FUNDAMENTALS
OF
GEOLOGY

John J. W. Rogers and John A. S. Adams

Department of Geology

Rice University

PHOTO FOR COVER AND FRONTISPIECE: Austin S. Post, U.S. Geological Survey

FUNDAMENTALS OF GEOLOGY

Contents

List of Tables

Symbols

$\mathring{A}$ = Angstrom unit (10^{-8} cm)

a, b, c, d, f, m, k = various constants for specific equations

A, B, C = soil horizons

C = amount of a substance

$[C]$ = concentration of a substance

d = distance; space between equivalent planes in a crystal; mean depth of a stream

e = base of natural logarithms

F = force

g = acceleration caused by gravity

G = constant of gravitational attraction

h = head (elevation) of water surface

H = elevation of stream above base level

K = equilibrium constant; distribution coefficient; solubility product

L = "long" seismic waves (surface)

m = mols; mass

M = mass of the earth

N = order of X-ray diffraction; also stands for numbers in a sequence, such as Bode's Law

p = pressure (and partial pressure)

P = primary seismic wave

Q = amount of stream discharge

s = distance

S = secondary seismic wave

t = time

$t_{1/2}$ = half life of radioactive material

T = temperature

v = velocity of stream

V = velocity of seismic waves

$w =$ width of stream surface

$X =$ distance

$Z =$ elevation

α, β, $\gamma =$ types of radiation

$\delta =$ a measure of the difference between the O^{18}/O^{16} ratio in a sample and the O^{18}/O^{16} ratio in a standard material; increase in δ signifies an increase in O^{18}/O^{16} ratio in the sample.

α and $\beta =$ phases of chemical systems

$\theta =$ angle of refraction of X rays

$\kappa =$ bulk modulus

$\lambda =$ wave length of X-ray beam; decay constant of radioactive material

$\mu =$ rigidity

$\rho =$ density

$\sigma =$ stress perpendicular to some surface

$^0/_{00} =$ parts of a substance per thousand parts

$_a X^b = b =$ atomic weight of isotope X

$a =$ atomic number of isotope X

$^\circ$C. $=$ degrees Centigrade

$^\circ$F. $=$ degrees Fahrenheit

ln $=$ logarithm to base e

log $=$ logarithm to base 10

Abbreviations

atm = atmosphere

cal = small calorie (1 cal raises T of 1 g of H_2O by 1° C.)

kcal = kilocalorie = 1000 cal

cm = centimeter

g = gram

in. = inch

km = kilometer

l = liter

m = meter

mi = mile

ml = milliliter

mm = millimeter

sec = second

yr = year

Editor's Introduction

FUNDAMENTALS OF GEOLOGY by John J. W. Rogers and John A. S. Adams is a new volume in Harper's Geoscience Series whose subject matter is limited specifically to physical geology in the classical sense. It represents more than a decade of preparation, for the writing and testing of materials have been carried on more or less continuously ever since the founding, in 1954, of the new Department of Geology at Rice University.

Fundamentals of Geology is a "modern" text in the sense that its subject matter is approached from the point of view of earth scientists who perhaps have been more broadly trained in the supporting fields of mathematics, physics, and chemistry than many, if not most, of the previous authors of the spate of texts in physical geology which have been published since the turn of the century. Nevertheless, all of the orthodox topics of the field are treated in such a fashion that instructors with limited training in the physical sciences should find the present text attractive and easy to teach; and students with or without a high degree of sophistication in the quantitative disciplines should discover in *Fundamentals of Geology* an interesting and rewarding volume.

The organization of the text into sixteen chapters involves nothing revolutionary, though the order and style of presentation is, generally speaking, "different" from that observed in any of the scores of somewhat similar volumes which have appeared on the market since Charles Lyell's *Principles* was issued more than a century and a quarter ago. Chapter 1 deals with "The Nature of Geology," under which title one finds up-to date discussions regarding the science of geology, uniformitarianism, and the complex subject of geologic time and correlation, including radioactive dating. Chapter 2, which is chiefly concerned with "The Earth's Size and Shape," gives the student, whom one commonly finds is surprisingly ignorant of such matters, concrete information about the earth's size, its magnetic field, the continents and ocean basins, mountain ranges, island arcs, and the climates of the earth. Chapter 3, which is devoted to "Gravity, Mass, and Density," takes up these important subjects and deals in a straightforward and effective fashion with gravity variations, gravity anomalies, isostasy, and the spheroid and geoid concepts. Chapter 4, entitled "Seismology," is concerned with the rather great range of subjects related to earthquakes, such as their waves, their energies, their recording, the interpretation of seismograms, and the principal earthquake belts. Also involved, however, is a summary of the properties of the earth, and a discussion of density, pressure and temperature, with particular reference to the earth's core, mantle, and crust. Chapter 5, entitled "Composition of the Earth," includes an outline of the formation of the elements and their abundance, as well as a discussion of chemical equilibrium. These topics lead naturally into an interpretation of the various theories that have evolved regarding the formation of the solar system and the geospheres.

Chapter 6 of *Fundamentals of Geology*, labeled "Components of the Earth's Crust,' is actually a synoptic outline of petrology and mineralogy, and has to do with the general characteristics of rock formations, stratification and sedimentation, and the kinds of igneous and metamorphic rocks, as well as their common expression in nature. There is also included here a discussion of rock cycles and a brief treatment of the subject of mineralogy, including the composition, crystal structure, and identification of the basic mineral groups. Chapter 7 is devoted to "Sedimentary Rocks" and Chapter 8 to "Igneous and Metamorphic Rocks." These two chapters, which involve elaborations of the subjects introduced in Chapter 6, are marked by relatively orthodox treatments of these two important topics.

Chapter 9, "Processes at the Earth's Surface," includes a summary of the development of soils through weathering, a discussion of mechanical deformation, and an interpretation of the rates of erosion and deposition. There is also an addendum on topographic maps. Chapter 10, entitled "Structural Geology," analyzes the major types of geological structures, deals with geological maps and mapping, goes into the problems of rock stress, strain and folding at some length, and discusses the effects of rock deformation as well as the history of the various orogenies. Chapter 11, "Rivers," not only describes stream transportation and deposition, as well as hydraulics and stream profiles, but treats of the subjects of land sculpturing, the origin of humid area landscapes, and the effect of various kinds of attitudes of rocks on the patterns which streams tend to develop. Chapter 12, "Secondary Sculpturing Agents and Processes," presents discussions of mass movements, such as landslides and creeps, the work of the wind, and the work of ice in its various expressions. Also included are the related subjects of continental glaciers and ancient climates. Chapter 13, labeled "The Oceans," which is concerned with the composition of sea water, the various water movements and their effect on shorelines, also includes a discussion of the life of the oceans with special reference to the formation of reefs, and submarine topography—subjects of rapidly growing general interest. Chapter 14, "Some Major Earth Processes," which is a particularly valuable discussion of continental drift, orogeny, epeirogeny, the geological effects of organisms, and paleotemperatures, concludes with an evaluation of the general concept of uniformitarianism. Chapter 15, "Economic Geology: Geologic Aspects," includes an analysis of energy relations in which oil, coal, and radioactive materials are discussed. Additionally, the metallic and nonmetallic ores are described, and the importance of ground water in all of its ramifications is underlined. Chapter 16 is a philosophical discussion of "Man in Geologic Perspective." The physical and chemical factors in his environment are analyzed, and the biological response is emphasized. The chapter concludes with a discussion of the future availability of minerals and energy.

There is also an extended Appendix, which is devoted to the identification of minerals.

It is possibly fair to state that the Rogers and Adams text presents a somewhat more explicit development of the basic mathematics, physics, and chemistry relevant to the earth sciences than that found in most of the other textbooks on physical geology. Moreover, the present authors take pains to discuss the physical and chemical reasoning behind geochemical and geophysical conclusions, whereas older authors, for the most part, have seemed content simply to state them. In spite of these facts, the Rogers and Adams text includes considerably less descriptive material and many fewer definitions than normally are employed. Nevertheless, the present text possibly will be considered more "advanced" than a number of books with somewhat similar titles, which commonly tend to be compendia of terms. This results from the fact that Rogers and Adams depend on a background in the basic sciences, and their presentation encourages, and indeed requires, concentrated thought on, rather than the memorization of the details of, the topics being presented.

In spite of what has just been said regarding the emphasis on thought rather than memory in *Fundamentals of Geology*, Rogers and Adams do discuss at some length many topics which are either mentioned not at all or receive relatively cursory attention in texts prepared by other geologists. These topics include heat flow, cosmology, diagenesis, and methods of modern research in sedimentation. Also included are man's control and use of his environment, the use of mathematical models to describe natural processes, a treatment of elementary mathematical crystallography, the explanation of X-ray techniques, and a discussion of chemical equilibrium considerations. Additionally, Adams and Rogers bring into their text detailed explanations of absolute age-dating methods, a discussion of the secretion mechanisms of invertebrates, and the development of their skeletal material. There are also included discussions of earthquake magnitudes, strain-release mechanisms, major problems concerning metamorphic facies, the orientation of structures in terms of stress directions, and paleomagnetism. All of these diverse topics have been presented in an integrating and illuminating fashion—their inclusion is by no means a mere attempt to demonstrate to instructor and student alike that the book is, indeed, "up to date."

The authors of *Fundamentals of Geology* were well qualified by training and experience to write the present volume. John J. W. Rogers is a native of Chicago, who received both the bachelor's and the doctor's degree from the California Institute of Technology, where he profited from a broadly-based advanced training in the physical sciences, but with a special emphasis on geology. Dr. Rogers also took his Master of Science degree from the University of Minnesota, with a major in geology and a minor in physical chemistry. Thus, he—like his coauthor—represents one of the increasing number of a new breed of geologists who are trained to a high level of competence in mathematics, chemistry, and physics, as well as in the earth sciences per se. Nevertheless, Dr. Rogers remains a generalist, as well as a specialist, being unusually successful as a teacher, as well as outstanding as a contributor to research. In the latter endeavors he has been active in geochemical fields—Adams-Rogers projects having been supported for a full decade by the Robert A. Welch Foundation. Additionally, he has received grants from the Oak Ridge National Laboratory and from the National Science Foundation. At Rice University Dr. Rogers, in a ten-year span, advanced through all of the academic grades, from instructor to full professor—an exceptional record even in these days of rapid promotions. Despite this author's partial preoccupation with geochemistry, he is perhaps best known for his research contributions as a sedimentologist, and for his effectiveness as a "visiting lecturer."

Dr. John A. S. Adams, chairman of the Department of Geology at Rice, was born at Independence, Missouri, but grew up in Chicago, Illinois, where he received his advanced education at the University of Chicago, from which institution he holds four degrees, including the doctorate. Dr. Adams was awarded two one-year Fulbright Fellowships to study in Norway, and while living in Europe had the opportunity to take part in a scientific expedition to the Arctic. He has also held a Postdoctoral Fellowship in the Department of Chemistry at the University of Wisconsin, and a National Science Foundation Senior Postdoctoral Fellowship at the University of Vienna. His contributions to geology, and particularly to geochemistry, to geochronology, and to the study of the radiation environment, have deservedly attracted international attention. At present he is serving as the Executive Editor of the Geochemical Society. His extensive researches have been carried on under the aegis of the Welch Foundation and the Oak Ridge National Laboratory.

Professors Adams and Rogers, together with the Editor of Harper's Geoscience Series, formed the nucleus of the Department of Geology at Rice University, which in little more than a decade has grown to be one of the larger graduate schools of geology in North America. The current text, *Fundamentals of Geology,* is in a very real sense an outgrowth of the curricular developments in that department. It represents a distillation of many trials and errors in the attempt to set up a new and improved course in physical geology sufficiently rigorous to challenge better-than-average students, and sufficiently interesting to hold the attention and sharpen the wits of geology registrants of average motivation and, initially, with no more than a casual concern for the earth sciences.

Perhaps the Editor may be permitted a point of personal privilege in concluding this Introduction. He has had the pleasure of witnessing the significant academic progress of Drs. Adams and Rogers, whom he invited years ago to join with him in the founding of the Rice Department of Geology. There is a great and understandable satisfaction in seeing scholars grow as their teaching and research projects flower. It cannot be maintained that the development and writing of *Fundamentals of Geology* was, or is, a prime objective in the building of a new department of geology from scratch. It can be stated, however, that the current text is a far from insignificant manifestation of the activities of Adams and Rogers—as well as those of a group of dedicated colleagues—who together have contributed to such success as the new department has already enjoyed. Through *Fundamentals of Geology* it is hoped that the impact of the department, its staff, and its graduates may have an ever-widening and increasingly beneficial effect in the geosciences.

CAREY CRONEIS

Rice University
January, 1966

Preface

THE READERS and authors of this volume share the special opportunities and problems that arise from the accelerating pace at which the scientific studies of the earth and space are now proceeding. A majority of all the scientists trained in the short history of science are active today, and with the resources and ever more powerful instrumentation at their command, knowledge of the earth doubles every few years. Well-publicized projects are now under way to sample directly the moon and the earth's interior. These samples and the results of many other researches will in a few years resolve some of the unanswered problems discussed in this volume; these forthcoming data will also necessitate the revision of some of the concepts presented and both simplify and complicate the already difficult problem of selecting and presenting topics in an introductory text of limited size.

On one hand, it is not difficult to discuss in simple terms the significance of the vast natural gas fields recently discovered in the North Sea region or the significance of the absence of any signs of canals in the recent Mariner V televised close-ups of the surface of Mars. On the other hand, it is difficult, even with some background in mathematics, physics, chemistry, and geology, to discuss simply all the major problems involved in the interpretation of absolute geologic ages or paleomagnetism. In this volume an attempt has been made to develop a limited, but representative, number of geologic topics that belong in any educated view of the earth. In the development of these topics the underlying mathematics, physics, or chemistry has been discussed in some cases; in other cases, in the interest of brevity, the basic concepts have been merely stated.

The authors have relied heavily on their colleagues and students for advice, criticism, and illustrations. We particularly acknowledge the assistance of Miss Letitia Zumwalt for editorial and other assistance and Mrs. Barbara Hawkins for repeated typing of the manuscript.

Any errors are the sole responsibility of the authors.

JOHN J. W. ROGERS
JOHN A. S. ADAMS

Houston, Texas
December, 1965

FUNDAMENTALS
OF
GEOLOGY

CHAPTER 1

THE NATURE
OF GEOLOGY

◀ Parícutin.(Courtesy of Mexican Government Tourism Department.)

THE SCIENCE OF GEOLOGY

The only unchanging aspect of the earth is the fact that it is always changing. The earth has been, and is being, affected by a myriad of interacting processes, and it is the task of geology to describe and understand these processes and their results. Not only are geologic processes as complex and delicately balanced as physiological reactions in man, but also the great age and size of the earth place special difficulties in the path of geological investigation. Yet we know of no human society so primitive that it has not speculated or constructed myths about the origin or the nature of the earth.

For modern scientific man, geologic processes may be discussed largely, though not wholly, in the terms and units of physics, chemistry, and biology. Many approaches to understanding, predicting, and partially controlling geologic processes require quantitative data and the mathematical treatment of these data, and limited success has been achieved with this approach. For example, both direct observation of natural crystals and mathematical theory agree point by point on the number of possible ways in which atoms can be arranged in crystals. Another example is the early forecasting of the time, but not the height, at which gigantic surface waves (tsunamis) generated by undersea earthquakes arrive at distant coasts. The ability to predict these tsunami arrivals has saved thousands of lives and is based on precise observation and measurement of the locations and times of many past earthquakes and the tsunamis caused by them; a direct experimental approach to this problem is precluded, because even the best placed and most powerful nuclear devices cannot produce a controlled oceanic surface wave as large as a full tsunami.

The lack of the means for a direct experimental approach to the study of tsunamis is not an isolated case in geology. Indeed, geologic phenomena generally involve so much energy, mass, and time that the possibility of direct, controlled experiment is rare. The range of phenomena that can be investigated by experimentation, however, increases each year as higher and higher temperatures and pressures are achieved in the laboratory and ever more refined techniques are developed for studying chemical reactions operating at the slow rates which characterize geologic processes. Scaled-down, laboratory models of such phenomena as the breakage and flowage of rocks have proven very useful in understanding the deformation of the earth's surface, and in recent years mathematical models handled by electronic computers have proven to be powerful methods for studying and predicting how waves generated by earthquakes are transmitted through the earth. Although a number of important scientific, economic, and military problems in geology have been solved by direct experimentation, model studies, or theoretical analysis, the majority have not. Thus, for example, there is no general agreement, despite much experimental and theoretical effort, as to the exact mode of formation of the simple and widespread mineral dolomite (essentially $CaMg(CO_3)_2$). Furthermore, it has not been possible in the laboratory to synthesize dolomite under the conditions in which it clearly forms in nature. At present, much of our understanding of the origin of dolomite and many other geologic problems must rest upon inductive interpretations of what we find in rocks. In fact, the "solutions" of many geologic problems must be based on interpretations of a large number of varied and separate pieces of evidence, and in this regard some aspects of geology are almost perfect examples of inductive reasoning.

To the extent that he can experiment directly with geologic phenomena, the geologist functions in the same manner and uses many of the same techniques as the biologist, chemist, and physicist. To the extent that the geologist is confined to observing what nature permits him to see, he functions much like the archeologist or the criminologist. Certain aspects of the past are gone forever. We may never know if or how the giant dinosaurs roared because we know of no way in which the sound would be recorded in the rocks, and it is unlikely that we will find enough well-preserved soft tissues of the dinosaur throat to settle the question. In this connection, the closest living relatives of the dinosaurs would provide only circumstantial evidence at best. Even with plentiful clues, the best inductive logic does not always yield a unique solution. Thus, a great deal is known about possible causes for the spread of glaciers over continents and the limits of climatic conditions in which such glaciation could occur; however, there is no general agreement about which cause or combination of causes produced the last great continental glaciation. As work continues on this problem of continental glaciation, each new piece of evidence must be tested in the context of several different hypotheses.

The types of data which geologists collect are quite varied and numerous. Ideally a geologist should be an expert chemist, mathematician, physicist, and biologist before he ever starts work on the earth itself; naturally, this is seldom so. In the course of an investigation into some geological problem, however, the typical geologist may encounter many questions well beyond his knowledge of the basic sciences or of some aspects of geology itself. The practicing geologist, therefore, must have a broad fundamental knowledge of many scientific fields. Furthermore, and even more importantly, he must know what areas of geology or related sciences he does not understand in order to ask specialists in these fields for help when the occasion arises.

One of the unfortunate aspects of modern science is its complexity and the necessity of specialization. No one person has the mental ability to grasp more than a small portion of modern scientific knowledge. The field of geology is subdivided for this reason, just as other sciences are subdivided, into fields of specialization. The geophysicist, for example, investigates the earth by studying its large-scale physical properties. Geophysicists may be interested in the variation of gravity over the earth's surface, in the transmission of sound waves through the earth, or in numerous other applications of the principles of basic physics. Geochemists are concerned with the earth as a chemical system. Rocks are

Fig. 1-1. An outcrop of horizontally bedded sedimentary rocks in the Theodore Roosevelt Monument, western North Dakota. (Photo by J. J. W. Rogers.)

considered in the light of their chemical compositions, and experimental studies may be done to synthesize the laboratory equivalents of common rocks. Other common geochemical studies involve the distribution of minor elements in various materials of the earth's surface or the distribution of individual isotopes of certain elements in the same materials. Paleontologists study the changing types of animals and plants which have inhabited the earth's surface and which have gradually evolved into the forms which we find at the present time. Their concern is not only a description of the ancient organisms, or fossils, found in rocks, but also an interpretation of the conditions under which these organisms lived before death. Petrologists are broadly concerned with the origin of rocks. The field of petrology is broken into several subdisciplines, depending on the type of rocks that are studied by a particular petrologist; subdivisions of the various rocks are discussed in considerable detail in later chapters. Mineralogists are interested in the composition, crystal structure, and occurrence of minerals, the naturally occurring chemical compounds which are the building blocks of all earth materials.

Stratigraphers are interested in the sequence of rock types formed on the earth's surface. As we shall discuss in later chapters, rocks such as the sands of beaches or the muds at the bottom of lakes are laid down sequentially on top of each other on the earth's surface and form roughly parallel, horizontal layers of different rock types. These layers, called *beds* or *strata,* are deposited on top of each other so as to give a continuing sequence from older to younger layers upward in the deposit (Fig. 1-1). The stratigrapher is most interested in determining which rocks in widely different areas have been deposited at the same time. This determination of time equivalents is called *correlation* and is a major problem facing geologists in all fields. Structural geologists are concerned with the mechanisms and the results of breakage and warping of the earth's surface. The object of their investigations is to determine the basic processes which cause this deformation. The geomorphologists are concerned with the shape of the land and with an understanding of the processes which have led to the present configuration of the earth's surface. Many other subdivisions could be listed, but most of the names are self-explanatory, such as glaciology, oceanography, ground water hydrology, engineering geology, and military geology. We shall discuss these various fields in later portions of this book and shall try to relate the results of studies in one field as much as possible to the information obtained in other fields.

UNIFORMITARIANISM

The science of geology is based largely on a proposition attributed primarily to James Hutton in 1785. Let us follow some of his original reasoning and that of his colleagues, without going into details of the exact observations which he made. If we go to a beach, we will see sand grains moving back and forth under the influence of waves and ultimately being deposited in some place and left there. If we look at a river, we will see that it contains mud and debris that is being carried along by the current. If we watch the river over a considerable period of time, perhaps only a few days, we will see that the banks of the river shift as material is carved off of a bank and the resultant debris is swept away by the river. In other places some of the material which the river carries may be deposited against one of the banks as the course of the river shifts away from that bank (Fig. 1-2). If we go to a volcano, we shall see volcanic material in the form of flowing liquid or exploded fragments being spewed out of the top and being deposited on the surrounding surface (Figs. 1-3 and 1-4). If we look at ancient maps of coastlines and compare them with modern maps, we shall find, despite the inaccuracies of mapping done several hundred years ago, that the coastlines in some places have distinctly moved back and forth. In deserts we can

Fig. 1-2. A bar in the Arkansas River. Sand has been deposited by slowly flowing water at the inside of the river bend. (Photo by R. Q. Oaks, Esso Production Research.)

Fig. 1-3. Izalco volcano, San Salvador, erupting during day.
(Photo courtesy of Instituto Salvadoreño de Turismo.)

Fig. 1-4. Izalco volcano, San
Salvador, erupting at night.
(Photo courtesy of Instituto
Salvadoreño de Turismo.)

observe sand being blown by the wind and accumulating in the form of dunes which move across the desert floor. We can feel earthquakes and see landslides tumbling down the sides of the mountains. All of these observations, plus many others not listed here, convince us that the earth is not inactive, that both its surface and subsurface are continually being affected by processes operating at the present time.

We can also look at a cliff face or the side of a sharply cut valley or a quarry and see rock buried below the earth's surface. Some of the rocks which we see, if we look hard enough, may look like beach sands. Some may look like the hardened equivalent of the liquid which came out of the volcano. Some may look like buried sand dunes. We may see sharp notches or channels cut in certain rocks and filled in by overlying materials. We can examine buried soils which are identical to modern soils and trace the topography of the ancient land surface as expressed by the positions of these soils. We may find rocks shifted past each other along planes of fracturing and compare these shifts with movements which have taken place along similar planes during modern earthquakes (Fig. 1-5). We can also find, in these partially buried rocks, the shells or other remains of organisms in many cases similar, or identical, to those which are alive today (Fig. 1-6). Even though many of the buried fossils are not equivalent to modern types, the similarities are close enough to make it unquestionable that they were living organisms at one time. In short, with some exceptions which we shall discuss later, we can find in ancient rocks most of the features which we can see now being formed by processes which are taking place on the earth.

The conclusion, then, is that the earth of the past underwent physical, chemical, and biological changes which are similar to, or perhaps equivalent to, the changes which are going on at the present time. This

Fig. 1-5. A fault separating two formations in a roadcut in east Texas. (Photo by H. B. Stenzel.)

proposition, formally stated by Charles Lyell, is given the technical name *uniformitarianism*, and the slogan is: "The present is the key to the past." We do not mean to imply by this theory that no events could have occurred in the geologic past which are not occurring today. We do imply, however, that it is possible to examine the present geologic processes and, from data obtained in this examination, interpret the processes which occurred in the past. Furthermore, there is no implication that the processes occurring at the present time are taking place at the same rate as equivalent ancient processes. The fact that the sand on some modern beach may be building upward at a rate of one inch per year does not mean that the sand on ancient beaches built up at a rate anything like one inch per year. Thus, the details of processes are not expected to be faithfully reproduced in the geologic past. We must, however, study the present in order to determine the history of the earth, and this effort to reconstruct history is based on the uniformitarian concept.

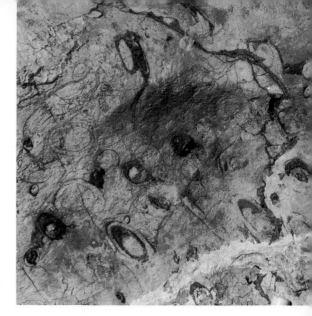

Fig. 1-6. Fossil-bearing (fossiliferous) sedimentary rock in the Franklin Mountains, west Texas. The rock is approximately 500 million years old, and fossils are similar to modern sponges. (Photo by D. F. Toomey.)

GEOLOGIC TIME AND CORRELATION

We have already used the terms "geologic past" and "time" and must continue to do so throughout the book. Geology is basically an historical science. The object of geologic investigation is to determine as accurately as possible the history of the earth. It is appropriate, therefore, to begin our discussion of geology with a brief outline of the two major methods by which geologic time can be estimated. We have already mentioned the correlation of rocks of identical age, and the task of stratigraphy is to establish such correlations over broad areas, even between separate continents. In detail, the procedure is quite complex, and more complete discussion will have to be deferred to later pages. In a simplified fashion, however, correlation is made largely on the basis of an identity of fossils found in widely separated beds. The idea is that, in the course of the evolution of the organic life of the earth, different organisms appear at different times of geologic history and occupy a particular and rather restricted time range. The time ranges of some types of organisms are quite broad; they are, consequently, not particularly useful for correlation purposes. The time ranges of other fossils, however, may be quite short, and hence the finding of such an index fossil implies that the enclosing rock was formed within that restricted period of time. Thus, ignoring the complications, we can establish sequences of events in various parts of the earth by setting up sequences of identical fossils. This idealized procedure is shown in Fig. 1-7.

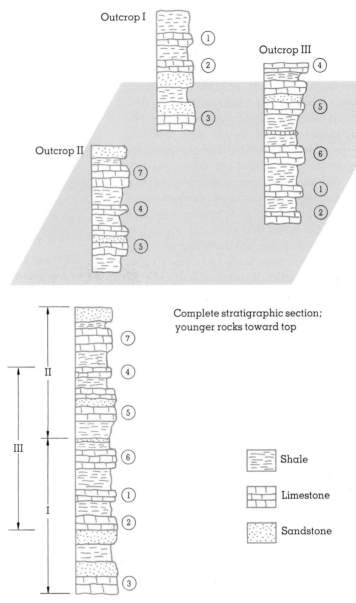

Fig. 1-7. Schematic representation of the technique of correlation by fossils. The three sedimentary sections shown in the upper part of the diagram may be combined into the composite section shown in the lower part. The reconstruction assumes that the beds at each outcrop are in the same relative positions in which they were deposited; i.e., rocks become younger upward in the sequence, and no overturning or other displacement has occurred. Numbers 1 through 7 indicate distinct fossils or suites of fossils; each of the seven suites is different from the others, although particular fossils occur in particular types of rock; identical suites have identical numbers.

We should note here the extremely important fact that paleontological dating is based on the ability of geologists to construct a sequence of fossil changes from their occurrence in sedimentary rocks. That is, fossils are originally dated by finding them in sequences of sediments that are deposited horizontally with progressively younger layers toward the top. Once a sequence is established as shown in Fig. 1-7, then the fossils can be used to date other rocks not found in a simple horizontally layered sequence.

There are two immediate difficulties which are apparent in the correlation procedure. At the present time, for example, the types of fish living in lakes are quite different from those living in oceans. Clams do not grow in flower gardens nor roses at the bottoms of rivers. That is, the types of organisms which occur in a rock depend in part on the conditions under which that rock was formed. Thus it is possible for rocks of identical age to contain different kinds of fossils. A further complication is that a particular organism may not necessarily have lived at the same time during the formation of all the rocks in which it occurs. It is known, for example, that some types of bottom-dwelling animals now living at depths of many thousands of feet in the oceans at one time lived at depths of a few tens of feet, a position in which they are now no longer able to live. There has, consequently, been a gradual migration of animals, including man, from one set of living conditions to another set of living conditions during time. Thus it is possible to find rocks formed under different conditions containing identical fossils which lived at one time under one set of conditions and at another time under another set. The apparent correlation between these rocks, therefore, would be erroneous.

Despite these difficulties, however, we can establish a time scale based largely on paleontological evidence. The drawback to this time scale is that it is only a relative one and does not give us any opportunity to attach an actual age in years to the various rocks and events. We may know that some fossils lived more recently than others, but by paleontological evidence alone, it is not possible to determine how much more recently. In order to attach quantitative significance to the geologic time scale it is necessary to turn to dating techniques based on radioactivity. Such techniques not only yield absolute ages in years but provide a check on the relative dates determined paleontologically.

RADIOACTIVE DATING

The general principles of radioactivity are sufficiently well known that we need not repeat them here. The important naturally occurring radioactive atomic varieties (isotopes) are U^{238}, U^{235}, Th^{232}, Rb^{87}, K^{40}, and C^{14}. The thorium and uranium decay through a complex series of alpha (helium nucleus) and beta (electron) emissions to various isotopes of lead. The rubidium decays by beta emission to strontium-87. Potassium-40 may decay in either of two ways. One path is by beta emission to calcium-40, and the other is by capture of the inner (K) electron to form argon-40. The ratio between calcium and argon produced by potassium decay is constant. The various decay equations are shown below, omitting intermediate steps.

Radioactive Parent Material		Daughter Product		Particles Emitted
U^{238}	$\longrightarrow$	Pb^{206}	$+$	$8\ \alpha$
U^{235}	$\longrightarrow$	Pb^{207}	$+$	$7\ \alpha$
Th^{232}	$\longrightarrow$	Pb^{208}	$+$	$6\ \alpha$
Rb^{87}	$\longrightarrow$	Sr^{87}	$+$	β
K^{40}	$\xrightarrow{\text{(K capture)}}$	Ar^{40}		
K^{40}	$\longrightarrow$	Ca^{40}	$+$	β
C^{14}	$\longrightarrow$	N^{14}	$+$	β

The rates of radioactive decay are independent of temperature, pressure, or the surrounding environment. Thus if we could, for example, incorporate a small amount of U^{238} in a rock at a particular time, we should be able to measure the time since its incorporation by measuring the amount of uranium left now and the amount of the daughter Pb^{206} formed. The calculations are based on the ratio of the amounts of parent and daughter product now in the rock and laboratory measurements of the decay rate of the parent material.

The amount of a radioactive element which decays within any period of time is proportional to the amount of the element present. That is, the percentage of material decaying at any time is constant, but the amount of material decaying decreases with time as the parent is used up. In mathematical terms

$$-dC/dt = \lambda C$$

$C =$ amount of radioactive material

$t =$ time

$\lambda =$ decay constant

This equation can be integrated to give the total amount of parent material decayed in a given time, and this amount is obviously equal in number of atoms to the amount of daughter product formed. The integrated form of the decay equation is:

$$\lambda(t_2 - t_1) = \ln(C_1/C_2)$$

where 1 and 2 refer to amounts present at the corresponding times.

The rate of radioactive decay is represented in the above equations by the decay constant, λ. Alternatively, the decay rate can be expressed by the half life, which is the amount of time needed for one half of the original parent material to decay to its daughter. The half life is related to the decay constant by the relationship

$$\text{half life} = t_{1/2} = (\ln 2)/\lambda$$

which can easily be derived from the integrated form of the decay equation.

The decay constants are known for all of the isotopes shown above (see Table 1-1). Thus, in theory, it is possible to take a rock, measure the concentrations of parent and daughter products, and calculate the time elapsed since the formation of the rock. In practice such calculations are based on several assumptions. First, it must be assumed that the parent material incorporated in the rock has remained within the rock and that there has been neither addition nor removal of parent or daughter. There is also the additional assumption that no daughter product was originally incorporated in the rock and that all of the daughter isotope, consequently, is formed by decay of the parent. This latter assumption is generally not valid, although in the case of the potassium-argon decay it can be assumed that most of the argon in the rock was formed by decay. In the case of the various isotopes of lead the amount of non-radiogenic lead (i.e., lead included in the rock at the time of formation) may be quite large. Of the various lead isotopes, only Pb^{204} is not formed from any naturally radioactive element occurring at the present time, and this permits, as shown below, a calculation of the percentage of the lead isotopes which are nonradiogenic. In the case of carbon-14 dating, only the absolute amount of remaining parent is measured.

TABLE 1-1. DECAY CONSTANTS AND HALF LIVES OF RADIOACTIVE MATERIALS

	decay constant	half life
U^{238}	$1.54 \cdot 10^{-10}$	$4.51 \cdot 10^9$ years
U^{235}	$0.97 \cdot 10^{-9}$	$7.1 \cdot 10^8$
Th^{232}	$4.96 \cdot 10^{-11}$	$1.39 \cdot 10^{10}$
Rb^{87}	$1.38 \cdot 10^{-11}$	$5.0 \cdot 10^{10}$
K^{40}	$5.28 \cdot 10^{-10}$	$1.31 \cdot 10^9$
C^{14}	$1.24 \cdot 10^{-4}$	5568

$$t_{\frac{1}{2}} = \frac{.69}{\lambda}$$

As an example of the determination of the age of a rock or mineral, let us consider the following data. A crystal of zircon ($ZrSiO_4$) is found by chemical analysis to contain the following small concentrations of isotopes:

	Percent by Weight
Uranium 238	0.106
Lead 206	0.0059
Lead 204	0.000021

A crystal of galena (PbS) adjacent to the zircon appears to have formed at the same time as the zircon. In analyzing the galena, we find that the ratio

$$\frac{Pb^{206}}{Pb^{204}} = 18.0$$

and also that the galena contains no uranium. Therefore, since the half life of uranium is so long that there would be some left if it had been originally present, we can assume that all lead in the galena is nonradiogenic in the sense that it entered galena as lead.

Laboratory studies show that isotopes as heavy as lead occur in constant ratios in all materials formed during chemical reactions such as the growth of crystals. Since the zircon and galena formed at the same time and in the same place, we can assume that the ratio Pb^{206}/Pb^{204} in the zircon was 18.0 at the time the zircon and the galena formed. Since the content of Pb^{204} has not been affected by radioactive processes, we can then assume that the amount of nonradiogenic Pb^{206} in the zircon is

$$18.0 \cdot Pb^{204} = 18.0 \cdot 0.000021\% = .00038\%$$

Therefore, the radiogenic Pb^{206} is

$$0.0059 - 0.00038 = 0.0055\%$$

In order to find the original U^{238} content we must now calculate the weight of U^{238} which contains the same number of atoms as 0.0055 percent of Pb^{206}. This amount of U^{238} is $(238/206) \cdot 0.0055$ percent, which equals 0.0064 percent, and we assume that this is the amount of U^{238} which has decayed. Thus the total amount of uranium originally in the zircon is 0.0064 plus 0.106, which equals 0.112 percent.

The age is now determined from the ratio of the original and present U^{238} concentrations by the formula

$$\lambda t = \ln \frac{\text{(initial concentration of } U^{238})}{\text{(final concentration of } U^{238})}$$

$$t = \text{age of zircon} = \frac{\ln (.112/.106)}{\lambda_U{}^{238}}$$

$$= \frac{.05}{1.54 \cdot 10^{-10}}$$

$$= 330 \text{ million years}$$

For geologic time we shall be using figures such as millions, hundreds of millions, and even billions of years. As will be discussed in Chapter 5, the total age of the earth is estimated at some time around 4.5 billion years. The period of geologic time in which abundant fossils have been found is approximately the last 600 million years. Owing to uncertainties of experimental measurement of the radioactive isotopes and to uncertainties in the various assumptions on which dating is based, we shall commonly state ages as approximations. For example, we may refer to some event as occurring 200 ± 20 million years ago. An error of 10 percent is not uncommon with present methods of age determination.

We should note here that not all rocks are datable; this is partly because the conditions for various assumptions necessary for dating are not always present, and partly because some rocks simply do not contain enough radioactive material for accurate measurement. Those rocks which can be dated, however, have been sufficiently numerous to establish a fairly complete time scale which can be related to, and used to confirm, the paleontological sequence. Conversely the paleontological sequence has been of great assistance in the original studies of radioactivity and in the development of absolute geochronological methods.

Other methods than paleontology and radioactive dating have been used to provide approximate ages of some rocks and even of the entire earth. For example, the amount of salt which has accumulated in the oceans has been used as an estimate of the age of the oceans, although we shall see later that this estimate is highly inaccurate. The rate at which sediments accumulate has yielded some data on the ages of thick deposits. No other methods, however, have provided the accuracy and consistency of paleontologic and radioactive dating.

THE EARTH'S SIZE
AND SHAPE

Since the subject of geology and some of its basic concepts have been introduced, it is now possible to begin a comprehensive examination of the earth itself. We shall want to know, for example, how big it is, how it is shaped, how much mass it has, how this mass is distributed, and whether the material which composes it is uniformly or heterogeneously distributed. We shall start in this chapter with the subject of the earth's size and surface configuration.

One of the most fundamental facts about the earth is that it is almost a perfect sphere. We can base this conclusion on several observations. In ancient times it was noted that the earth cast a curved shadow on the moon during lunar eclipses. The fact that the surface is curved is demon-

Fig. 2-1. Astronaut E. H. White II shown floating in space outside the Gemini-4 spacecraft on June 3, 1965. Curvature of the earth is clearly visible. (Photo courtesy of National Aeronautics and Space Administration.)

strated quite easily by the observation that the tops of tall objects can be seen at distances, whereas the bases are not visible. Thus, for example, early seafarers could use the phrase "hull down on the horizon" to refer to a ship whose hull was no longer visible but whose sails were still clearly seen. Now, in the days of satellites and high-altitude rockets, the curvature of the earth is clearly shown in direct photographs (Fig. 2-1).

SIZE

Once it is established that the earth is essentially spherical, the next problem is the determination of its radius. This measurement can be made quite easily, and indeed early estimates by such Greek scholars as Eratosthenes in the third century B.C. have proved to be remarkably accurate. The procedure is to observe the angle which the sun makes with the perpendicular to the earth's surface at two different points along a north-south line. The procedure and calculations are shown diagrammatically in Fig. 2-2. The basic assumptions for this measurement are that the earth is a sphere, thus causing a vertical to the surface to be pointed directly at the earth's center, and that the sun is sufficiently distant so that its rays reaching the earth are parallel at the two points measured. On the basis of these assumptions, if the two points lie on a north-south line, the distance between them is the length of an arc on the earth's surface whose angular value equals the difference in the angles between the verticals and the sun's rays at the measured points. We have shown the calculation in Fig. 2-2 for the case in which the sun is vertically above point A. In actuality it is not necessary for either of the points to be so placed, although the calculations are simpler if they are.

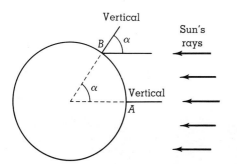

Fig. 2-2. Simplified technique of measuring the circumference, and hence the radius, of the earth. The sun is sufficiently distant so that rays striking the earth at two different points are parallel. Thus the angle α represents the angle of the arc from A to B, and distance from A to B may then be used to calculate total circumference.

Measurements of the type shown in Fig. 2-2 can be made at various places on the earth's surface and lead to the conclusion that the earth is not exactly a sphere. In particular, the radius of curvature is found to increase as we go from the Equator toward either the North or the South Pole. A gradual increase in the radius of curvature from the Equator toward the Poles can only signify that the earth is somewhat flattened at the Poles; that is, the distance from the center of the earth to the Equator is larger than the distance from the center to either of the Poles. Accurate measurements of the variation in the earth's radius from place to place have yielded the following results for the size of the earth.

Distance from earth's center to Equator	Distance from earth's center to Pole	Volume of earth
3,963.5 miles	3,950.2 miles	$2.5 \cdot 10^{11}$ cubic miles
6,378.4 km	6,356.9 km	$1.1 \cdot 10^{12}$ cubic km

You will notice that the radius of the earth is some 13 miles shorter at the Poles than at the Equator (Fig. 2-3). The flattening at the Poles is quite easily related to the earth's rotation. As is clearly demonstrated by the sun's daily progression from east to west, the earth is spinning from west to east with a 24-hour period of rotation. Thus the velocity of rotation of the earth at the Equator is more than 1000 miles per hour. This velocity of rotation diminishes toward the Poles and is, of course, 0 at the Poles themselves. This tremendous spin of the earth causes a bulging outward at the Equator and consequent polar flattening.

Locations on the earth's spherical surface are based on a latitude and longitude grid system. Latitudes (termed "parallels") refer to degrees of arc north and south of the Equator, with the poles of rotation being 90° N. or 90° S. Lat. Longitude in the English-speaking world is measured east and west of an arbitrary north-south line, or "meridian," through the observatory at Greenwich, England. This 0° Long. is matched by Long. 180° on the opposite side of the earth. Longitude 180° is, by convention, the International Date Line at which a traveler moving westward gains one day and moving eastward loses one day. In order to conform to international boundaries and for local convenience the Date Line departs in places from the 180° meridian. The latitude lines are referred to as parallels, owing to the fact that they do not intersect at both Poles.

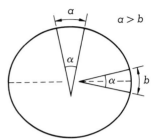

Fig. 2-3. Effect of flattening of the earth at the Poles of rotation. The arc encompassed by a given angle α is greater near these Poles than near the Equator, and the radius of curvature increases toward the Poles. Flattening is greatly exaggerated in the diagram.

MAGNETIC FIELD

We have referred to the Poles of the earth as the points of no rotation, that is, the points of emergence of the axis of the earth's rotation. It is well known that these Poles are not the points indicated by magnetic compasses. The magnetic poles of the earth toward which compasses point are approximately 20° away from the true North and South Poles at the present time. The magnetic poles are not diametrically opposite each other, though the line joining them passes near the center of the earth. A complete picture of the earth's magnetic field is given in Fig. 2-4, in which the *isogonic lines* are drawn parallel to the orientation of a horizontal compass needle at all points. These isogonic lines are essentially meridians of magnetic longitude.

As shown in Fig. 2-4, the magnetic field of the earth can be explained fairly well in terms of the field of a simple bar magnet with its poles at the two magnetic poles. Irregularities in the isogonic lines, however, indicate that there are deviations from this ideal field. Some of these deviations can be related to the presence of magnetic ore bodies, such as iron deposits, which tend to concentrate lines of magnetic force. Some deviations, however, are not clearly related to any features of the earth itself and are probably caused by weak magnetic fields originating outside of

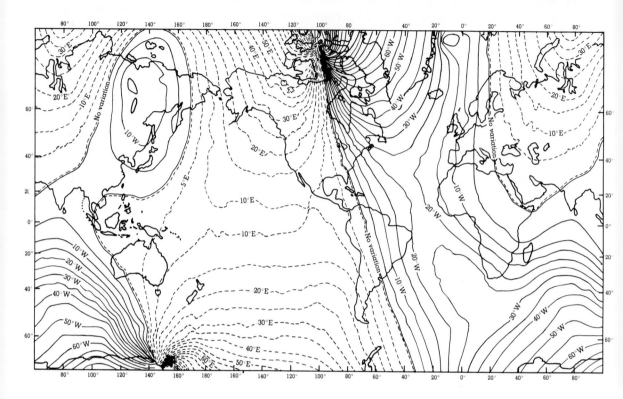

Fig. 2-4. Isogonic chart. The figures by the various lines indicate the deviation of a compass needle from true north and south. Solid lines are for westward deviations, dashed lines for eastward deviations. (Reproduced by permission from *Dutton's Navigation and Piloting,* copyright © 1956 by U.S. Naval Institute, Annapolis, Maryland.)

the solid earth. The origin of such magnetic fields is not clear, though one possibility is the interaction between charged particles radiating outward from the sun and the magnetic field of the solid earth.

The fact that the major portion (at least 95 percent) of the earth's magnetic field can be described in terms of a bar magnet within the earth indicates that most of the field is generated by some process within the earth. We shall see in Chapters 3 and 4 that the earth is presumed to have a large "core" consisting primarily of metallic iron and nickel. Material in the core obviously rotates, more or less, with the rest of the earth, and if some electrical charge differences were set up between different portions of this easily ionized metal, then the rotation of the charge would set up a magnetic field. The mechanism for establishing charge differences, however, is uncertain.

Observations of the orientation of a magnetic needle (the magnetic *declination* and *inclination*) at different stations over a period of 350 years show that the magnetic field changes systematically during time (e.g., Fig. 2-5). It is tempting to ascribe the movement shown in Fig. 2-5 to a shifting in the position of the north magnetic pole. Observations from a large number of observatories at different places during the last few decades, however, indicate that variations in direction of the magnetic field cannot be explained in terms of a simple movement of the magnetic poles. The earth's magnetic field is not sufficiently regular to be accounted for in this fashion; that is, it is not a simple dipole.

The reason for the deviation of the magnetic poles from the axis of rotation is not known, nor indeed is the reason for the movement of these poles near the axis of spin. It is important for us to note here, however, the fact that the magnetic poles are now in the vicinity of the true North and South Poles, and thus, over a long period of time, the general direction of magnetization probably indicates the direction of the axis of spin. We shall make considerable use of this fact when we study the direction of remnant magnetization of ancient rocks. In Chapter 12 we shall see that the slight preferential magnetization of rocks can yield information on relative displacements of the axis of rotation of the earth. This study of paleomagnetism has provided valuable information concerning the movements of continents and perhaps even relative shifting of the whole outer shell of the earth itself.

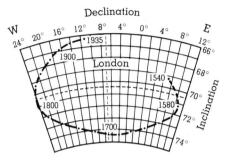

Fig. 2-5. Direction of magnetic force at London between 1540 and 1935. Declination is the horizontal angle between a magnetic needle and the Greenwich meridian. Inclination is the angle between the needle and the earth's surface. (Courtesy of S. A. Chapman; from *Geomagnetism*, vol. I, The Clarendon Press, Oxford, 1940.)

CONTINENTS AND OCEANS

The spherical surface of the earth is virtually impossible to show accurately on a two-dimensional book page or map. The major surface features of the earth are best seen by careful inspection of a globe, and if you wish to follow this and future discussions carefully, it is best done with a globe at hand. The first major feature which we notice upon looking at the earth is the distribution of continents and oceans. The oceans cover nearly three-fourths of the earth's surface, and continental areas are clearly not distributed uniformly over the surface. The Pacific Ocean occupies nearly an entire hemisphere, the International Date Line cutting it approximately in two. The Atlantic Ocean, though much smaller than the Pacific, is still an area larger than any single continent. The other two major bodies of water are the Indian and Arctic oceans.

The major landmass is the Eurasian continental area, extending over 6000 miles from the west coast of Spain to the east coast of Siberia and China. This large mass has no distinctive geometric pattern, and the same is true of the Australian and Antarctic continents. When we look, however, at Africa, South America, and North America, we see a rather striking similarity in general geometric form. All three of these continents are, very roughly speaking, triangular, with the points directed toward the south. Geology often requires the correlating of miscellaneous or isolated observations in the hope of arriving at some usable generalizations. We have now noted an isolated observation, namely the triangularity of three of the six major continental areas. We must ask ourselves the question of why those continents have this vague triangular shape and whether this shape has any significance in regard to other facts concerning the general evolution of the earth's surface. At this stage in our discussion the questions cannot really be answered, as we do not have enough additional facts concerning the evolution of continents and other surface features to construct a worthwhile theory. We shall, however, return to the matter in a later chapter.

Before leaving the subject of triangularity, it is necessary to mention the "continent" of India. India appears as a somewhat triangular appendage hanging on to the bottom side of the Eurasian landmass. The question then arises as to whether India has originated geologically as a part of the Eurasian continental area, or whether it is more closely related to Africa, South America, and possibly North America. This point also must be discussed in more detail in a later chapter.

While looking at Africa and South America, we should observe a surface configuration which has puzzled geographers and geologists for many years. It is peculiar that if we were to move Africa westward or South America eastward they would fit into each other very much like a hand into a glove. The bulge of Brazil in South America very nicely occupies the concavity in the coast of Africa marked by the Gulf of Guinea. We shall see in Chapter 14 that the two continents actually fit together almost perfectly when we take into account the underwater configurations of their outer margins. We are immediately tempted, merely by this geographic observation, to the conclusion that the two continents were once a part of the same mass and have simply split along this irregular line. We might even be willing to add India, with its appendage-like position, to this larger continental grouping and consider the possibility that all three of these triangularly shaped continental or subcontinental land areas (Africa, South America, and India) were at one time joined together. We have touched here on the subject of *continental drift,* which refers to the splitting apart of a continental mass and relative lateral movement of the resulting fragments. This concept will be discussed in more detail in Chapter 14.

MOUNTAIN RANGES

Let us look now at the distribution of surface features within the continental areas themselves. The most striking portions of the earth's land surface are mountain ranges, and the highest mountain area in the world is the Himalayan chain along the northern edge of India. If we consider that India may be only "accidentally" placed against the Eurasian continent, it is possible that the Himalayan chain really forms the southern margin of Asia. To the east, the Himalayan Mountains spread out into an area of lower but generally mountainous country in western and central China. To the west, however, the Himalayan range continues through Afghanistan, Iran, the Caucasus area of Russia, and connects with the eastward extension of the Alps. Exceptionally high elevations are found throughout this generally east-west belt, with the highest peak in the Alps being Mont Blanc, with an elevation of 15,781 feet, and in the Himalayas being Mt. Everest, with an elevation somewhat over 29,000 feet, the highest point on the globe.

One of the interesting features about this Alpine-Himalayan trend is that it is not simply a straight line. At least two major loops are visible at different points in the chain, the best known of which is the Transylvanian Alps of Rumania. The Transylvanian Alps appear as a north-easterly directed bulge or projection from the general east-west trend, with the mountains to the east of the Transylvanian bulge being farther south than the main Alpine extension to the west. A similar bulge, which is not so well displayed owing to the general high elevation of surrounding areas, is found in northern Pakistan and eastern Afghanistan. Here in the Pamir area, sometimes referred to as "the roof of the world," is a bulge, and further offsetting of the mountain trend toward the south occurs as we go eastward.

These loops and abrupt offsettings are a major part of virtually all regional structural trends in the earth. Their presence implies, at the very least, that the mobility of the earth's crust prevents straight-line trends from being continued over extremely long distances. It is an open question as to whether or not there is some more fundamental explanation for the presence of such loops.

The other major mountainous area of the earth's surface is along the west coast of North and South America, the Rocky Mountains and the Andes. The Rockies extend from Alaska and northern Canada in a virtually unbroken pattern down through the western United States and into northern Mexico. In Alaska they may be interpreted as forming into two broad loops, the Alaska and Brooks ranges. At the southern end, the Rockies are terminated quite abruptly by a series of smaller east-west trending mountain ranges just south of Mexico City. The Andes extend from the southern tip of South America up the west coast and then trend in a loop toward the east through Venezuela and Colombia. There is, thus, a break in the straight-line join of the Andes and Rocky Mountains in the general Central American area. The mountainous and rugged topography and general land area of Central America is constructed almost exclusively by outpourings of volcanic rock and does not represent a real structural join of the mountains of North and South America. As will be discussed below, the mountain structures form a broad loop, or arc, extending through the Antilles and other Caribbean Islands, and the continents are geologically linked by this broad eastward-extending bulge. Before discussing the configuration of these and other sets of islands, however, we should note the one-sided nature of continental topography.

The highest elevations of most continents are not in the center. The mountainous areas of North and South America are all on the western edge of the continents, and similarly, the mountainous areas of Europe and Asia are all on the southern edge. (We are here omitting certain details such as the Appalachian Mountain chain along the eastern edge of the United States; this is, however, a much lower region than the Rockies.) The continental divide in the United States is also far toward the western margin, and similarly, the continental divide in Asia is near the southern margin.

OCEAN BASINS

This one-sided nature of the continents may be an indication of a different character of the different ocean basins which border the continental areas. Of particular significance, perhaps, is the fact that the lands bordering the Atlantic Ocean are completely different from the continental margins on the shores of the Pacific Ocean. The western margin of the Atlantic Ocean is formed by the broad and generally low-lying coastal plains of eastern North and South America. On the eastern margin of the Atlantic are similar, though not as well developed, low-lying coastal plain areas in Europe and Africa. Thus the Atlantic Ocean is bordered by generally low land areas around its entire margin. Indeed, as will be discussed later, if we examine the configuration of the ocean bottom offshore from these continental coastal areas, we shall see that the slopes in the margin of the Atlantic Ocean are comparatively slight.

The Pacific Ocean presents a marked contrast to the Atlantic. The western margin of the Pacific, though not bordered by continental mountainous areas, is the site of extensive development of islands and, as will be discussed later, is similar to the eastern margin in such aspects as earthquake and volcanic activity. These types of activities are virtually absent from the margins of the Atlantic Ocean. In contrast to the relatively shallow slopes of the Atlantic under the ocean, the margins of the Pacific Ocean are quite abrupt and fall off sharply to extreme depths. This fact, indeed, partly explains such a simple observation as the comparison of the extremely heavy surf along the Pacific coast of North America with the generally lighter surf along the Atlantic coast. We are thus led inescapably to the conclusion that the Atlantic and Pacific oceans are geologically quite distinct. This may mean that they differ somewhat in their mode of formation, though exactly what these differences may be must be left for discussion after we have obtained more observations on the geology of the ocean basins and surrounding land areas.

ISLAND ARCS

In discussing the Alpine-Himalayan trend, we mentioned broad loops which occurred within the general east-west belt. We saw also that the structural connection between the North and South American continents appeared to be a loop swinging toward the east through the Caribbean Islands and the Antillean chain. We should notice, now, that there are really two broad loops, or arcs, of islands extending eastward into the Atlantic Ocean from the western margin of the North and South American continents. One of these is the Caribbean arc referred to previously.

The other is an arc which passes through South Georgia Island and the area around the Scotia Sea and connects with mountains extending north along the Palmer Peninsula of the Antarctic. This connection between South America and the Antarctic may lengthen the Andes-Rocky Mountain chain, in a structural sense, into the Antarctic continent and leave it as a chain extending virtually halfway around the earth.

The presence of two broad loops into the Atlantic Ocean raises the immediate question as to why such loops occur. We have already mentioned the fact that this must indicate the extent of the mobility of the outer portion of the earth, but we have left unanswered the reason for the generally arcuate character of the deviations from the straight-line structural trends. Unfortunately this is a question which geologists have not yet answered, and we must for the present content ourselves with considering it as "intriguing."

Although we have found two broad loops of islands in the Atlantic, circular or semicircular island patterns are far more characteristic of the western Pacific than they are of the Atlantic Ocean. A glance at the map of the western Pacific will show a large number of island chains which have an arcuate trend. By starting in the north with the Aleutians we can follow down through the Japanese Islands, the Ryukyus and the Marianas, and into several less well-defined arcs in the southwestern Pacific. These arcs of islands are all characterized by similar geologic features. They are all, for example, the site of extensive volcanic activity, and much, though in some cases not all, of the land surfaces of these islands are composed of volcanic material. The arcs, additionally, are all sites of extensive earthquake activity. We shall find, in studying the oceans, that to the seaward side of these arcs occur the deepest oceanic areas, with depths of over 35,000 feet to the east of the Marianas arc.

It has been pointed out that a plane intersecting the surface of the earth at some angle other than perpendicular will form an arcuate intersection. Some geologists, therefore, believe that these island arcs may be the result of some planar feature in the earth intersecting and deforming the earth's surface along the zone represented by the island buildup. The evidence for this theory will be demonstrated in our discussion of oceanic features, where it will be shown that the arcs are underlain by a broad and gradually deepening zone of earthquake centers. As mentioned earlier, this volcanic and earthquake activity on the western side of the Pacific is matched by similar activity, though without the development of island arcs, on the eastern side of the Pacific.

The question now arises as to whether the arcuate form of these volcanic chains bears a relationship to the somewhat more extreme loops that extend eastward into the Atlantic Ocean or that characterize the Himalayan-Alpine chain. Are the same forces in the earth responsible for the arcuate and loop-like form of both features? Although this question will be discussed in more detail in later portions of the book, it is also one which we will not be able to answer.

It should be noted that the detailed study of surface features and configurations like that summarized above has also been applied to the moon; indeed, such study is at present a major means of gleaning some information about lunar processes and history.

CLIMATES

Although the study of climates quite properly occupies the attention of specialists in the field of meteorology, it is necessary for geologists to have some knowledge of the distribution of the earth's climates. The principal reason is that certain topographic features, such as deserts, or soils, such as the red laterites of the tropics, or other geologic features are at least partly determined by climates. In turn, climates are affected by the surface configurations summarized earlier in this chapter. In order to understand ocean currents we must know something about the distribution of winds and wind directions. We study climates and related features not only to better understand those processes which are apparently taking place on the earth but also to enable us to determine features which might be preserved in rocks in the geologic past and which might enable us to construct climatic patterns for the ancient earth. We shall find, in fact, that some climatic patterns which we may construct for ancient periods of time differ considerably from those which occur today. Indeed, we may wish to examine those geological hypotheses which conclude that these different climatic patterns are indicative of a relative change in the positions of poles and present continental areas.

The dominant factor controlling the earth's climate is the far higher proportion of sunlight, and thus of heat, received by the Equator than the polar regions. The point of the earth receiving the greatest amount of sunlight, that is, the point at which the sun's rays are perpendicular, shifts north or south with changes in the seasons. This shift results from the earth's axis being inclined at an angle of $23\frac{1}{2}°$ to the plane of the earth's revolution about the sun. Thus, since the axis of rotation retains the same orientation in space as the earth revolves about the sun, the point on the earth perpendicular to the sun's rays moves from $23\frac{1}{2}°$ N. Lat. on June 21 to $23\frac{1}{2}°$ S. Lat. on December 21. These two dates are called *solstices,* and the times when the sun is directly above the Equator are called *equinoxes.* Latitude $23\frac{1}{2}°$ N. is referred to as the Tropic of Cancer; $23\frac{1}{2}°$ S. is referred to as the Tropic of Capricorn. In like fashion, the region north of $66\frac{1}{2}°$ Lat. (the Arctic Circle) receives continual sunlight in the summer and experiences continual night in the winter; a reciprocal relationship obviously exists below the Antarctic Circle.

Regardless of the seasons, there is a continual tendency for air to be heated at the Equator and to spread north or south after rising to high altitudes over the equatorial regions. As the warm equatorial air moves north or south it cools off and ultimately descends to the earth roughly in Lat. 30° N. and 30° S. This motion establishes a convection cell in the earth's atmosphere in the fashion shown in Fig. 2-6. At latitudes above 30° the warm air encounters cold air moving away from the Poles, and the area in which they meet is generally one of high precipitation and storm activity. Naturally, the latitude along which the equatorial and polar air masses meet moves back and forth with the seasons.

Owing to the earth's rotation from west to east, warm equatorial air moving north from the Equator has an eastward velocity imparted to it at the Equator which is somewhat higher than the velocity of rotation at more northerly latitudes, and similarly in the southern hemisphere. The air, therefore, descending around Lat. 30° and moving toward the poles tends to slip eastward, thus creating a set of winds from the west referred to as the *westerlies*. This relative movement of the earth's surface and fluids above it is referred to as a *Coriolis effect* and will be described in more detail in Chapter 13 when we discuss ocean currents. In equatorial regions, slippage between the earth's surface and the air above it creates a set of westward-directed winds known as *equatorial easterlies* or *trade winds*. Along the 30° latitudes, winds are not generally as strong as they are to the north or south, and they are more variable in direction. These regions are commonly referred to as the *horse latitudes*. The general direction of the various winds is shown diagrammatically in Fig. 2-6.

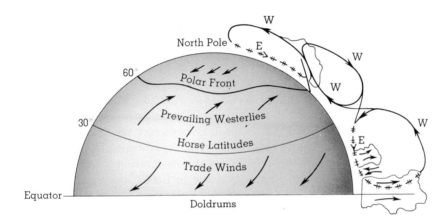

Fig. 2-6. Diagram showing prevailing wind directions and circulation in the atmosphere. Explanation in text. (From *U.S. Department of Agriculture Yearbook, 1941*.)

As a result of the upward movement of heated air at the Equator, there is a considerable amount of precipitation in equatorial regions. The reason is that the hot air rising above water surfaces, such as the oceans, brings with it a large amount of water vapor. Upon rising to higher altitudes the air is cooled and can no longer hold as much water vapor as it could at a higher temperature. This is why equatorial regions are generally noted for high rainfall. The air, however, which moves to the north or south of the Equator has lost most of its moisture, and thus the air which descends near the 30° latitudes and then moves back toward the Equator is relatively dry. It is interesting to note that most of the desert areas of the earth such as the Sahara, the southwestern deserts of the United States, and certain arid belts in South Africa, South America, and Australia, are largely concentrated between the 15° and 30° latitudes north or south.

The amount of precipitation at a particular location is not controlled solely by latitude. For example, coastal areas in general tend to be relatively moist owing to the proximity to water and the tendency for winds to blow onshore. Conversely, areas in the center of continents tend to be more arid, owing to precipitation of most of the moisture in the air along the coastlines. In particular, where a continental area is shielded by a high range of mountains, extreme aridity may develop. This shielding is the explanation for the deserts of the southwestern United States, which are in the path of westerly winds coming from the Pacific Ocean. The winds, however, must pass over the major mountain ranges of southern California, such as the Sierra Nevadas, and it is in these ranges that virtually all of the moisture is precipitated. Consequently, air passing farther to the eastward in the westerly wind belt is comparatively dry. Winds reaching this area from the east have passed over several thousand miles of the North American continent, and the tendency for moisture to precipitate near the coast is shown by the gradually decreasing rainfall from east to west between the Atlantic coast and the Rocky Mountains.

The climate at any particular place is obviously controlled by a variety of factors including the complex interplay between general atmospheric circulation and local topography. For example, the tendency for coastal areas to be humid is not followed in the extremely arid coastal region of northern Chile. The aridity here arises from the fact that the surface air is cooled by the upwelling of cold polar water, and hence the cool air carries little moisture to the warmer land.

In later chapters of this book we shall describe features in ancient rocks which may be used to indicate the climate under which the rocks were deposited. We shall, for example, reconstruct the temperature of sea water in equilibrium with some types of chemically precipitated rocks. We shall also discuss criteria for the recognition of arid climates or of tropical climates. With this evidence in hand, and presuming that we can correlate rocks of equivalent age in various parts of the earth, we will be able to draw paleoclimatic maps for different periods of time. This synthesis will be more fully developed in Chapter 12.

CHAPTER **3** GRAVITY, MASS, AND DENSITY

◀ A marine gravimeter. (Photo by T. W. Donnelly.)

We have discussed the size of the earth and the general configuration of its surface, and it is now logical to investigate the earth's interior. In this section we shall be particularly interested in the mass of the earth.

Several simple methods are available for studying the earth's interior. One is to determine the mass of the entire earth and, having already determined its volume, the average density. Then, by investigating the densities of surficial rocks, we will be able to draw some conclusions concerning the density and composition of the interior. Another method that we mentioned earlier and shall discuss in more detail in Chapter 4 consists of studying the travel times of elastic waves generated by earthquakes. These waves, called seismic waves, pass through the earth, and the relative velocities with which they travel provide distinct clues concerning the nature of the subsurface features of the earth. In later chapters we shall also be able to infer properties in the earth's interior from features which occur on the surface. We will, for example, be able to investigate the earth's shallow interior by finding rocks which have been erupted onto the surface through volcanoes or brought up to the surface from shallow depths by earthquake movement repeated over and over in the long span of geologic time. Furthermore, in studying the methods by which the earth's crust was formed, we will arrive at a moderately accurate appraisal of processes that have gone on in the earth's interior.

LAW OF GRAVITY

The first line of investigation is the technique which we can use to determine the mass of the earth. Newton's fundamental law of gravitational attraction states that any two infinitely small particles attract each other with a force proportional to the products of their masses and inversely proportional to the square of the distance between them. Mathematically, this law may be formulated as follows:

$$F \propto \frac{m_1 m_2}{d^2}$$

or

$$F = \frac{G m_1 m_2}{d^2}$$

where m_1 and m_2 = masses
d = distance between points
G = the constant of gravitational attraction

This formula refers to the force of attraction between infinitely small particles whose size or shape are inconsequential compared to the distance between them and not to the attraction between irregularly shaped bodies of finite size. This fundamental law of gravitation can be tested in a variety of ways, such as by studying the acceleration of particles falling toward the earth's surface or by interpreting the motion of the planets, as was done in the early days of the development of classical physics. Mathematical derivations from this basic formula prove that it also applies for two spheres outside of each other, even if one sphere is relatively very small. In the case of two such spheres the gravitational attraction is inversely proportional to the square of the distance between their centers. This formula is the starting point for the construction of a method for determining the mass of the earth.

MASS OF THE EARTH

Consider a small sphere as shown in Fig. 3-1 which is constrained by a rigid bar to move only in a horizontal plane parallel to the earth's

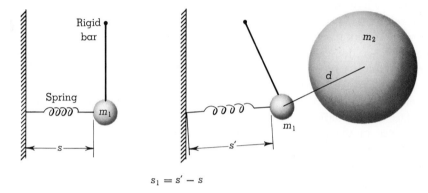

Fig. 3-1. Establishment of a proportionality constant for the gravitative attraction between two spheres. Explanation given in text.

$$s_1 = s' - s$$

gravitational field. This sphere is restrained in this horizontal motion by a spring. Now we bring a heavy mass in the form of a large sphere from an infinite distance away up to a position very close to the small sphere, also as shown in Fig. 3-1. This small sphere will be attracted toward the large sphere, and the spring will stretch. We know, in arbitrary units, the masses of the small and large spheres and also the distance between the center of the large mass and the center of the smaller one. We have, thus, been able to calibrate the spring restraining the small sphere in terms of the force of attraction between the two spheres.

If we now take the small sphere and the spring and hang the sphere vertically below the spring, the sphere will be attracted toward the center of the earth (Fig. 3-2). The force of attraction will stretch the spring, and if the amount of stretching is proportional to the force exerted, we will then know the force of attraction between the earth and the small sphere. We know the distance between the sphere and the center of the earth, since we have already measured the earth's radius by methods discussed in the previous chapter. We now have the following information: the masses of the large and small spheres; the distance between the large and small spheres in Fig. 3-1; the distance between the small sphere and the center of the earth; and the ratio of the force generated by the large sphere when it is brought near the small one and the force generated by the earth when the small sphere is allowed to hang freely in the earth's gravitational field. We thus have all of the quantities necessary to measure the mass of the earth in terms of the mass of the large sphere. The mathematical formulation of this procedure is as follows:

Let m_1 = mass of the small sphere

m_2 = mass of the large sphere

d = distance between the centers of the large and small spheres

s_1 = distance of stretching of the spring when the large sphere is brought close to the small one

s_2 = distance of stretching of the spring when the small sphere hangs in the earth's gravitational field

r = radius of the earth

M = mass of the earth

then

$$F_1 \propto s_1 = \frac{Gm_1m_2}{d^2}$$

$$F_2 \propto s_2 = \frac{Gm_1M}{r^2}$$

$$\frac{s_2}{s_1} = \frac{Gm_1M}{r^2} \cdot \frac{d^2}{Gm_1m_2} = \frac{d^2}{r^2} \cdot \frac{M}{m_2}$$

We know the ratio s_2/s_1 and all quantities except M and can thus calculate M.

Without going into the details of establishing a set of physical units, we can say that the gravitational constant or measure of gravitational attraction, g, equals 978 cm/sec² or 32 feet/sec² at the Equator. Similarly, the constant of gravitation, G., which appears in the above equations, is equal to $6.67 \cdot 10^{-8}$ cm³/g · sec². With the fundamental unit of mass established by letting 1 gram be the mass of 1 cm³ of water at 4° C. (the maximum density), we can say that the total mass of the earth is $6 \cdot 10^{27}$ g or $5.4 \cdot 10^{21}$ tons. If we divide this mass by the earth's volume (determined in Chapter 2), the average density is found to be 5.5 g/cm³.

Actual measurements of the gravitational constant are clearly more complicated than has been shown here. For example, no single spring is usable for both experiments. It has been the purpose of this discussion, however, merely to present the basic principles which permit us to obtain the overall mass and density of the earth.

GRAVITY VARIATIONS

The force of gravity is not constant over the earth's surface, and it is, therefore, of interest to discuss methods by which we might measure the variation in g from place to place. In theory we need only construct an instrument containing a calibrated spring as shown in Fig. 3-2 in order to determine variations in gravitational attraction. This has, indeed, been

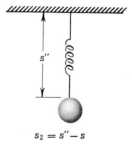

$s_2 = s'' - s$

Fig. 3-2. Determination of mass of earth based on information derived from experiment shown in Fig. 3-1. Explanation and derivation given in text.

done, and many gravimeters operate essentially on this principle. Another method, however, and one which was the only satisfactory one in the early days of gravity investigations, involves the use of a simple pendulum. A pendulum with a length, *d,* and a mass ideally concentrated at one point at the end of the pendulum bar, has a period of oscillation given by the formula

$$\text{period} = 2\pi \frac{\sqrt{d}}{\sqrt{g}}$$

It will be observed in the above formula that the period of oscillation is inversely proportional to $\sqrt{g}$. Thus, by moving a standard pendulum from place to place on the earth's surface and measuring its period of oscillation as accurately as possible, we can determine variations in the force of gravitational attraction. With these methods of measurement in mind, let us turn, now, to the causes of variations in *g* from place to place on the earth.

Variations in gravitational intensity can be attributed to a number of causes. In this section we shall try to analyze the reasons for major variations in gravitational attraction and, consequently, provide a framework with which to study local or minor variations in the gravitational field. One major cause of change in gravitational intensity is entitled the *latitude effect*. This effect is the result of two phenomena: (1) the centrifugal force caused by the earth's rotation decreases from a maximum at the Equator to zero at the Poles; and (2) the shorter radius at the Poles causes a stronger attraction toward the earth's center than at lower latitudes. Both forces act in the same direction, and *g* increases smoothly with the latitude from 978 cm/sec² at the Equator to 983 cm/sec² at the Poles.

In addition to the latitude effect, a particle on the earth's surface exhibits different degrees of gravitational attraction toward the earth, depending upon its elevation. As we go to higher elevations, the distance from the earth's center increases, and the gravitational attraction decreases. Thus, in constructing a map of gravitational intensity for any given area, it is necessary to correct all readings to the values which they would have at any point if all points were at a constant level. It is customary, though not necessary, to use sea level for the purposes of this correction. A correction in which all gravitational measurements are reduced to the value that they would have at a predetermined elevation is entitled *free-air correction*. The term results from the fact that this correction does not take into account the amount of rock existing between the actual elevation of the measured point and the reference elevation.

In order to effect a complete correction of a single gravitational measurement, it is necessary to take into account this mass of rock which exists between the reference and actual elevations. If, as is commonly the case, the actual point is above the reference elevation, then the gravitational attraction on a particle will be decreased by the higher elevation but will be somewhat increased by the mass of rock occurring between the particle and the reference elevation. Thus, a measured *g* at an elevation above sea level could be corrected to sea level by adding a free-air correction, to take into account the fact that the measured *g* is less than it would be at sea level, and subtracting a correction for the amount of rock between the point and sea level, to take into account the fact that this mass of rock has caused additional gravitational attraction at the measured point. This correction for the amount of excess rock is called a *Bouguer correction,* for the man who first developed the process. In order to make a Bouguer correction it is necessary to know not only the densities of rock in the area but also to have a very accurate map of the configuration of these rocks. The whole correction is difficult to make, but approximate techniques are routinely used in geophysical surveys (Fig. 3-3).

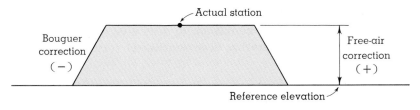

Fig. 3-3. Conversion of measured gravity to theoretical value at a reference surface. If the actual station is above the reference elevation, a positive free-air correction must be added to the actual value in order to obtain the theoretical value, and the Bouguer correction for the rock beneath the station is negative.

ANOMALIES

In summary, in order to make a meaningful map of gravity variations over a broad region, it is necessary to apply a correction for change in latitude, for elevation, and for the amount of rock existing between the elevation of the measured point and a chosen reference level. Once these corrections are made, the result should be a map which, in theory, shows no gravity variations from place to place. That is, all corrections that might be predicted on an *a priori* basis have been accounted for, and any residual variations in gravitational intensity must result from local or minor features. These residual variations are commonly referred to as *anomalies,* because they represent unexpected deviations from the measured *g*. We shall discuss anomalies in more detail in various later sections of the book. Here, however, it would be appropriate to mention several examples of the causes of gravitational anomalies.

On the Gulf Coast of North America a number of major oil fields have been developed in the neighborhood of large domes of salt which pushed their way upward from an underlying salt bed into near-surface sediments. This salt has risen because its density is less than that of the surrounding rocks. The presence of comparatively low-density salt near the surface causes gravitational attraction over these salt domes to be less than the gravitational attraction in other parts of the area. Thus it is a reasonably simple matter to prospect for salt domes and their accompanying petroleum deposits by means of a gravimeter. A map showing values of *g* suitably corrected for latitude, height, and the Bouguer factor should, in an area of salt domes, show the outline of the domes in terms of areas of relatively low g (negative anomaly). Prospecting by this technique has resulted in finding large quantities of petroleum.

By contrast, a positive gravity anomaly may be expected where particularly dense rock is concentrated near the surface. As an example of such concentrations, we might mention various metallic ore bodies in which heavy-metal sulfides in high concentration give the rock a higher density than an unmineralized rock of similar composition. Therefore, it is also possible to prospect for such ores by suitable gravity-measurement techniques.

With regard to major features, we shall find that mountain ranges in general have sizable negative Bouguer anomalies. The implication is that there is a large mass of comparatively light rock underlying the mountain range, and indeed, in the next section we shall show how this conclusion is supported by a second, independent line of evidence. Extremely high negative gravity anomalies are also found along the ridges and oceanic sides of the island arcs discussed in Chapter 2. The reasons for these negative anomalies are more difficult to determine than for mountain ranges, and no one theory has been conclusively demonstrated to date.

SPHEROID AND GEOID

It is now useful to relate gravity and the shape of the earth in terms of two idealized surfaces which conform fairly closely to the actual surface of the earth. One surface, called a *spheroid,* is an ellipsoid of revolution around an axis through the North and South Poles and is purely geometric. The spheroid is simply the surface which the earth would have if it had a polar radius 13 miles shorter than an equatorial radius, a smooth increase in radius from either of the Poles to the Equator, and a complete lack of surficial features such as mountain ranges and valleys. The spheroid, being a smooth surface of revolution, is therefore a sort of ideal geometric earth. In contrast to the spheroid, the *geoid* is a somewhat irregular surface defined by gravitational attraction. The geoid is the surface which is perpendicular to a plumb bob at any point on the earth. Thus, where a mountain range causes deflection of a plumb bob

Fig. 3-4. Relationship between spheroid, geoid, and topography. The approximately vertical lines are drawn perpendicular to equipotential (equal gravity) surfaces at all points. Note that the geoid is an equipotential surface. (From G. Bomford, *Geodesy,* 1st ed.; courtesy of The Clarendon Press, Oxford.)

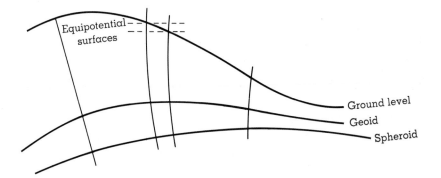

away from a valley, or a continent causes deflection away from an ocean basin, the geoid shows this deflection by rising toward the high land and away from the low areas. Diagrammatically, the geoid and the spheroid bear the relations shown in Fig. 3-4. In the last few years artificial earth satellites have provided both more accurate and much more plentiful data on the exact shape and gravity field of the earth. The huge amount of data generated by such geodetic satellites permit the determination of any selected radius of the earth to within a few tens of feet.

ISOSTASY

One object of introducing the concept of the geoid was to arrive at a very fundamental geologic principle. In extremely accurate topographic surveying it is necessary to take into account deflections of the plumb bob from the perpendicular to the spheroid. For example, a surveying instrument which is used to measure vertical angles is oriented vertically by means of a plumb bob. If this vertical plumb bob is not perpendicular to the spheroid surface that is approximated by the earth's surface, then a correction factor must be applied to angles measured by the instrument. In making these corrections it is important to note that the only "vertical" measurement which can be made at a particular location is the orientation of a plumb line. That is, the perpendicular to the spheroid cannot be obtained by direct measurement. In order to correct the plumb line so that it is perpendicular to the spheroid, it is necessary to make some rough calculation of the deviation of the plumb line caused by adjacent land masses or land deficiency, such as valleys.

All of these surveying techniques were well-known in the 1800s, and it was during the course of an accurate topographic survey of India that a number of difficulties were noted. The difficulties were best shown by noting discrepancies in latitude and longitude measurements made by surveys from a reference station (using a plumb bob) and correlative astronomical measurements (which are independent of the orientation of a plumb bob). An Englishman by the name of V. H. Pratt found that errors in the survey were caused by the inaccurate representation of the orientation of the plumb bob in the neighborhood of the Himalayan Mountains. This immense mountain range on the northern border of India must, of course, cause a deflection of the plumb bob toward the north at stations on the plains south of the mountain range. The deflection, however, is found by calculation to be less than would be expected if the Himalayan Mountains were treated simply as a mass of rock lying on top of the Indian plains. That is, if rocks of equal density were placed in the topographical configuration shown in Fig. 3-5, the deflection of the plumb bob should be greater than the actual deflection. The only conclusion which Pratt could reach was that the rocks of the Himalayan Mountains and their underlying roots must be less dense than rocks in the neighboring plains area. From this conclusion it is logical to extrapolate to the possibility that the mountains are high, because they consist of lighter rock than that underlying neighboring plains (Fig. 3-6).

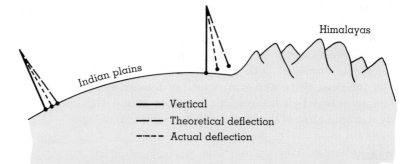

Fig. 3-5. Deflection of the plumb bob caused by the Himalayas. "Vertical" line is the perpendicular to the earth's surface (spheroid) at a point. Theoretical deflection is calculated by assuming that the Himalayas consist of rock with the same density as the rock underlying the plains. The fact that actual deflection is less than theoretical proves that the Himalayas consist of low-density rock. All elevations and angles are greatly exaggerated.

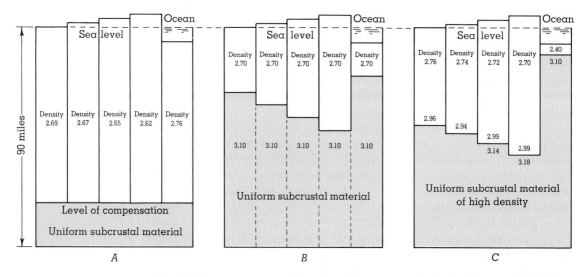

Fig. 3-6. Three concepts of the nature of floating crustal blocks. (From *A Textbook of Geology*, Robert M. Garrels, Harper & Row, New York, 1951.) *A.* Crust composed of floating uniform blocks of different densities. They all sink to the same depth in the subcrustal material, but the different densities account for the variation in surface elevation. There is small variation in the four blocks on the left, representing continental blocks of granitic material, but a marked change to the low-lying ocean block on the right. *B.* Crust composed of blocks of uniform density, sinking to unequal depths in the subcrustal material, and rising to unequal heights above mean sea level. This is one of the earliest views advanced, and its obvious difficulty lies in the low density assigned to the oceanic block on the right. Earthquake waves have shown that the material immediately underlying most of the ocean floors is basaltic, with a density of 2.9 or 3.0. *C.* A modern picture, combining parts of the two fundamental pictures (*A* and *B*). In this concept, the crust is composed of blocks of densities increasing downward to a nearly uniform value from varying densities at the surface. An oceanic block is shown consisting of deposited sediments of low density. The crust grades downward into subcrustal material and is much less a separate unit than in the original views.

This conclusion requires the assumption that surficial materials can move freely, essentially in adjustment to "hydrostatic" equilibrium. Thus, light materials float higher than heavier materials and cause the elevation of mountain ranges or other high land areas. The floating of these surficial materials also implies that below the near-surface rocks is a denser, reasonably mobile layer in which the "hydrostatic" adjustments take place. The term "hydrostatic" is, of course, not wholly accurate, since all materials involved are silicate rocks rather than water. Geologists commonly use the term "lithostatic" to refer to adjustments in rocks which permit equalization of pressures at some level within the rock mass. Once the possibility of elevations controlled by floating of surficial blocks is accepted, it is possible to construct an alternative theory to that of Pratt. The alternate theory, developed by G. B. Airy, assumes that all surficial materials have approximately the same density and are floating in a heavier substratum. The difference in elevations, then, is simply caused by difference in thicknesses of individual blocks. On the basis of this concept it is not necessary for there to be a density difference from one type of surficial rock to another. The Airy concept implies that mountain ranges should have deep roots extending down into the substratum below the level reached by the blocks of lower-standing land regions.

Additional modern evidence concerning these two theories is based on the negative Bouguer anomalies of mountain ranges discussed earlier in this chapter, on the seismic studies which will be discussed in the next chapter, and on general geologic investigations of rock types at various parts of the earth's surface. There is now clear evidence that mountain ranges do indeed have roots which extend to greater depth than surficial material under land areas of low elevation. It also appears likely, however, that there is some type of density difference between rocks characteristic of mountain ranges and rocks characteristic of other regions. Thus, both the Pratt and the Airy hypotheses may be partially correct.

The concept of lithostatic floating of surficial materials has been refined since the original publication of the Pratt and Airy hypotheses and has been given the name *isostasy*. Essentially the hypothesis of isostasy states that the total weight of rock between the center of the earth and the earth's surface at any point is constant regardless of its position on the earth (although ignoring the effects of variation in the earth's radius with latitude). Thus the earth's surface can be considered as being in lithostatic equilibrium. The consequences of this conclusion are as follows:

1. Surficial rocks must be considerably less dense than immediately underlying rocks.

2. The substratum for surficial material must be fluid, at least to stresses exerted over long periods of time.

3. The earth's crust must not be very strong; that is, portions must *not* be so rigidly linked together as to cause any major region to be held above or pushed below the level of lithostatic equilibrium. For example, as shown in Fig. 3-7, a rigid bar whose density changed from one end to the other would float at an angle as shown, and individual portions of

the bar are clearly not in lithostatic equilibrium with a column of fluid directly below them. The occurrence of isostatic equilibrium, therefore, implies that the earth's crust does not have the type of rigidity shown by the bar in Fig. 3-7, and we may conclude that the crust is not particularly strong as viewed from a large scale and over a long period of time.

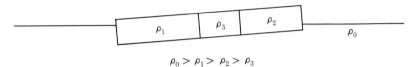

$$\rho_0 > \rho_1 > \rho_2 > \rho_3$$

Fig. 3-7. Floating rigid bar in which the density varies from place to place. Rigidity of the bar prevents each portion from establishing an independent position of hydraulic equilibrium (isostasy). Note particularly that the region of lowest density (ρ_3) has a lower elevation than a region of higher density (ρ_2).

We shall return to the applications and ramifications of the concept of isostasy throughout this book.

DENSITIES IN THE EARTH

Some of the most fundamental geologic observations are also the simplest. One of the major clues to the structure of the outer part of the earth is the fact that the earth's surface appears to show two preferred levels of elevation. If we plot the percentage of the earth's surface, including the sea bottom, having elevations in different ranges above and below sea level, we obtain a cumulative frequency distribution as shown in Fig. 3-8. Figure 3-8 clearly shows two preferred elevations for the earth's outer surface. One is at a depth of 2 to 3 miles (12,000 to 15,000 feet) below sea level, and the other is approximately at sea level.

Fig. 3-8. Cumulative percentage of elevations on the earth's surface. Note the very large proportion of elevations between sea level and 1 km above sea level and also between 3 and 5 km below sea level.

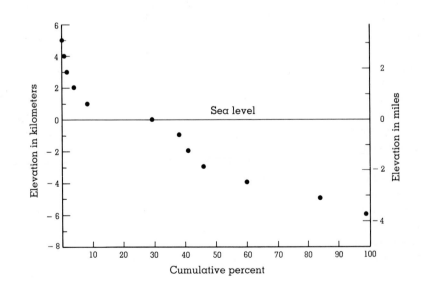

This fact, together with all other observations of general geologic validity, must be explained in terms of some major feature of the earth.

One logical explanation for these two preferred levels of the earth's surface is that the outer portion of the earth consists of two major rock types. One of these rock types we can call *continental,* and we can attribute the presence of continental land areas to an accumulation of this comparatively light rock. The other type of rock is presumably characteristic of oceanic areas, which are depressed as a result of the fact that this oceanic rock is heavier than that of the continents. The discovery of the occurrence of mountain roots and of isostatic compensation represents a major line of evidence in favor of the subdivision of the outer portion of the earth into continental and oceanic rock types. In this view the continents are presumed to be masses of comparatively light material floating on a subcrust of a density closer to that of the oceanic rock. If we sample the continental areas extensively, particularly with drill cores below the immediate surficial layers, we find that most of the continental mass consists of a rock called *granite,* which we shall study later. This granite has a specific gravity of approximately 2.7. Although granite is the principal rock of the continents, it is virtually absent from oceanic islands or in materials dredged from the ocean floor. Most of these materials are another type of silicate rock known as *basalt,* a heavier material with less silica and more calcium, magnesium, and iron than granites. Basalt has a density of approximately 3.0.

At first we might be tempted to say that the material in which the granitic continents float is simply the typical oceanic basalt. In the next chapter, however, when we study seismology, we shall find that the fundamental discontinuity between continents and the underlying material is also present under the surface of the ocean floor, although at a much shallower level. The continents apparently are underlain by material which has a specific gravity estimated as approximately 3.3. This estimate of 3.3 is based on the thicknesses and specific gravities of continental and oceanic rocks and the average elevations of continents and oceans. The major discontinuity between material of density 3.3 and the overlying granites and basalts of the continents or oceans is entitled the *Mohorovicic discontinuity.* This surface was originally discovered by seismological work and must be documented more fully in the next chapter.

We have already mentioned the fact that the average specific gravity of the earth is approximately 5.5. The fact that continental areas have a specific gravity of approximately 2.7 and oceanic areas of 3.0 indicates that at some depth there must be specific gravities considerably greater than 5.5 in order to give that overall average for the earth. It is well to speculate here on the various causes for high densities deep in the earth. Basically there can be two causes for high densities. One is a progressive or sudden change in composition downward in the earth, with material having a higher density becoming more abundant at greater depth. The other possible cause is the effect of pressure on materials similar to those which occur at the surface. It is conceivable that, at great depths, the high pressures generated by the weight of overlying rock cause the mineral phases present in the rocks to change to denser phases, and these changes to higher-density phases may account for extremely high specific gravities toward the center of the earth. This latter possibility is indeed a tempting one for density variations in the outer portion of the earth.

Geologists are just beginning to be able to build equipment which can simulate, for brief periods of time, the temperatures and pressures which exist in the outer few hundred miles of the earth. Within these ranges of temperatures and pressure, there certainly are transformations from one type of crystal phase to another type, with increasing density at higher pressures. The laboratory transformation of graphite to diamond under high pressure and temperature is one example of such density changes. Nevertheless, there has been no opportunity to duplicate conditions at great depth, and there seems to be considerable doubt that specific gravities above 5.5 could be generated from surficial material exposed simply to high pressures. The leading working hypothesis at present is that there must be some sort of compositional change at great depth in the earth to account for the high densities towards the earth's center.

This hypothesis is supported by the study of meteorites. Meteorites come in a variety of forms and compositions, and this subject will be discussed in much greater detail in Chapter 5, when we consider the evolution of the earth from a compositional point of view. Most meteorites reaching the earth's surface in coherent form consist of silicates with compositions similar to normal surficial rocks. These are called *stony meteorites,* and although their compositions and the types of minerals they contain are different from those of granites or basalts of the earth's surface, nevertheless they are not sufficiently different in composition to account for major high-density zones within the earth. A significant portion of meteoritic material, however, perhaps on the order of 10 percent of observed meteorite falls, consists of metallic material in which iron and nickel predominate. The significance of these *nickel-iron meteorites* is that they demonstrate the existence in the solar system of a mass of high-density metal which occurs as a separate phase.

The origin of meteorites is disputed, though some scientists hypothesize that they represent the remnants of a fragmented planet. Whether or not this origin is correct, the fact that nickel-iron meteorites exist in some abundance in the solar system gives rise to the suggestion that similar material may have gone into the formation of the earth. If this is true, we have a very logical explanation for the high density which must exist at depth within the earth. Possibly toward the earth's center there is a region of nickel-iron, either as a liquid or solid. Then the density of this area would be sufficiently large to counterbalance the comparatively light rock of the earth's surface. It is largely for this reason that geologists speculate on the existence of a nickel-iron *core* in the earth.

We have now discovered density variations in the earth that could be summarized as follows: light continents with a specific gravity of approximately 2.7 and oceanic rocks with a specific gravity of 3.0 all float on something slightly heavier, apparently with a specific gravity of about 3.3; at depth there is material with a specific gravity considerably above 5.5 in order to give an average of 5.5 to the earth as a whole; this high-density material is probably composed of iron and nickel in solid or liquid form, though it is conceivable that high pressures near the center of the earth might convert other materials into some high-density phase.

We do not as yet have information concerning the depths to the boundary between continental and subcontinental rock or to the boundary, if there is one, between high-density nickel-iron and overlying lighter rock. In fact, on the basis of the evidence thus far developed we cannot even determine whether or not these boundaries are comparatively sharp or whether they are broad gradations from material of one density to the next. We shall discover in the next chapter that the nature and position of these boundaries can best be determined by the study of earthquakes.

CHAPTER 4

SEISMOLOGY

◀ Seismic exploration at sea. (Courtesy of Robert H. Ray Co.)

When you hear sounds, such as a person talking, you are listening to movements in the air around you. Sound waves, in fact, are simply alternating bands of compressed and rarefied particles which spread outward from the source of the noise. The bands which form the "sound wave" travel through air with a particular velocity depending upon the density of the air being traversed. In similar fashion such waves may pass through solid objects, such as doors or walls of houses, with velocities characteristic of all of the various media that they move through. Where the media are completely uniform in all directions the waves move with equal velocities in all directions. Where there are nonuniformities in the media, as in many types of solids, the waves move with different velocities in different directions.

In an exactly similar manner, waves may be caused by motions within the earth, and the waves (called *seismic waves*) pass through the surrounding solid rock much as a sound wave passes through air. In fact, all waves caused by such movements could be considered as kinds of sound waves, though most of those formed within the earth are far from audible. Waves are generated naturally in the earth by earthquakes. In earthquakes, in addition to the compressional-rarefactional waves characteristic of sound transmission, other types of wave motions are set up. We shall discuss these various types of complex waves in the next section of this chapter after a brief discussion of the general principles of seismologic investigation based upon a simple study of modern exploration techniques.

SEISMIC EXPLORATION

Seismology is the branch of geology which deals with the movement of waves through the earth. Many of its practitioners are engaged in the search for petroleum based on various seismic surveying techniques. In its essentials, the methods of seismic exploration appear quite simple. The technique consists of drilling a hole in the ground, inserting a charge of dynamite, and exploding this charge in the presence of various listening devices. Waves emanate out from the point of explosion, and their times of arrival are recorded at the listening devices, essentially small *seismographs,* distributed over the ground surface. Alternatively, waves can be generated by dropping weights on the ground (thumping) or any other technique that periodically puts energy into the medium.

If the outer portion of the earth were homogeneous, this procedure would provide us with no information which we did not already have. The outer part of the earth, however, is generally layered, for, as we shall see in Chapter 6, most of the land surface is covered by sedimentary rocks deposited in a series of beds which have relatively sharp contacts between different types of rocks. Without going into detail concerning the materials which constitute these individual layers, we can say that most materials have different seismic properties; that is, they transmit seismic waves with different velocities. In general the more compressed rocks at greater depth, and thus under higher pressure, are the more rigid, and therefore the velocities of seismic waves in them are higher than in rocks closer to the surface.

As a result of these faster velocities at depth it is possible for waves following a rather deep path, as shown in Fig. 4-1, to arrive at a particular listening device before waves following the more direct path from explosion to seismograph. Thus, by placing a series of seismographs at different distances from the shot point, we will be able to detect the depth to various layers of high velocity by virtue of the fact that the arrival times of seismic waves at distant seismographs will not lie on a straight line (or smooth curve) as would be plotted for arrival times for waves traveling directly from the shot point to seismographs near the shot. This situation is shown diagrammatically in Fig. 4-2, where you will notice that a distinct break in the curve of travel time versus distance from the shot point is shown at a distance determined by the depth to the "discontinuity" between materials of different seismic velocities. By knowing the depth of the explosion and the velocities of seismic waves in different rock types, it is a comparatively simple matter to calculate depth to layers with different seismic velocities.

As an example of such a calculation, consider the situation shown in Fig. 4-2. For our purposes here we shall make a few simplifying assumptions which, in actual practice, would cause some modification of the results. These assumptions are: (1) seismic velocities are constant in all directions within the layers; (2) the depth of the hole is negligible with respect to the depth to layer 2; and (3) the path followed by a wave which passes through layer 2 consists of vertical portions from the shot hole down to layer 2 and up from layer 2 to the seismograph, plus a horizontal portion along layer 2. In actual practice, the path followed will be somewhat curved. The seismograph at station III is clearly at a distance d from the shot point, such that the wave which travels solely in layer 1 reaches the station at the same time as the wave which travels down to and through layer 2. At greater distances the lower wave arrives first, and at smaller distances the upper wave arrives first. Thus, at station III the travel time for a wave wholly in layer 1 is

$$t_1 = \frac{d}{V_1}$$

Similarly, the travel time for a wave which travels down to and through layer 2 is

$$t_2 = \frac{d}{V_2} + \frac{x}{V_1} + \frac{x}{V_1}$$

Since $t_1 = t_2$, we may solve for x, the thickness of layer 1.

In the above paragraph we have assumed that velocities of the various waves in different layers are known. In practice these velocities are also determined from travel time-distance curves simply as the slopes of the straight portions of the time-distance curves.

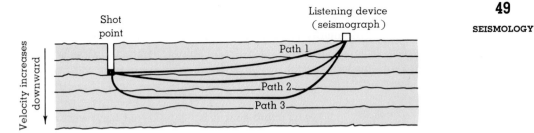

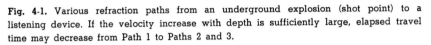

Fig. 4-1. Various refraction paths from an underground explosion (shot point) to a listening device. If the velocity increase with depth is sufficiently large, elapsed travel time may decrease from Path 1 to Paths 2 and 3.

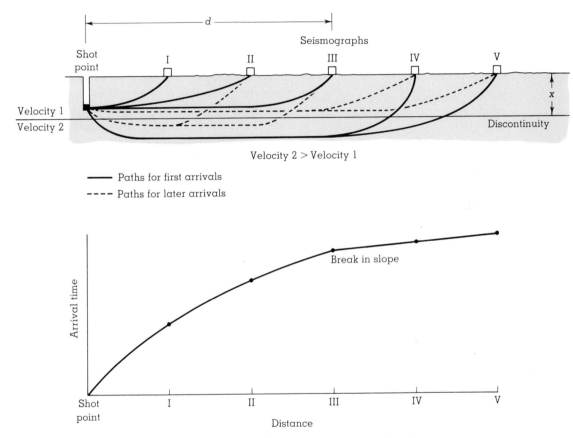

Fig. 4-2. Effect of discontinuity in seismic velocities. First arrivals at stations I to III are from waves traveling in the upper layer, and those at stations IV and V are from waves in lower layer. Difference in velocities is shown by the break in slope in the lower graph. The symbols x and d refer to the calculation given in the text.

We have been discussing a seismic prospecting technique known as *refraction*. It is also possible to measure the depth to various horizons by *reflection* methods. This method is based on the fact that the surfaces between layers of markedly different seismic velocities will reflect seismic waves. Thus we might find a travel path such as shown in Fig. 4-3, and here we would want to measure not only the time of the arrival of the first, or direct, wave from the shot but also the arrival of the next wave, which is presumably reflected from the highest major surface of discontinuity between materials of different seismic characteristics. We would also, of course, expect a whole series of reflections from various layers, with the only restrictions being that ultimately the seismic energy is sufficiently dissipated at depth that it is not reflected back with sufficient intensity for us to measure on the seismograph.

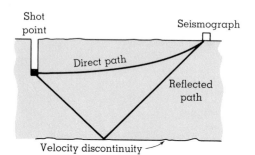

Fig. 4-3. Comparison of reflected and direct seismic paths.

The examples which we have used thus far have assumed a horizontal layering within the earth. It should be apparent that if the layering is inclined in some way at an angle to the earth's surface, then this fact should be fairly easily detected by placing listening devices on both sides of the shot hole. The travel times in Fig. 4-4, for example, will be considerably shorter for waves extending to the right of the shot hole than for waves extending to the left. A complete interpretation of complex orientations of these underground layers is very difficult and occupies a large part of the time of a large number of seismologists. Fortunately most of the numerous and tedious calculations involved can now be done quickly on electronic computers.

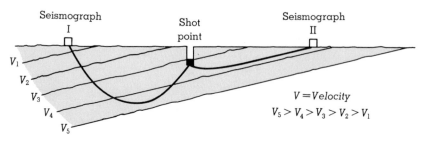

Fig. 4-4. Paths of seismic waves in tilted layers. Times of first arrivals of seismic waves from shot point would be different at stations I and II.

SEISMOGRAPHS

We have mentioned the listening devices, or *seismographs,* used to record the time of arrival of various seismic waves. Thus far, however, we have not discussed the construction of these instruments. The basic principle in the construction of a seismograph is that it must consist of a heavy enough weight suspended in such fashion that the weight will not move when the earth on which the seismograph rests does move. That is, as seismic waves impinge on the earth's surface, the surface shakes. Except in the largest earthquakes, the total movement is sufficiently small, however, to be undetectable by human beings. Nevertheless, small movements can be picked up by delicate instruments constructed on the general principles shown in Fig. 4-5. Here you will notice that a weight with a high inertia is suspended such that when the instrument carrying the recording scale is suddenly shaken, the weight itself will not move, or at least it will be moved much less than the rest of the instrument. The relative movement of the weight and scale is recorded by some suitable mechanism, such as a pen-and-ink tracing, a photographic recording, or an electronic recording. The record produced is called a *seismogram,* and we shall discuss character- istics of seismograms in more detail after a descrip- tion of the types of waves produced by earthquakes. The seismograph shown in Fig. 4-5 will record only the vertical motions in earthquakes. For a complete recording of earth movements, it is necessary to record motions in two directions parallel to the earth's surface by the use of similarly designed, but differently oriented, instruments.

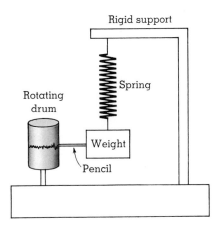

Fig. 4-5. Basic principle of seismograph. Weight remains in fixed position as frame (attached to ground) moves during earth- quake. This seismograph records vertical movements only. (From *A Textbook of Geology,* Robert M. Garrels, Harper & Row, New York, 1951.)

CAUSES OF EARTHQUAKES

An earthquake results from the energy released by rapid motion of two portions of the earth past each other. The surface along which they move is termed a *fault* (Figs. 4-6, 4-7, and 4-8). The rapid motion sets up seismic waves, which emanate outward from the point of major motion on the fault and pass through overlying rocks to the earth's surface. Most earthquakes are so small that they are completely unnoticeable by anything other than the most delicate seismographic instruments. Occa- sionally, however, major movements release im- mense quantities of stored elastic energy, and the rapid dissipation of this energy in the form of seismic waves causes sufficient ground move- ment for considerable surface damage to result. Ground movement rarely exceeds a few inches, but sudden motions of even this small size can be catastrophic to buildings or other man-made structures. The actual ground motion in a quake consists of waves set up at the earth's surface by the internal waves rather than the motion of the internal waves them- selves.

The location of the first major movement on the fault which causes the earthquake is called the *focus.* The focus may have any depth from essentially the earth's surface down to several hundred kilometers, though these deep focus earthquakes are much more rare than shallower ones. A point directly above the focus on the earth's surface is entitled the *epicenter,* and this is commonly, though not invariably, the site of the greatest ground movement and consequently the greatest damage. The amount of ground movement (or, to be more accurate, the amount of energy dissipated at any point on the ground) is referred to as the *intensity* of an earthquake at that point. The intensity of most quakes naturally decreases rapidly away from the epicenter.

For the many quakes where sufficient information is available, it is possible to draw lines of equal intensity (*isoseismal lines*) around the

Fig. 4-6. Fault scarps developed during 1964 earthquake in Anchorage, Alaska. The strip of ground through the center of the photograph has dropped below the surface seen on both edges and has stretched and cracked in the process. (Photo by J. P. Gates.)

epicenter. Such lines generally show a roughly circular or elliptical pattern, and a typical example is given in Fig. 4-9. In Fig. 4-9, the numbers on the various isoseismal lines refer to an arbitrary scale of intensity which need not concern us here in its details.

The causes of earthquake motions must be sought in the fact that the earth's crust is constantly being warped or deformed. The reasons for these deformations are not clearly understood, and a more complete discussion will be deferred until Chapter 14. Nevertheless, we may say that as a result of the development of strains, warps, and deformations in the earth's crust there is a tendency for movement to occur in certain

Fig. 4-7. Aerial view of fault scarp associated with 1954 earthquake near Fairview Peak, Nevada. Scarp is the slight cliff dividing the gullied area near the mountains from the flat land in the foreground. (Photo by C. R. Allen.)

portions of the earth. We have already seen in Chapter 2 that this deformation and consequent earthquake activity is concentrated along certain major belts, such as the margin of the Pacific Ocean. Regardless of location, however, we can say that fault movement occurs wherever the amount of warping of the earth exceeds the ability of the deformed rock to resist fracturing. Rocks are, to a certain extent, elastic. Thus where they are warped slightly, the deformation may be absorbed by a simple bending of the rocks without fracturing. This bending takes place within the range of elasticity, and thus the rocks would return to their original position if the forces causing the deformation were removed.

We might envision a deformation such as is shown diagrammatically in Fig. 4-10, in which a line of points across a potential fracture surface is warped elastically. If continued warping takes place, at some point the resistance of the rock will be exceeded, and fracturing and rapid

Fig. 4-8. Fault scarp along west flank of Panamint Range, California. (Photo by C. R. Allen.)

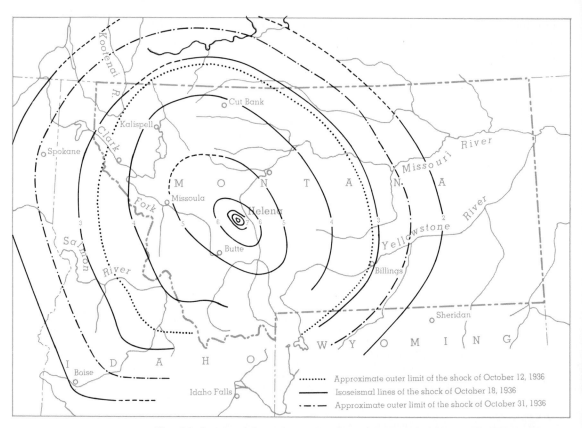

Fig. 4-9. Isoseismal lines for earthquake of October 18, 1936, near Helena, Montana. Limits of earthquake effects for a fore- and an aftershock are also shown. Numbers on isoseismal lines refer to an arbitrary intensity scale. (From *Montana Bureau of Mines and Geology Memoir 16*, 1936.)

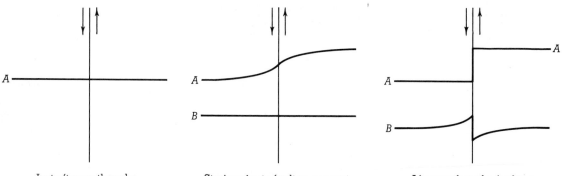

Just after earthquake has removed all strain

Strain prior to fault movement

After earthquake faulting

Fig. 4-10. Elastic rebound method of releasing seismic energy. A straight line drawn in a position of no strain will be progressively deformed until rupture occurs. A straight line constructed during a time of strain (middle diagram) will take on a configuration shown at the bottom after faulting. This diagram is applicable to release of strain energy on faults with any kind of movement, and a natural example for a fault with horizontal movement is shown in Fig. 4-12.

movement will occur as shown in the figure. This fracturing will release all or most of the strain energy stored in the rock by the deformation. The line of points will return to positions as shown, and the dissipation of the energy will take place in the form of seismic waves spreading out through the surrounding rocks.

Verification of this explanation for sudden release of energy by fracturing has been found in actual surveys made across relatively active faults in California. The San Andreas fault, a major zone of movement which was responsible for the San Francisco earthquake of 1906 and others before and after, has been continually surveyed over a long period of years (Fig. 4-11). Displacements on opposite sides of this fault parallel

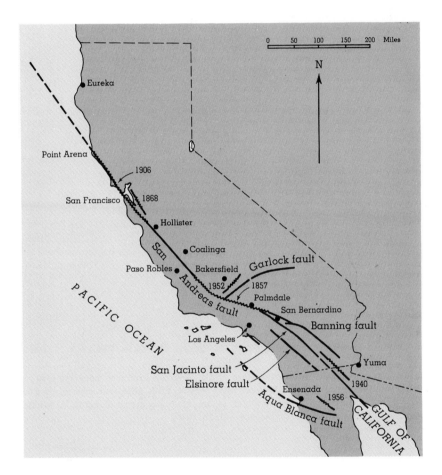

Fig. 4-11. Map of San Andreas and associated fault zones in California and northern Mexico. Actual ground breaks during earthquakes are shown by zigzag lines and dates of movement. (After C. R. Allen.)

to the earth's surface are shown in Fig. 4-12, which resembles very closely the theoretical diagram given above. This explanation for the origin of earthquake faulting is called the *elastic rebound* theory.

One of the best-studied examples of modern earthquakes is the San Francisco shock just mentioned. On April 18, 1906, a portion of the San Andreas fault in an area extending many tens of miles north and south of San Francisco suddenly underwent a rapid shifting. This lateral

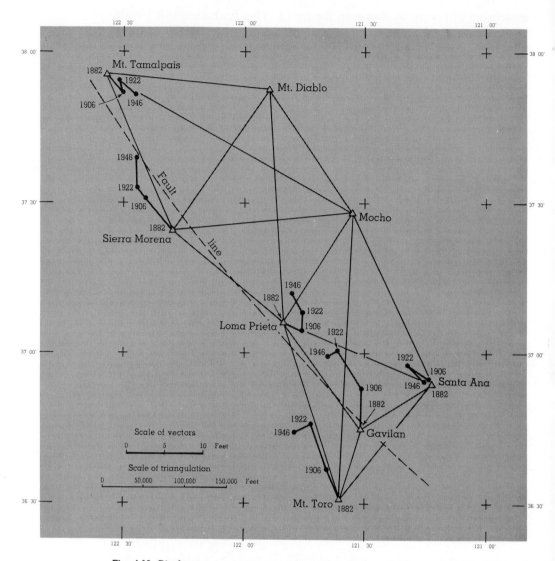

Fig. 4-12. Displacements on opposite sides of San Andreas fault zone between 1882 and 1946. Note that stations west of the fault have moved north. Note that scale of displacement vectors is much smaller than scale of geographic triangulation. (From C. A. Whitten, *American Geophysical Union Transactions,* vol. 29, 1948.)

shifting offset roads, fences, and other surface features in places by as much as 21 feet (Fig. 4-13). Vertical movement was absent or very small. The earthquake produced had a catastrophic effect on San Francisco. Many buildings were shaken down outright, and many others were so irreparably damaged that they later had to be completely destroyed (Figs. 4-14, 4-15, 4-16). Not only were buildings damaged directly by earthquake action, but as a result of a complete disruption of the water-distribution system, fires which broke out shortly after the quake could hardly be checked. Total damage in the San Francisco earthquake was

Fig. 4-13. Road displaced by movement on fault associated with San Andreas zone during San Francisco earthquake of 1906. (From *Carnegie Institution of Washington Publication 87,* 1908.)

Fig. 4-14. Damage in San Francisco caused by earthquake of 1906. (From *Carnegie Institution of Washington Publication 87,* 1908.)

Fig. 4-15. Damage in San Francisco caused by earthquake of 1906. (From *Carnegie Institution of Washington Publication 87,* 1908.)

Fig. 4-16. Damage to Geology Building at Stanford University caused by San Francisco earthquake of 1906. (From *Carnegie Institution of Washington Publication 87,* 1908.)

estimated in the range of several hundreds of millions of dollars, which was worth considerably more in 1906 than it is in the present time. Over 700 people lost their lives.

EARTHQUAKE ENERGIES

The energy released by an earthquake travels outward from the focus in the form of the seismic waves which we have already defined. Such waves are essentially vibrations which can be described in terms of: (1) their period, the time elapsed between the passage of two identical positions; (2) their wave length, the distance between equivalent points; and (3) their amplitude, the extent of the vibration. In terms of a wave on the surface of water, the period is the time needed for two wave crests to pass one point, the wave length is the distance between the crests, and the amplitude is the wave height. On the basis of the classical physics of vibrating particles, which we shall not discuss in this book, it can be shown that the energy carried by waves such as those which travel through the earth is proportional to the square of their amplitude, or displacement.

For any one seismograph, the amplitudes of various earthquake waves are proportional to the displacements on the seismogram traces, though the seismograph greatly magnifies the tiny actual ground movements. Thus, at any one seismograph it is possible to determine the relative energies of the various seismic waves. We shall discuss later the comparatively simple methods for determining the distance of earthquakes from seismographs. Then by knowing the distances between some reference seismograph and various earthquake foci, together with experimental knowledge of the rate at which seismic energy is dissipated as waves move through the ground, it is possible to calculate relative energies of earthquakes at their foci. All of these measurements provide only relative energies of earthquakes, but it is possible to establish an absolute energy scale by measurements of seismic waves sent out by underground explosions of known size, for example some of the underground nuclear tests. The amount of energy released by a major earthquake is about the same as that of a large hydrogen bomb. As discussed earlier, the energy dissipated by an earthquake wave in the form of ground motion at any point is called the intensity of the quake at that point. The energy produced at the focus of an earthquake is termed the *magnitude*.

The energy produced by an earthquake is not necessarily all of the energy which is stored in the rock as a result of elastic deformation. Most earthquakes have either a short series of minor shocks which precede the major one and/or a long series of after-shocks following the major quake. Some of these after-shocks may be nearly as large as the original quake itself. When we calculate the energies released in a major earthquake and its related fore- and after-shocks, we get a comparatively smooth "curve" with time. A typical graph is shown in Fig. 4-17. Of even greater importance to the study of the earth as a whole is the fact that "curves" such

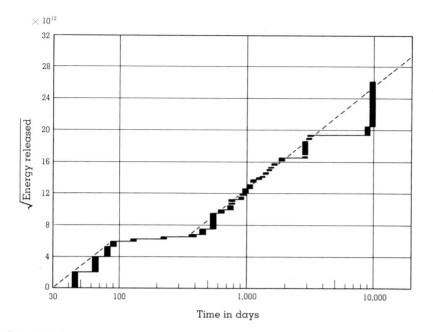

Fig. 4-17. Strain released at various times during a sequence of earthquakes in the Indian Ocean. The vertical scale is proportional to the displacement on the fault or faults causing the quakes and is calculated as proportional to the square root of the energy (magnitude in ergs) of each quake. The height of each block represents the energy released by each quake, and the dashed line shows the general trend of total energy release with time. (From H. Benioff in *Geological Society of America Special Paper 62*, 1955.)

as shown in Fig. 4-17 can be constructed to show the energy released for the entire earth for given periods of time. The procedure is simply that of adding the energy released by all of the major earthquakes produced during a given period of time and plotting them graphically. A typical example is shown in Fig. 4-18, which demonstrates very nicely the fact that the total amount of energy released in any given period of time in the earth's surface is comparatively constant. The conclusion which we might draw from this fact is that the earth is undergoing a rather constant amount of deformation or warping. Although a particular deformed area may not release its energy as soon as deformation occurs, nevertheless, on the average and over the whole earth, the amount of warping and the release of strain take place at roughly the same rate with time. This fact shows that we must construct a theory for the deformation of the earth's crust which will provide continual warping rather than intermittent activity, at least over periods of time measured in a few years. The prevalence of earthquakes throughout historical times and the inferred prevalence of earthquakes and related mountain buildup processes throughout geologic time may be cited as an additional verification of the concept of uniformitarianism. This concept does not necessarily require or imply, however, that any process proceed at an uniform rate throughout geologic time.

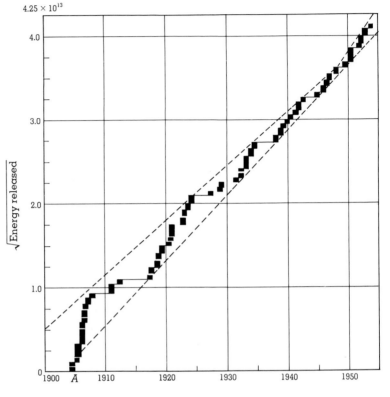

Fig. 4-18. Diagram similar to Fig. 4-17, showing strain release by major earthquakes for the entire earth. The height of each block represents the energy released by each quake, and the dashed lines outline the band of total energy released by all quakes up to the indicated dates. (From H. Benioff in *Geological Society of America Special Paper 62*, 1955.)

Longitudinal or *P* waves

One wave length

Compression   Rarefaction

Direction of wave travel

Transverse or *S* waves

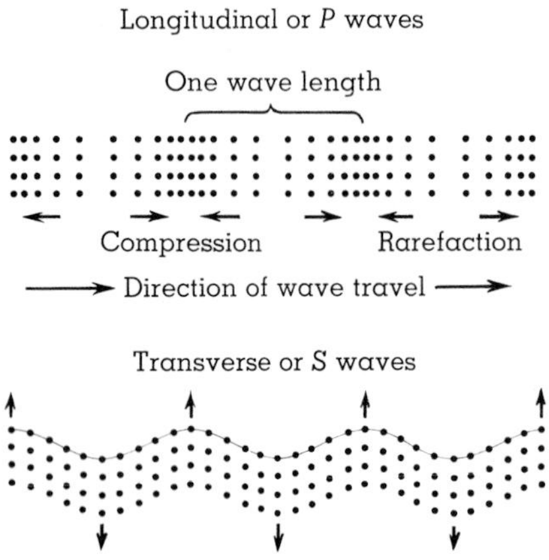

Fig. 4-19. Diagrammatic representation of particle motions in longitudinal (*P*) and transverse (*S*) seismic waves. (From A. N. Strahler, *The Earth Sciences*, Harper & Row, New York, 1963.)

EARTHQUAKE WAVES

In our discussion of the seismic waves produced by explosions, we mentioned the compressional-rarefactional analogs of sound waves which pass through rocks in the same manner as a sound wave passes through air. An explosion causes the rock to be thrust radially outward from the point at which the charge is set off, and thus the compressional-rarefactional waves are the only ones which are developed by this type of source. Earthquakes, however, are caused by a lateral movement and not simply by a sudden radial thrusting. As a result of this lateral movement, not only are the compressional-rarefactional waves produced, but also a set of transverse waves is generated which move through the rock with a side-to-side motion. The relationships between these two types of waves are shown in Fig. 4-19.

Fig. 4-20. Seismogram of the Helena, Montana, earthquake of October 18, 1936, as recorded at the University of Chicago. This is a record of the same earthquake for which isoseismal lines are shown in Fig. 4-9. (From *Montana Bureau of Mines and Geology Memoir 16, 1936.*)

The compressional-rarefactional wave is the *primary,* most rapid, wave and is called the *P wave.* The transverse, or shear, wave is the *S (secondary) wave* and moves with a velocity approximately three-fifths that of the primary wave in ordinary rocks. Both *P* and *S* waves are capable of being refracted and reflected. In addition to these *P* and *S* waves, the ordinary earthquake produces a surface wave called an *L,* or *long,* wave which emanates from the epicenter of the earthquake and travels at a comparatively low velocity across the surface of the earth. The *L* waves are essentially combinations of *P* and *S* waves which travel along the earth's surface.

The ordinary seismogram contains records of all of these waves. In fact, in a layered earth in which there are different zones in which *P* and *S* waves may travel with different velocities, the seismograph receives a whole series of *P* and *S* waves and, in addition, the *L* wave. Thus the seismogram of a large earthquake becomes extremely complicated. An example is shown in Fig. 4-20, where arrivals of the first major waves are indicated. For extremely large earthquakes, the seismograms become even more complicated as a result of the fact that waves may pass through the earth several times and be reflected either from the opposite side of the earth or from layers deep within the earth. A few of the waves resulting from these complex reflections are shown in the diagram in Fig. 4-21. (We shall have to wait until the next section, however, to explain the evidence on which this diagram is constructed.)

As mentioned in our discussion of exploration seismic work, interpretation of seismic waves generally involves the establishment of a time-distance graph, in which arrival time of different waves is plotted against distance. The construction of such a graph is not particularly difficult for the simpler

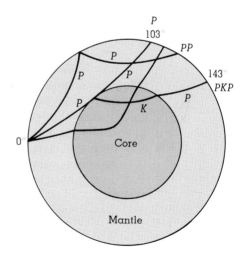

Fig. 4-21. Paths followed by seismic waves through the earth. Paths are shown for a direct *P* wave, reflected (*PP*) wave, a *P* wave passing through the core (*PKP*), and a deeply penetrating wave (unlabeled). Note the "shadow zone" from 103° to 143° in which direct arrivals do not occur.

waves. For example, the direct *P* wave from an earthquake is generally the first seismic arrival at a number of seismographs stationed at various places around the earth. If the focus is located, then it is easy to plot arrival time of the *P* wave against distance from the quake, to extrapolate this line backward to zero distance and thus establish the time of the quake, and to calculate the travel times for various distances. (For an example of a time-distance graph for major earthquake waves, see Fig. 4-23.) Construction of a time-distance graph for later arrivals is more complex than for the *P* wave, largely as a result of difficulty in recognizing the nature and path of some of these slower waves. By comparison of seismograms from many stations for each of a number of earthquakes, however, it has been possible to construct such graphs for waves which have undergone a variety of reflections and refractions.

SEISMOGRAM INTERPRETATION

Several important conclusions may be drawn concerning the earth's internal structure from a study of seismograms produced by earthquakes. For this purpose assume that there is an earthquake at the point marked 0° in Fig. 4-21 and that seismographs are located at various distances around the earth from this quake. The travel times of various waves including the direct *P* and *S* waves will be noted at these seismographs, and from these travel times we shall make several important observations.

The first observation is that at stations within a few degrees of the earthquake there is a break in the travel time-distance curve very similar to that shown for explosion seismometry in Fig. 4-2. Very clearly, the waves arriving at stations a short distance away from the quake have passed below a sharp transition in the earth's internal structure and have entered a comparatively high-velocity zone in which the refracted wave travels much faster than it does in the rock above this transition. If we make detailed measurements and assume that the earthquake occurs in a continental area, then the transition between the low- and high-velocity layers will generally be found to be a transition between *P* waves with a velocity of approximately 6 to 7 km/sec above the transition and 8 km/sec below the transition. In fact, we may construct a velocity profile for the average continental area and also for the average oceanic area, and these profiles are shown in Fig. 4-22. What we have done here is delineate a very sharp discontinuity between shallow crustal rocks, primarily those of the continental areas, and deeper-seated rocks of considerably higher velocity. The discontinuity is very abrupt and, having been discovered by a Yugoslavian by the name of A. Mohorovičić, has been named the *Mohorovicic discontinuity* (often shortened to *Moho*). The depth to the Moho varies considerably from place to place, being fairly deep under continents (several tens of kilometers) and shallow under oceans (a few kilometers). The depth is particularly large where mountain ranges extend their roots down below the normal continental level, as discussed in the section on isostasy in Chapter 3. The general relationships of the Mohorovicic discontinuity to the earth's surface are diagrammed in Fig. 4-22.

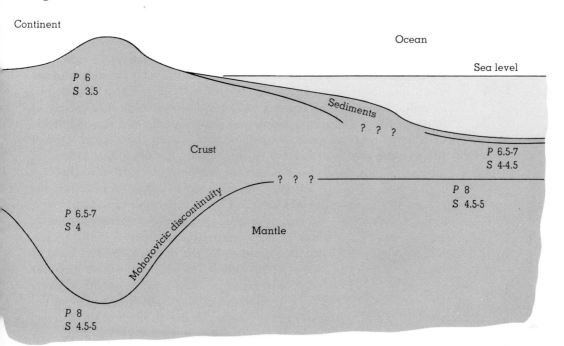

Fig. 4-22. Presumed relationships between crust and mantle. Velocities of *P* and *S* waves in various portions of crust and mantle are shown in kilometers per second. Note the downward bulge of the crust under the mountain range. Question marks indicate uncertainty of configurations near continental margin. All vertical distances greatly exaggerated.

Now let us consider the arrival times of seismic waves at stations somewhat distant from a major earthquake. With regard to first arrival of the *P* waves, we obtain a time-distance graph as is shown in Fig. 4-23. In this figure we see that the time-distance curve is not a straight line, and this clearly indicates that the velocity of travel increases as the waves pass deeper into the earth. This increase in velocity is found not only for *P* but also for *S* waves. The only conclusion is that there is a velocity profile within this deeper zone such that gradually increasing rigidity of the rock, as a result of higher pressure, has given rise to faster travel times.

Now as we proceed farther around the earth from our hypothesized earthquake, we note a very interesting phenomenon. At a depth of approximately 1800 miles (2900 km), there is another break in the travel time-distance curve (Fig. 4-23). This depth in the earth corresponds to an arc of approximately 103° around the earth from the earthquake to the measuring seismograph. In a zone from 103° to 143° two effects are noticed. First, there is almost a complete absence of direct *P* waves; that is, no arrivals at seismographs within this zone fall on a curve extrapolated from that constructed for *P*-wave travel time versus distance in the zone from the epicenter to 103°. The conclusion from this fact is that there is a major discontinuity at a depth of approximately 1800 miles, and this discontinuity is such that rock with a lower *P*-wave travel velocity occurs below the discontinuity and rock of higher velocity above. This conclusion is seen quite clearly from the fact that the broad band without direct *P*-wave arrivals, known as the "shadow zone," has to be explained in terms of refraction of the direct *P* wave at the discontinuity down into the medium below the discontinuity (Fig. 4-21). That is, just as light waves are refracted more toward the vertical into media of lower velocities of travel, so also sound waves are refracted into the media of lower travel velocities, and thus this interior zone must have a velocity of travel less than that of the immediately overlying material.

A second phenomenon is observed in stations beyond 103°: no shear waves appear to penetrate the zone below the 1800-mile discontinuity. Wherever a seismic wave strikes a discontinuity, there are set up both reflected and refracted *P* and *S* waves regardless of the nature of the original, incident, seismic waves. Thus the waves which travel through the earth and arrive at seismographs on the side opposite an earthquake may actually be combinations of *P* and *S* waves with the different mode of travel characteristic of different parts of their path through the earth. Assuming, however, that *S* waves within this lowermost region of the earth have velocities about three-fifths that of *P* waves—as they do in the outer portions of the earth—no arrivals at seismographs opposite earthquake foci can be attributed to combinations of travel paths through the earth which involve the transmission of *S* waves through the interior below the 1800-mile discontinuity. Apparently, therefore, this region will not transmit *S* waves. The conclusion drawn from this observation is that this interior portion of the earth must be fluid, because only a liquid or gas will transmit *P* waves and not *S* waves.

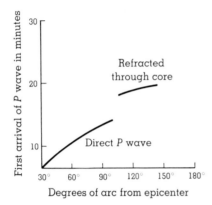

Fig. 4-23. Travel times of a direct *P* wave and a *P* wave refracted through the core plotted against distance from epicenter. Note separation at 103°.

The conclusion that this inner region of the earth is a fluid may have to be modified slightly. It is very difficult to determine the exact paths and travel velocities of waves which have undergone a complex series of refractions and reflections, possibly combined with transitions between *P*- and *S*-type motions at reflecting boundaries. These difficulties are magnified for waves which penetrate the deep interior, and some seismologists believe that *S*-wave velocities can be found for the innermost portion of the region below the 1800-mile discontinuity. This interpretation would indicate that the innermost part of the earth is a solid which is surrounded by a fluid below the 1800-mile discontinuity.

We mentioned in Chapter 3 the fact that the inner part of the earth is presumed to consist of iron and nickel because of the presence of meteorites with this composition and the necessity for a region of high density to occur somewhere near the earth's center. Seismic evidence has recently provided a tentative verification of this composition. The velocities of seismic waves in this region are very similar to the velocities of high-pressure shock waves measured in samples of iron and nickel in the laboratory. The laboratory technique consists essentially of applying an extremely high pressure at a small point on a sample and measuring the rate at which the deformation spreads through the sample. These rates are closely related to velocities of seismic waves, and the transmission properties of iron and nickel match those of the inner part of the earth far more closely than do those of other elements.

We are now in a position to construct a graph of travel velocities versus depth in the earth for the entire earth. This graph is shown in Fig. 4-24.

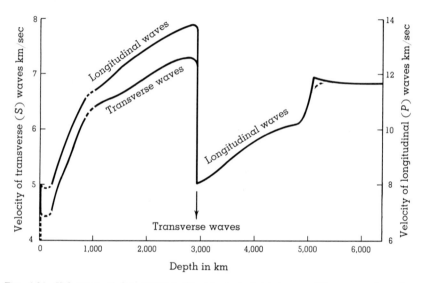

Fig. 4-24. Velocities of longitudinal (P) waves and transverse (S) waves at various depths in the earth. Uncertainties are shown as dashed lines. (From *Internal Constitution of the Earth* by B. Gutenberg. Published by Dover Publications, Inc., New York 14, N.Y., 1951.)

CORE, MANTLE, AND CRUST

It is almost entirely on the basis of the graph shown in Fig. 4-24 that geologists have been able to subdivide the earth into three broad, concentric spheres. The outermost thin spherical shell, containing the granitic continental material and the associated rocks of relatively low travel velocity, is the *crust*. Below the crust (that is, below the Mohorovicic discontinuity) is a thick concentric spherical shell of solid rock extending downward to the liquid inner portion. This zone of gradually increasing velocities of *P* and *S* waves is the *mantle*. The interior portion of the earth below the discontinuity at approximately 1800 miles is called the *core*. For reasons cited above, the core is presumed either to be wholly liquid or to consist of an inner, solid, core and an outer, liquid, core. The boundary between the mantle and core is very sharp and smooth, forming a nearly perfect spherical surface.

DENSITY, PRESSURE, AND TEMPERATURE

Having constructed a graph of the variation of seismic wave travel times with depth, it is interesting to consider what graphs we might develop to show the variation in other physical properties with depth. Consider, for example, the variation of density with depth. We know that the specific gravity of continental material (granite) is approximately 2.7 and that the material of the ocean floors (and presumably that which directly underlies the continents) is approximately 3.0. We have no direct measurement of the material of the upper mantle, but from the levels reached by mountain roots in attaining isostatic balance and from the differences in levels of the continental and oceanic portions of the Mohorovicic discontinuity, we can estimate that the upper part of the mantle has a specific gravity probably in the range of about 3.0 to 3.5; a figure commonly cited is 3.3. Farther down in the mantle this density must, of course, increase as a result of the increase in pressure to which the rock is subjected. If, however, there were some exceptional change in density at some point within the mantle, there would almost assuredly be a rather noticeable seismic discontinuity. Although some geophysicists have postulated discontinuities of moderate sharpness within the mantle, apparently most of the changes occurring within it are comparatively smooth. This does not prove that the density does not increase sharply downward, but probably the density at the base of the mantle is not enormously higher than that at the top.

Another reason for believing that the density variations are not extremely large within the mantle will be discussed in Chapter 14, in which we will describe the possibility that major convection currents are set up within the mantle as a result of the heating of the lower part of the mantle and comparative cooling of the upper portion. This heating and cooling causes a density inversion with the heavier rock at the top and the lighter rock at the bottom, and convective overturn then results. This density inversion could hardly exist if there were major density changes within the mantle as a result of pressure or compositional variations.

The core is obviously a zone of extremely high density. It must have a high density in order to compensate for the low density of the crust and, possibly, the comparatively low density of the mantle, for the earth as a whole must have an average specific gravity of approximately 5.5. Estimated density values in the core are, as described in the preceding chapter, obtained largely on the basis of the supposition that the core consists of nickel-iron meteoritic material. The density of such material under the high pressures of the core has, of course, not been measured, because these pressures cannot be attained in laboratory experiments. Nevertheless, specific gravities in the range of 10 to 15 seem reasonably plausible. We can, on the basis of this rather tenuous evidence, construct a graph of density variations with depth, and this graph is shown in Fig. 4-25. The density values shown in Fig. 4-25 must be consistent with the velocities of P and S waves as given in the following experimentally derived formulas for seismic velocities:

$$v_p = \frac{\varkappa + 4/3\mu}{\varrho}$$

$$v_s = \frac{\mu}{\varrho}$$

$v_p =$ velocity of P wave

$v_s =$ velocity of S wave

$\varrho =$ density

$\varkappa =$ bulk modulus (a measure of compressibility)

$\mu =$ rigidity modulus (a measure of shearability)

Furthermore, the μ and $\varkappa$ must increase downward in the earth more rapidly than the ϱ, in order to account for the observed increases in seismic velocity despite density increases.

Since we have constructed a graph of density variations, it is obviously a simple matter to develop a graph of pressure variations with depth. We merely add up the weight of rock above a certain level in the earth and plot the pressure accordingly. Such a graph of pressure variations is also shown in Fig. 4-25.

It is more difficult to construct a graph of temperature variations within the earth. We know from measurements in drill holes in the outer portion of the crust that, near the surface, temperature increases at a rate of about 1° C. per 50 to 100 meters. This rate of increase varies markedly from place to place, being relatively high in areas of recently deposited sedimentary rocks which are undergoing compaction and generating frictional heat, and being comparatively low in areas of old, stable rocks in the central parts of the continent where underground activity of any type has been almost completely absent in recent times. This average figure for the temperature gradient of 1° C. for each 50–100 meters obviously cannot hold true for the entire earth. This would give a temperature in the range of 10,000 or more degrees for the center of the earth, and such a temperature is highly unlikely. Exactly what the temperature of the center of the earth might be is a matter of almost sheer speculation. Most tentative estimates would place it in the range of 3000° to 4000° C. (Fig. 4-26).

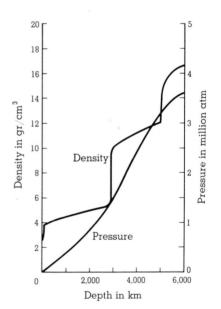

Fig. 4-25. Variation of density and pressure in the earth. Calculations are made as indicated in the text. (From *Internal Constitution of the Earth* by B. Gutenberg. Published by Dover Publications, Inc., New York 14, N.Y., 1951.)

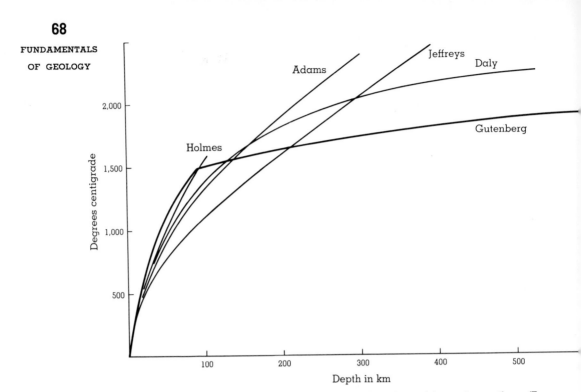

Fig. 4-26. Temperature variations in the earth as hypothesized by various authors. (From *Internal Constitution of the Earth* by B. Gutenberg. Published by Dover Publications, Inc., New York 14, N.Y., 1951.)

LOCATION OF EARTHQUAKES

We have discussed the use which we can make of seismograms after the distance from the seismograph to the epicenter of the earthquake is known. Before leaving our discussion of seismic phenomena, however, it is well to indicate just exactly how geophysicists determine the epicenter of an earthquake and also the depth from epicenter to focus.

After the establishment of known travel times in various portions of the earth, it is clear that the difference between the arrival of the initial *P* and the initial *S* wave at a particular seismograph must be a function of the distance from the seismograph to the epicenter. With the travel times of the *P* and *S* waves known, it is then a simple matter to calculate the distance from the seismograph to the epicenter. For example, assume that we want to locate a fairly shallow earthquake in a part of the crust in which the *P* wave has a velocity of 5 km/sec, the *S* wave has a velocity of 3 km/sec, and the *S* wave arrives at the seismograph 100 sec after the *P* wave. The distance, *d,* is then found by

$$\frac{d}{5} + 100 = \frac{d}{3}$$

At any one seismograph it is possible only to determine the distance away and not the direction of the epicenter. That is, around a seismograph we must draw a circle whose radius is equal to the distance of the epicenter, but we cannot tell from one station exactly where on this circle the epicenter occurs. From two stations we would be able to draw two circles intersecting in two points and thus narrow the epicenter down to one of two possible locations. Clearly, a third reporting station will give us a third fix on the earthquake and allow an accurate location of the epicenter (Fig. 4-27).

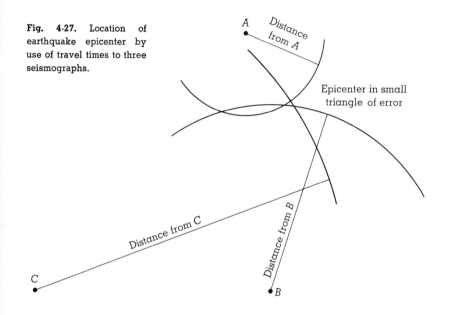

Fig. 4-27. Location of earthquake epicenter by use of travel times to three seismographs.

It is a considerably more difficult task to determine the depth of focus than to locate the epicenter. Two pieces of evidence lead to the conclusion that some earthquakes do occur at great depth: (1) the fact that such earthquakes do not give rise to surface L waves; and (2) the fact that seismic waves from the same earthquakes arrive earlier at seismographs than would be predicted from measurement of the distances between the seismographs and the epicenter. This last fact obviously indicates that the focus was deep in the earth so that seismic waves did not have to travel through the upper, low-velocity layers before reaching the higher velocity material of the deep interior. Measurement of the depth is made possible by the fact that earthquakes give rise not only to direct P waves but also to P waves which are reflected from the earth's surface near the epicenter. That is, a wave will originate at the focus, travel almost directly up to the surface near the epicenter, be reflected at the surface, and then travel through the earth as a P wave just as if it had originated at a shallow focus. The difference in arrival times of these reflected P waves and the direct P waves is obviously a function of the depth of focus and permits calculation of that depth with fair accuracy.

Most earthquakes originate in the upper few tens of miles of the earth. A small number, however, have a deeper focus, and the greatest depth recorded is in the neighborhood of 450 miles (700 km). The seismograms for deep-focus earthquakes show that direct S waves result from the quake, thus presumably indicating that fault movements are possible at the depths involved.

SUMMARY OF THE PROPERTIES OF THE EARTH

In the last three chapters we have completed our survey of the solid earth. It is appropriate, therefore, to summarize some of the data which we have obtained. The earth is roughly spherical with an equatorial radius of 3963.5 miles (6378.4 km). A slight deviation from sphericity is shown by the fact that the polar radius is 13 miles shorter; thus the earth is very much like an oblate ellipsoid with the bulge at the Equator caused by the higher velocity of spin in equatorial than in polar regions.

Continents and ocean basins are distributed with marked nonuniformity over the earth's surface. The Pacific Ocean covers almost an entire hemisphere, and the Atlantic and Pacific are apparently quite different geologically as shown by the margins of the two oceans. The border of the Pacific Ocean is characterized by earthquake and volcanic activity, whereas that of the Atlantic Ocean is characterized by shallow, gently sloping plains on the land areas adjacent to it. The continents themselves are generally one-sided though not invariably so. The one-sidedness is shown particularly well in South America, with the Andes on the west and the continent sloping off to the east, and in Europe and Asia, with the Alpine-Himalayan trend on the south and the lower plains areas to the north.

The earth has an average specific gravity of 5.5 and an overall mass of $5.4 \cdot 10^{21}$ tons. The density is distributed with considerable nonuniformity, as shown by the fact that surficial rocks have specific gravities in the range of 2.7 to 3. Presumably the highest-density rocks are concentrated in the earth's core, where specific gravities up to 10–15 are probably present. These high densities appear to be caused largely by the presence of a nickel-iron mixture, as attested to by the fact that this material is a common constituent of meteorites.

It is possible that the transition from crust to mantle, referred to as the Mohorovicic discontinuity, and from mantle to core represent changes in phase of the minerals present rather than changes in composition. Thus, for example, it is conceivable that the mantle and the core have the same general composition but consist of more-dense compounds in the core than in the mantle. Neither the hypothesis of a rapid change in composition at the discontinuities nor of rapid phase change owing to increased pressure can be proven with the data now available.

In the outer part of the earth an isostatic balance is established in which areas of comparatively high-standing land appear to be elevated as a result of the fact that they are underlain by thicker columns of light rock than neighboring areas of lower elevation. Thus the outer portion of the crust appears to consist of floating blocks which apparently show some variation in both thickness and density. The fact that most mountain ranges have deep roots indicates that there are differences in thicknesses of blocks, but the additional fact that the continental areas are regions of rock considerably lighter than that of the oceans indicates that a large part of isostatic balance is accomplished by density variation.

CHAPTER 5 ———————— COMPOSITION

OF THE EARTH

◄Comet Ikeya-Seki. (Photo by Armand Yramategui, Burke Baker Planetarium, Houston Museum of Natural Science.)

In the past few chapters we have studied the physical properties of the earth and have inferred some of the major features of the earth's chemical composition. We are now in a position to study the earth's composition more completely and to relate it to the composition of the solar system and of the universe itself. Before embarking on this discussion, however, it is necessary to describe some of the basic chemical principles and identify some of the chemical terms which we shall use in this and later chapters. We shall primarily be concerned with the concepts of chemical equilibrium.

CHEMICAL EQUILIBRIUM

Let us consider a chemical system that consists of a number of different phases, all enclosed in some container. A "phase" is some part of the system which can be separated physically from the remainder. For example, in a mixture of liquid gasoline and liquid water in a jar with no free air space, there are two separate phases, namely the gasoline and the water; in a jar containing ice floating on the surface of water there are three phases, namely ice, water, and vapor above the water. A condition of chemical equilibrium in a system exists when there is no tendency for any reaction to occur except under the influence of some outside change. For example, if the ice and water are at a temperature of 0° C., there will be no change unless heat is added to the system to melt the ice or unless heat is removed from the system to freeze the water.

In our definition of equilibrium we used the phrase "no tendency for any reaction to occur" rather than "no reaction," because an absence of reaction does not necessarily mean that equilibrium has been attained. For example, at the temperature and pressure of the earth's surface, diamond is unstable and ought to invert to graphite, the other crystalline form of carbon. The rate at which the inversion takes place, however, is so slow that human beings would never observe it, and in fact the rate may be so slow that inversion could not take place within the entire age of the earth. A phase which should undergo reaction but does not do so because of slowness of reaction is said to be "metastable." Most reactions involving geologic materials take place very slowly, and it is difficult both in laboratory experiments on rocks and also in investigations of naturally occurring materials to know whether or not equilibrium has been reached in the process being studied.

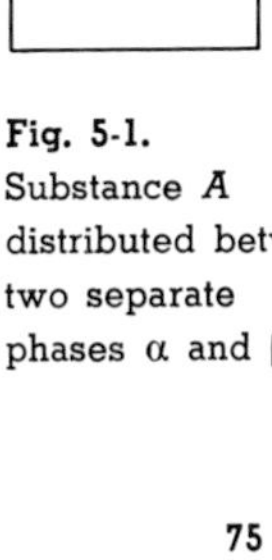

Now let us consider a system, such as is shown in Fig. 5-1, which contains two phases, α and β (e.g., gasoline and water). Assume that we take some substance A which dissolves in both phases and add it to the system. If equilibrium is reached, for example by shaking or stirring the two phases together to insure complete contact, the substance A will be distributed between the two phases so that the ratio of its concentrations in α and β has some particular value. If we add more and more A to the system and distribute it between the two phases, we will increase the

Fig. 5-1. Substance A distributed between two separate phases α and β.

concentration of A in both phases, and ultimately we can plot the concentrations in the two phases in some manner as is shown in Fig. 5-2. Figure 5-2 is a typical result for experiments of the kind which we have performed, and it signifies that the ratio of concentrations of A in α and β is a constant within the range of concentrations studied. Thus we can construct a constant "distribution coefficient" defined by the formula

$$K_A = \frac{[A]_\beta}{[A]_\alpha}$$

brackets are used to represent concentrations, and subscripts represent phases

This coefficient may be used for predicting the concentration of A in either phase, if its concentration is known in the other, and providing that equilibrium is established.

Unless equilibrium is established, it is not necessary that the ratio of concentrations in the two phases equal K_A. For example, if we insert a small amount of A at the bottom of the jar holding α and β, the A will spread through α before it reaches β, and the ratio $[A]_\beta/[A]_\alpha$ would be much smaller than K_A. Ultimately, the A will diffuse through both phases, equilibrium will be established, and the ratio of concentrations will be K_A.

The distribution coefficient discussed above is essentially the "equilibrium constant" for the reaction

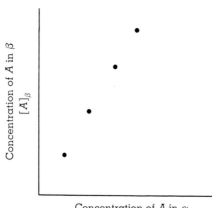

$$A_{\text{in } \alpha} \rightleftharpoons A_{\text{in } \beta}$$

Any chemical reaction may reach a state of equilibrium which can be described in terms of the concentrations of the materials undergoing reaction. For example, in the ionic reaction

$$H^+ + HCO_3^- \rightleftharpoons H_2CO_3$$

Fig. 5-2. Relationship between concentrations of A in phases α and β under conditions of equilibrium.

the equilibrium constant is

$$K_1 = \frac{[H_2CO_3]}{[H^+]\,[HCO_3^-]}$$

A similar relationship is valid for

$$H^+ + CO_3 = \rightleftharpoons HCO_3^-$$

where

$$K_2 = \frac{[HCO_3^-]}{[H^+]\,[CO_3^{--}]}$$

We can combine equilibrium constants and reactions to obtain constants for other reactions. For example, for the reaction

$$\frac{H^+ + HCO_3^- \rightleftharpoons H_2CO_3}{\text{plus} \quad H^+ + CO_3^= \rightleftharpoons HCO_3^-}$$

$$\text{overall reaction} \quad 2H^+ + CO_3^= \rightleftharpoons H_2CO_3$$

$$K_{H_2CO_3} = K_1 \cdot K_2 = \frac{[H_2CO_3]}{[H^+]^2[CO_3^{--}]}$$

The squared term in the denominator of $K_{H_2CO_3}$ results from the fact that two hydrogen ions take part in the reaction.

We can write a generalized expression for equilibrium constants as follows: assume a reaction of the type

$$aA + bB \rightleftharpoons cC + dD$$

where A, B, C, D are reacting materials and a, b, c, d are the number of mols involved in the reaction. For this reaction

$$K = \frac{[C]^c[D]^d}{[A]^a[B]^b}$$

For materials not dissolved in solution or otherwise dispersed through a solid or liquid phase, the unit of concentration is different from that for dissolved materials. For ions in solution the common unit of concentration is mols per liter, i.e., the number of gram molecular weights in one liter of solution. For gases the concentration is measured in terms of partial pressure, which is the fraction of the total pressure exerted by the substance being investigated. For pure solids and liquids the concentration is clearly constant regardless of the amount of the phase and is set equal to 1 by convention.

The procedure of setting the concentration of a pure solid equal to 1 enables us to write "solubility products." The process of solution in the system shown in Fig. 5-3 can be represented by the reaction

$$PbS \rightleftharpoons Pb^{++} + S^{--}$$

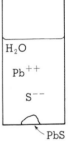

Fig. 5-3.
Lead sulfide
in contact
with water and
partially dissolved
in it.

For this reaction

$$K_{PbS} = \frac{[Pb^{++}][S^{--}]}{[PbS]} = [Pb^{++}][S^{--}]$$

$$= \text{solubility product of PbS}$$

One very important use of equilibrium constants is in determining the direction which a reaction ought to take. For example, if we mixed two solutions containing Pb^{++} and S^{--} so that the product of their ionic concentrations exceeded the solubility product of PbS, then PbS would precipitate. If we placed a grain of PbS in a solution that contained no Pb^{++} or S^{--}, the grain would dissolve until the solubility product of the PbS was attained.

ABUNDANCES OF THE ELEMENTS

The only naturally occurring materials which we can lay our hands on for direct study are from the outer part of the crust or from meteorites. Upon performing detailed analyses of these materials, we find that they consist largely of about one dozen minerals (crystalline compounds) or chemical phases. This small number of phases reflects the fact that the accessible crust and meteorites are composed primarily of ten elements; the rest of the chemical elements occur in only minor (a few tenths of a percent) or trace (below hundredths of a percent) quantities. The distribution of elements in materials subject both to direct and indirect analysis provides many important clues to the history of the earth and the nature of geologic processes, and we shall find that minor and trace elements are as useful for this purpose as the major ones. In this section we shall discuss primarily the distribution of the nonradioactive (stable) isotopes; age dating by means of radioactive materials has already been discussed in Chapter 1.

The data presented have been derived in a variety of ways. The "average" compositions of the crust and the meteorites have been obtained by analyzing a large number of samples and calculating an average based on "weighting" each sample in proportion to the estimated abundance of the rock type or meteorite which it represents. This weighting is, of course, subject to considerable error. The abundances of elements in the stars, including the sun, are obtained by spectrographic methods. These methods are based on the fact that the outer portions of stars consist of relatively cool gases which transmit only a portion of the radiation emitted from the hot center of the stars. These gaseous atoms absorb light of particular wave lengths, and the wave length absorbed differs from one element to another and is controlled by the different electronic configurations in the atoms. By measuring the amount of absorption of different wave lengths of light emitted from the stars, it is possible to estimate the composition of their outer portions, and it is assumed that this composition is representative of the stars as a whole.

Inspection of the data reveals a number of relationships that must be explained by any theory for the origin of the earth and universe. Among the more important relationships are the following:

1. Over 90 percent of the matter of the universe consists of hydrogen and helium.

2. The earth is greatly deficient in hydrogen and also in the inert gases helium and neon relative to the visible stars, including the sun.

3. A plot of the atomic numbers of elements versus the abundance of the elements in the universe yields a graph as shown in Fig. 5-4. We see here that abundance of elements generally decreases as atomic number increases and that elements of even atomic number are more abundant than those of odd number. Iron is unusually abundant relative to other elements of similar atomic number.

In order to explain these data and other information contained in Fig. 5-4, we must realize that the abundances of elements in the earth are the result of a long sequence of events. This sequence begins with the formation of the elements in the universe, continues with the formation of the solar system, the separation of the earth from the rest of the solar system, the separation of elements among various portions of the earth, and ends with modification of the near-surface rocks by various geologic processes discussed in the following chapters. Thus, obtaining a complete explanation of the abundance data is much like working a jigsaw puzzle with an unknown number of pieces. Year by year new pieces are found, and many can be fitted together to form small parts of a complete picture of the formation of the elements, the universe, and the earth. Each overall guess at the whole picture represents a "cosmology" (a theory of the universe) that attempts to synthesize all of the data developed by astronomy, astrophysics, nuclear physics, geophysics, geochemistry, and geology.

FORMATION OF THE ELEMENTS

Theories for the formation of the universe are intimately related to theories for the formation of the elements. These theories can be subdivided into two groups: (1) a continuous, essentially uniformitarian process of element formation going on at the present time in much the same way as in the past; and (2) formation of most elements at one time and in one small space during a "big bang." This big bang is presumed to have shot material out in all directions, and the resultant expansion of the universe is still continuing. The evidence for an expanding universe is quite interesting and is based on the fact that light waves emitted from more distant celestial objects are shifted toward the longer wavelength end of the spectrum (the red end), in comparison with light from closer objects; this "red shift" is best explained by assuming that the distant objects are traveling away from us at high velocities. The present expansion of the universe, however, does not constitute complete proof of the big-bang hypothesis; indeed, this hypothesis poses a number of fundamental questions which may well not be answerable on the basis of physical evidence and rigorous theory. For example, if there were one single big bang at one time in the past, what went on before? Does something strange happen to time on the scale of billions of years in the same way that our customary Euclidean geometry breaks down on the scale of astronomic distances? These are questions which students soon learn not to ask, because they cannot be answered as yet.

A study of the abundances of the elements may help to distinguish which of the two cosmologies described in the preceding paragraph is correct. For example, if elements have been continually formed at different times and places and in slightly different ways throughout the past, then it is possible that the elements in a few of the meteorites that fall onto the earth represent a mechanism of element formation different from that of the solar system. There are approximately 1500 known meteorites, and although most of them are sufficiently similar to the earth to be presumed part of the solar system, some of them may have originated outside of the system. If these extrasolar-system meteorites have developed by a process different from those in the solar system, then they may be expected to show marked deviations from the abundance data presented in Fig. 5-4; for example, it might be possible to find material in which a few elements had entirely different percentages of stable isotopes. If the surface of the moon proves to be

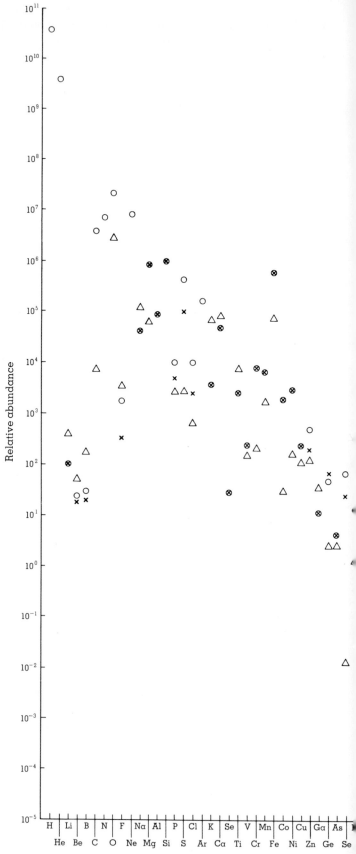

○ Abundance in universe

✕ Abundance in chondritic meteorites

△ Abundance in continental crust

Fig. 5-4. Abundances are ratios of number of atoms of each element to the number of atoms of silicon, which is set equal to 10^6 for convenience in reporting data. Note that data are not reported for all elements. Abundances in the continental crust are those calculated by Vinogradov by assuming that the crust consists of 2/3 granitic, continental, material and 1/3 basic, oceanic, material. (Figures for the continental crust are obtained from L. H. Aller, *The Abundance of the Elements*, 1961, published by Interscience Publishers.) Chondritic meteorites are characterized by small aggregates of the mineral olivine. They appear to represent the average composition of all meteorites. (Data are from H. E. Suess and H. C. Urey, *Reviews of Modern Physics*, 1956.) Abundances of elements in the universe are calculated by a combination of methods. Elements of low atomic number are estimated from abundances in the sun and nearby stars. Elements of high atomic number are generally assigned the abundances which they have in chondritic meteorites. (Data are from H. E. Suess and H. C. Urey, *Reviews of Modern Physics*, 1956.)

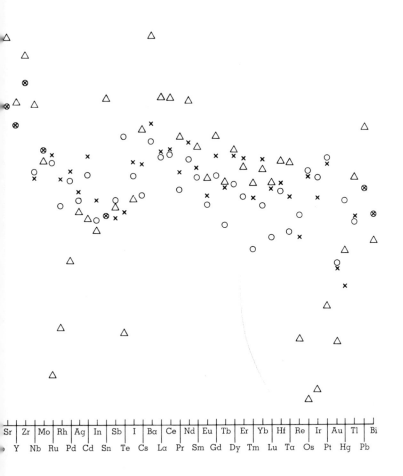

rich in meteoritic material, the chances of finding extrasolar-system matter will be enhanced. It is interesting to note that a presumed meteorite which caused an enormous explosion, flattening a thick forest over an area of hundreds of square miles in Siberia in 1908, has been hypothesized to have been a small piece of antimatter; antimatter is simply atoms which have a negatively charged nucleus with positive "electrons" around it, and the reaction of this material with normal earth matter would cause immediate annihilation of the mass and conversion of it into large amounts of energy.

Regardless of the time and place of formation of the elements, two separate mechanisms must have been involved. The major series of elements has almost certainly been built by repeated combination of subatomic particles, primarily protons, neutrons, and electrons. Sequential combination of these particles proceeded in such way as to produce smaller and smaller amounts of elements of higher atomic weights. The other mechanism operating in the formation of elements is radioactive decay to form some, possibly a large percentage, of the isotopes.

Extremely minute amounts of elements are being produced in the solid earth and its atmosphere at the present time. Cosmic-ray bombardment of nitrogen in the upper atmosphere produces small amounts of carbon-14 and tritium (hydrogen-3). The total natural amount of carbon-14, however, in the earth and atmosphere is only about 50 tons, and significant amounts of this total have been produced by artificial nuclear reactions such as atomic bombs. The total amount of tritium is even smaller than that of carbon-14. Within the earth uranium-238 is decaying to lead-206 and helium-4, and the other radioactive elements of long half life, mentioned in Chapter 1, are forming their own daughter products. Relative to the mass of the earth, however, the total amount of new elements produced by these natural radioactive processes today and in the past is inconsequential, and there is every reason to conclude that essentially all of the elements now found in the earth have existed in their present form from the origin of the earth.

If we assume that most of the elements now found in the earth were formed at the same time, some estimates of that time of formation can be made on the basis of the half lives of the longer-lived radioactive elements. For example, by assuming that all of the lead-207 in the earth was formed by the decay of uranium-235 and that none of this comparatively rare isotope was present in the original earth, we can calculate the time necessary to form all of this lead by normal radioactive decay. This time is approximately $5 \cdot 10^9$ years, which matches rather closely with estimates based on other radioactive decay series. We may conclude, therefore, that the earth is approximately $5 \cdot 10^9$ years old, and this conclusion is supported by the fact that the ages of meteorites and the oldest rocks found to date are invariably less than this figure.

Astronomical estimates of the maximum ages of star clusters and galaxies, through methods which we shall not discuss here, exceed the age of the earth by something like a factor of two. This difference may be interpreted as the result of error in one or both methods of age estimation, or it may be interpreted as real and indicating that elements have formed at different times. This last interpretation leads to the comforting thought that our earth may be of average age. Present knowledge of the possible mechanisms of element formation is too incomplete to resolve the difficulties regarding these time relationships.

By means of ever more powerful beams of nuclear particles and isotopically purer targets for bombardment, modern nuclear accelerators have yielded data with which to interpret some of the relative element abundances shown in Fig. 5-4. Thus the lack of technetium and promethium, which have never been found on the earth, is confirmed by the fact that artificial isotopes of these elements have half lives which are much shorter than the age of the earth. The spectra of certain stars, however, show small amounts of technetium, which indicates that nuclear processes for changing one element to another have operated, at least in some stars. These processes of transmutation or formation of elements must proceed at rates considerably shorter than the half lives of the isotope formed, for otherwise there would not be enough technetium to detect. It is possible that the particular mixture of heavy elements which characterizes the earth could form in stars at some time in their history.

A particular type of star, the "exploding star" or "supernova," is considered by some scientists to be responsible for continual production of elements of high atomic weight. There is no apparent reason for the sudden explosion of supernovas. Those close to the earth may become almost as bright as the moon, and the light may last for several days or weeks. The extraordinarily high temperatures and pressures which must be caused by such explosions undoubtedly have a tremendous effect on atomic nuclei in the stars, but it is uncertain as to whether or not they are capable of producing elements with the ratio of abundances observed on the earth. The explosions presumably send atomic nuclei throughout space until they are attracted by a planet or another star, and the residue of the supernovas has been hypothesized to contract to masses of very high density. High-density stars, called "white dwarfs," are fairly common, and their estimated densities in the range of several thousand pounds per teaspoonful indicate that they consist of atomic nuclei pressed together without their normally spacious, surrounding, electron cloud.

Despite the progress which we have mentioned above, no theory for the formation of atomic nuclei has succeeded in explaining all of the abundances of the various elements and isotopes. For example, iron is far more abundant than elements near it in the atomic number sequence, and lithium, beryllium, and boron are much less abundant than their position in the sequence would indicate. Nevertheless, chemical and isotopic analyses of earth and meteoritic samples are so similar in many details, including age of formation, that they, as well as other members of the solar system, probably represent one episode of element formation.

FORMATION OF THE SOLAR SYSTEM

Astronomical observations have provided a great deal of information about the solar system which is valuable in discussing the formation of the earth. Among the more pertinent observations are:

1. All planets revolve around the sun in a counterclockwise direction when viewed from a position above the North Pole of the earth.

2. All planets lie in roughly one plane, and with the exception of Uranus, the axes of rotation of the planets are nearly perpendicular to this plane. Furthermore, the planets rotate on their axes in the same west-to-east direction in which they revolve around the sun.

3. The inner planets (Mercury, Venus, Earth, and Mars) are comparatively small and have high densities, whereas the outer planets have large radii and low densities (Table 5-1).

TABLE 5-1.   DATA FOR THE SOLAR SYSTEM

	distance from sun	diameter	mass	density
Sun	—	$1.39 \cdot 10^6$ km	$1.7 \cdot 10^{33}$ grams	1.4 grams/cm^3
Mercury	$0.57 \cdot 10^8$ km	$5 \cdot 10^3$	$0.25 \cdot 10^{27}$	5.0
Venus	$1.1 \cdot 10^8$	$12.4 \cdot 10^3$	$4 \cdot 10^{27}$	4.9
Earth	$1.5 \cdot 10^8$	$12.7 \cdot 10^3$	$6 \cdot 10^{27}$	5.5
Mars	$2.2 \cdot 10^8$	$6.6 \cdot 10^3$	$0.5 \cdot 10^{27}$	4.2
Jupiter	$7.8 \cdot 10^8$	$139 \cdot 10^3$	$1600 \cdot 10^{27}$	1.3
Saturn	$14 \cdot 10^8$	$115 \cdot 10^3$	$475 \cdot 10^{27}$	0.7
Uranus	$29 \cdot 10^8$	$51 \cdot 10^3$	$73 \cdot 10^{27}$	1.3
Neptune	$45 \cdot 10^8$	$50 \cdot 10^3$	$86 \cdot 10^{27}$	1.6
Pluto	$59 \cdot 10^8$	(?)	$4.5 \cdot 10^{27}$	(?)

These observations are consistent with the hypothesis that the solar system was once a large, diffuse mass rotating counterclockwise. Under gravitational forces, this mass is presumed to have split up into the sun and the various planets by some type of condensation process. The composition of the earth enables us to deduce a number of the features of this condensation.

The initial stages of formation of the earth apparently took place at temperatures roughly the same as those of the present earth's surface. This conclusion, in sharp contrast with earlier theories of the formation of the earth as a "fiery ball," is based on the presence on the earth of such materials as water and mercury. The reasoning stems from the fact that both water and mercury vaporize at comparatively low temperatures; at 1 atm pressure the boiling point of water is 100° C., and of mercury is 357° C. Slow accretion of the earth at higher temperatures would lead to almost complete loss of water and mercury to space, and none would now be present on the earth.

Despite an atomic weight equal to the molecular weight of water, neon is quite impoverished on the earth in comparison with its cosmic abundance. A plausible explanation is that neon, being unable to form chemical compounds, as does water, was not retained by the gravitational field of the accreting body that was to become the earth. By the time the earth had a large enough mass to retain neon, the abundant neon originally present had been pushed far away by the light pressure from the sun. This light pressure was first noted in the tails of comets—the tails point away from the sun as the comet nears the sun; light pressure effects were also noted to affect the orbit of the large balloon-like Echo satellite. Many gases with atomic or molecular weights less than neon, such as hydrogen and helium, may also have been partially removed by this "degassing" process.

One of the reactions which almost certainly occurred during an early period in the earth's history resulted in the formation of two major and distinct portions of the earth, namely a central core of an iron-nickel alloy and an outer mantle consisting of complex silicates. With the aid of some simple equilibrium considerations, we can demonstrate that metallic iron was not an original phase in the earth. We have already shown that water was present in the initial earth and that its presence implied a comparatively low temperature of accretion. In the presence of water, metallic iron undergoes a series of reactions to form various oxides, the simplest being ferrous oxide (FeO). The reaction might be written as follows:

$$FeO + H_2 \text{ (gas)} \rightleftharpoons Fe + H_2O \text{ (gas)}$$

with an equilibrium constant found experimentally to have the values

$$K = \frac{p_{H_2O}}{p_{H_2}} = \frac{1.7 \cdot 10^{-3} \text{ at } 25° \text{ C.}}{0.97 \text{ at } 825° \text{ C.}}$$

$$p_{H_2O} = \text{partial pressure of } H_2O$$

$$p_{H_2} = \text{partial pressure of } H_2$$

The equilibrium constant can be shown experimentally to decrease with decreasing temperature. At any temperature, ratios of water pressure to hydrogen pressure greater than K will cause FeO to be the stable phase, and vice versa for lower ratios, assuming equilibrium is established. We can calculate the ratio of p_{H_2O}/p_{H_2} in the formative stages of the earth, if we assume that the earth originally condensed from material having the average composition of the universe. By calculating all of the oxygen as water, we obtain an abundance ratio of water/hydrogen approximately equal to 10^{-3}, and in a simple gas the ratio of abundances is the ratio of partial pressures. From Fig. 5-5 we see that at temperatures above 0° C. the FeO would break down to metallic iron for the ratio of partial pressures assumed, whereas below this temperature FeO would be stable. In similar fashion we can find decomposition temperatures for other iron oxides such as Fe_2O_3 and Fe_3O_4, and we may conclude that unless the earth originally accumulated at temperatures higher than several hundred degrees, the original iron was in an oxide form. We know, however, from the examination of meteorites that metallic iron and nickel occur in the solar system at the present time, and the high density of the core and other evidence discussed in Chapter 4 yield the strong presumption that the core is iron-nickel. If the original earth did not contain such material, then it must have formed later, and we are led to the conclusion

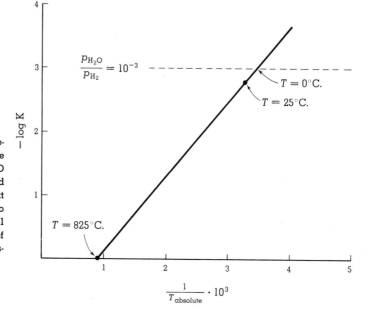

Fig. 5-5. Relationship between temperature and equilibrium constant for the reaction $FeO + H_2$ (gas) $\rightarrow Fe + H_2O$ (gas). The plot of log K vs. $1/T$ is based on the two points mentioned in the text (25° C. and 825° C.) and presumed to be linear on the basis of chemical theory. The line intersects a ratio of $p_{H_2O}/p_{H_2} = 10^{-3}$ at 0° C., as discussed in the text.

that reduction of the original iron oxides may have taken place at higher temperatures after the original accretion. As in much of present cosmology, the last argument does not yield unique answers. The possible answers, however, are limited in number by the boundary conditions, that is by the limits of possible physical-chemical conditions.

Obviously not all of the planets have gone through the various processes which we have outlined above. The outer planets, with their low density and great size, have not been degassed and probably have never reached particularly high temperatures. The equatorial bulge of Mars is considerably larger than that of the earth and is higher than would be expected if Mars contained a large portion of its mass in a high-density core. Apparently the separation of silicate and iron-nickel portions has not been as complete on Mars as on the earth, thus leaving dense material near the planet's surface and causing the equatorial radius to bulge outward by the centrifugal force of rotation.

The presence of iron-nickel phases in many meteorites may indicate that they have formed from a body which underwent the high-temperature reactions and phase separations characteristic of the earth. Such reactions could not have occurred in bodies having the size of the average meteorite, which are far too small to exert any appreciable gravitational force. Thus the meteorites may be fragments of a larger body, and many scientists believe that they may be related to the belt of *asteroids* which is in orbit between Mars and Jupiter. The distances of most of the planets from the sun can be calculated from the following series:

$$\frac{(N = 0, 3, 6, 12, 24, \text{etc.}) + 4}{10}$$

where 0 represents the distance of Mercury from the sun, 3 represents Venus, etc.; the distances are in terms of the earth-sun distance set as 1 astronomical unit. Astronomers have provided no explanation for this series although it is usable. From Mercury to Uranus, a planet is present in orbit at distances corresponding to each value of N except for $N = 24$. Along the orbit for $N = 24$, however, are a very large number of small objects (asteroids), the largest having diameters of a few hundred miles and most being much smaller. The leading hypothesis for the formation of these asteroids is that they represent a planet broken apart by some mechanism. It seems possible from the fact that meteorites have an average composition similar to that of the earth that the meteorites may represent fragments of this disintegrated planet. This hypothesis is compatible with the observation that many meteorites travel together in swarms that orbit the sun.

Although we have described a time of accretion of the earth, we should realize that the earth is still growing. In the open ocean, far from land, very little material accumulates on the sea floor. We shall discuss the formation of deep-sea deposits in Chapter 13, but we may say here that meteoritic dust, recognized by its content of iron-nickel, is an important fraction of deep-sea deposits. By measuring the rate of accumulation of these deposits and the percentage of meteoritic material, we can calculate that approximately 10^3 to 10^6 tons of meteoritic material, largely fine dust, falls on the earth each year. At the higher rate it would take about $6 \cdot 10^{15}$ years to accumulate the present $6.6 \cdot 10^{21}$ tons ($6 \cdot 10^{27}$ grams) of the earth, assuming that the earth has the composition of meteorites. This period of time is impossibly long, particularly if we assume that $5 \cdot 10^9$ years is the age of the elements. Obviously, a much higher rate of accumulation of material occurred during the initial stages of the growth of the earth.

We have already estimated the age of the earth as approximately $5 \cdot 10^9$ years from its content of lead-207. We can also estimate its time of formation, and presumably the time of formation of the remainder of the solar system, by a study of meteorite ages. Meteorites have been dated by all of the methods (except carbon-14) discussed in Chapter 1, as well as by the decay of rhenium-187 to osmium-187. The loss of radiogenic argon-40 and helium-4 from meteorites while they are in space and the contamination of their low strontium-87 content by terrestrial strontium after they land are but a few of the difficult problems encountered in such studies. The bulk of the evidence, however, is consistent with a maximum age of about $4.5 \cdot 10^9$ years for meteorites. This age is nearly the same as that found for the earth by uranium-lead and thorium-lead methods and can be interpreted as signifying that the earth and most, if not all, meteorites formed at almost the same time. An additional conclusion is that the abundances of lead isotopes found in the outer portion of the earth are fairly representative of the whole earth as well as of the meteoritic material accumulating on it today.

The age of formation of the earth and meteorites appears to be roughly the same as that estimated earlier for the formation of the elements, namely about $5 \cdot 10^9$ years. This conclusion is supported by a small, but important, bit of evidence provided by the unusually high content of xenon-129 found in some meteorites. We have mentioned that extinct (fossil) radioactive elements formed in the original synthesis of the elements might leave evidence of their presence by anomalously large accumulation of their stable daughter isotopes. Iodine-129, which does not occur now in nature, has been made in nuclear reactors and found to decay to the stable xenon-129 with a half life of $17 \cdot 10^6$ years. The conclusion which may be drawn from these data is that the xenon-129 is the product of decay of the iodine-129 which was formed during the original cosmic synthesis of the elements. This conclusion implies that meteorites containing unusual amounts of xenon-129 must have formed soon after element synthesis, because all of the iodine-129 in the universe would decay within a period of time equal to several of its half lives, and the meteorites must have contained this iodine-129. This interpretation, of course, assumes one period of formation of the elements rather than a continuous synthesis.

In our discussion of the process of formation of the solar system, we have made quite a number of assumptions. Some (we hope not all) of these assumptions may not be correct. One of the interesting tasks of geology is to determine which assumptions are, and which are not, correct.

SEPARATION OF THE GEOSPHERES

In the preceding sections, we have outlined the evidence for the existence of two major types of material in the earth, namely silicate and iron-nickel. In Chapters 3 and 4 we discussed the likelihood that the earth had a core of iron-nickel, the outer part of which is probably liquid and the inner part probably solid. These facts imply that the various phases formed by reactions in the condensing earth underwent physical separation into different spherical shells, the major ones being the core, mantle, and crust which have been defined on the basis of seismic evidence. These three subdivisions of the solid earth, plus the atmosphere, hydrosphere, and biosphere, can be termed *geospheres*. Quantitatively, the last three geospheres are unimportant, but their effect on the surface of the modern earth has obviously been enormous. The biosphere processes its own weight in material many times each year. Separation of components into different phases is commonly referred to as *fractionation;* the mechanism of fractionation will be discussed in relation to some concepts of crystal chemistry in Chapter 6 but will be referred to in general terms in the remainder of this section.

The fractionation of an iron-nickel core from a silicate mantle is easily understood on the basis of simple physics. Dense materials, such as metallic iron, tend to sink toward the center of gravitational attraction and displace less dense materials outward; in this fashion, the total potential energy of the system (the earth) is reduced, and the system becomes more stable. This fractionation on a global scale presumably takes an extensive period of time. We have shown that the fractionation of the core probably did not occur in Mars, and the degree of complete-

ness of separation in the earth is a matter of conjecture; probably fractionation is still occurring at the present time, thus moving the boundary
between core and mantle outward.

The gravitative separation of materials may permit evolution of heat
because of loss of potential energy, although the energy may in large
part be utilized in speeding up the earth's rotation. This heat source, in
addition to the heat evolved by radioactive processes, has been largely
responsible for bringing the interior of the earth to its present temperature. We have discussed in Chapter 4 the immense uncertainties regarding the temperatures within the earth, but the few facts concerning the
earth's heat supply which seem to be available lead to some very interesting conclusions regarding major chemical fractionation in the earth. For
this purpose, we combine data from two sources: (1) the present flow of
heat out through the earth's surface; and (2) the amount of radioactive
material in surface rocks and in meteorites.

We can calculate the amount of heat flowing through the earth's surface by the following process. Drill a hole approximately 1000 feet into
the earth and measure the temperature at various points in the hole.
This depth is needed in order to be sure that we are measuring temperatures below the area affected by surface processes. The result of such
measurements is generally a temperature-gradient curve similar to that
shown in Fig. 5-6. Next we must measure the heat conductivity of the
core removed from the hole by taking a piece into the laboratory, heating one end, and determining the rate at which the temperature increases at the other end. The total amount of heat flowing through the
earth is then the temperature gradient in the hole multiplied by the heat
conductivity of the rock; the figure must, of course, be adjusted for the
cross-sectional area of the hole. In order to calculate the amount of heat
actually flowing from the interior of the earth, we must subtract from

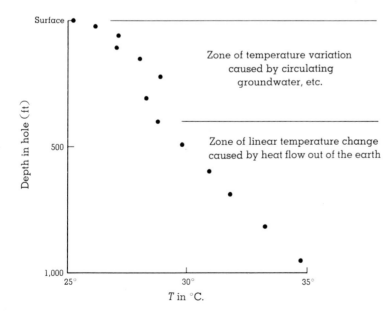

Zone of temperature variation
caused by circulating
groundwater, etc.

Zone of linear temperature change
caused by heat flow out of the earth

Fig. 5-6. Typical relationship
between temperature and
depth in bore holes. Use of
these data to determine
crustal heat flow is discussed
in the text.

the total heat flow at any point the amount of heat generated by radio-active elements in the surface rocks in which the hole is drilled. In theory, then, we can drill a large number of holes around the earth, calculate an average heat flow, and determine the total amount of heat generated in the earth's interior. In practice, the heat flow measurements show sufficient variation from place to place, and the available data are so few, that the amount of heat generated can only be approximated rather roughly.

Averaging the rough heat flow data which are available yields a value of $1.4 \cdot 10^{-6}$ cal/sq cm/sec for the amount of heat liberated over the earth. (One calorie is the heat needed to raise the temperature of 1 gram of water 1 degree Centigrade.) Multiplying the heat flow just given by the surface area of the earth yields a value of $7 \cdot 10^{12}$ cal/sec or $2 \cdot 10^{20}$ cal/yr emitted by the whole earth.

Let us turn now to the concentrations of radioactive materials in the accessible part of the earth. In continental areas the average concentrations of the important radioactive elements are: 2.6 percent potassium, 0.0010 percent thorium, and 0.0003 percent uranium. From laboratory studies of the heat generated by radioactive decay we know that these elements in their natural isotopic ratios produce heat at the following rates:[*]

	Cal/gram/yr
Uranium	0.73
Thorium	0.20
Potassium	$2.7 \cdot 10^{-5}$

We know from gravitational and astronomic measurements that the earth weighs $6 \cdot 10^{27}$ grams. It is then a simple matter to calculate that if the radioactive elements were distributed throughout the entire earth with the concentrations which they have at the surface, the total heat emitted by the three elements within the earth would be $2.5 \cdot 10^{22}$ cal/yr. This figure is 100 times larger than the measured heat flow across the earth's surface, and we must either assume that the interior of the earth is heating up at an alarming rate (remember the planet which distintegrated to form the asteroids) or that the average concentration of radioactivity within the earth is much smaller than at the surface.

Actually, a heat production of $2.5 \cdot 10^{22}$ cal/yr is so high that the earth would have vaporized long ago if that figure were valid. Therefore, we must determine a distribution of radioactivity within the earth which yields a heat production of roughly $2 \cdot 10^{20}$ cal/yr. We do not know, of course, whether the earth is in "thermal equilibrium," that is, without change of internal temperature with time; if the yearly radioactive heat production is larger than $2 \cdot 10^{20}$ calories, then the interior is heating up, and vice versa for a heat production smaller than the surface heat flow. In the case of radioactive heat production smaller than the heat flow, the extra heat flow is derived from the heat caused by initial condensa-

---

[*] After F. Birch, in H. Faul, ed., *Nuclear Geology*, New York, John Wiley & Sons, 1954.

tion of the earth and gravitative separation of the core and other inner regions. We shall assume that the earth is in rough thermal balance, though this assumption bears much additional study.

In pursuing an explanation for the earth's heat flow, the next data we note are the concentrations of radioactive elements in the silicate and iron-nickel phases of meteorites (Table 5-2). Owing to the intimate

TABLE 5-2. **RADIOACTIVE ELEMENTS IN METEORITES**

	abundances in percent	
	silicate meteorites	iron-nickel meteorites
uranium	$10^{-6}\%$	$10^{-9}\%$
thorium	$4 \cdot 10^{-6}$	too small to detect
potassium	0.1	< 0.01

admixture of these phases in many meteorites, we can assume that equilibrium has been established with regard to the distribution of these elements, and the ratios of concentrations are true distribution coefficients. We have already mentioned the general similarity between the compositions of meteorites and the earth, and if we assume that the earth has the overall composition of chondritic meteorites, then we may assume that the core has the radioactive concentrations of the iron-nickel meteorites and the mantle has the concentrations of the silicate meteorites. From the radius of the core, we may calculate that the core occupies roughly 15 percent of the earth and the mantle the remaining 85 percent; (the crust is volumetrically insignificant). From these data the total amount of radioactive material and the heat produced within the earth is as shown in Table 5-3.

TABLE 5-3. **RADIOACTIVE MATERIAL AND HEAT PRODUCED WITHIN THE EARTH**

	core		mantle	
	mass	heat	mass	heat
uranium	$0.9 \cdot 10^{16}$g	$0.7 \cdot 10^{16}$ cal/yr	$5 \cdot 10^{19}$g	$3.5 \cdot 10^{19}$ cal/yr
thorium	0	0	$2 \cdot 10^{20}$g	$4 \cdot 10^{19}$ cal/yr
potassium	0	0	$5 \cdot 10^{24}$g	$1.3 \cdot 10^{20}$ cal/yr
Total				$2 \cdot 10^{20}$ cal/yr

The total heat production, wholly from the mantle, is in line with the measured heat flow.

We must now explain the concentration of radioactive elements in the outer part of the earth. The chondritic hypothesis assumes that the entire earth has a composition equal to that of the average meteorite. On the basis of this assumption the total abundance of radioactive elements would be as shown in the table above. At the concentrations in surficial continental rocks, all of this radioactive material could be included within the outer few tens of miles of the earth. Since the continents occupy only one-fourth of the earth's surface, and rocks from oceanic islands invariably have lower concentrations of thorium, uranium, and potassium than do those of the continents, the radioactive elements would actually extend to somewhat greater depths than a few tens of miles. Regardless of the exact depth figure, however, it is obvious that these three elements have been concentrated toward the earth's surface by some process occurring within the earth, probably within the mantle. We can find such an upward enrichment for other elements also; for example, sodium and all of the other alkalies have concentrations in rocks of the continental crust which are much higher than in the average meteorite.

In explaining an upward concentration of certain elements, we may note the fact that all elements which show their greatest abundance near the earth's surface form ions of comparatively low density. In the case of the alkali metals, individual ions are large in comparison with their mass. In the case of thorium and uranium, both elements are closely associated with oxygen in a low-density anion composed of several different atoms. It seems fairly clear that individual ions within the mantle have separated gravitationally in much the same way as the core and the mantle separated, with the lighter material moving upward. This separation appears to be more complete in the continental masses than in the oceanic crust, thus leading to the idea that the floating continents consist of material which has moved upward out of the mantle and separated as a low-density phase. The relationships between continents and ocean basins will be discussed more fully in Chapters 13 and 14.

The formation of the atmosphere, hydrosphere, and biosphere is more easily discussed than fractionation in the solid earth, but not all of our questions concerning these geospheres can be answered. Water was obviously a part of the original earth, and it must have been incorporated in crystalline compounds while the earth was accreting. The water content of material with the composition of chondritic meteorites is sufficient to account for all of the water now on the earth, and we must, therefore, assume that water has been separating from its compounds in the interior and moving out on the surface throughout geologic time. Much, though probably not all, of this water was released as vapor through volcanoes. This origin of the hydrosphere implies a gradual increase in the volume of the oceans during the earth's history, and we shall discuss this question more fully in Chapter 13.

The early history of the atmosphere contains several events of enormous significance for the subsequent evolution of life. The early atmosphere was clearly dominated by chemically bound hydrogen, a cosmically most-abundant element. Some process or processes liberated the hydrogen from water (and ammonia). The free hydrogen then escaped from the earth's gravity field into space in the same way as helium does today. Since many forms of life as we know it require oxygen directly, such life could not have developed before the formation of an oxygen-rich atmosphere. Anerobic forms of life, particularly bacteria that can extract bound oxygen from iron oxides or sulfates may have been some of the earliest life on the earth. The date of the emergence of any form of life is highly uncertain, but it must have been at a fairly early time during the earth's history, for evidence of life has been found in rocks as old as $2 \cdot 10^9$ years. By this time, the atmosphere must have accumulated sufficiently to provide a shield against the primary cosmic ray and solar radiation. If all of the nitrogen in the present atmosphere had been originally combined with hydrogen to form ammonia, then the dehydrogenation of this ammonia and the loss of its resultant free hydrogen to space must have been largely completed by the time life developed. Otherwise, the poisonous ammonia would have prevented the evolution of present-day forms of life. (This last conclusion does not necessarily imply that no form of life could evolve in the presence of abundant ammonia.) However, present forms of life represent an adaptation to the earth's surface and to each other that has developed slowly over at least $2 \cdot 10^9$ years.

CHAPTER 6 COMPONENTS
OF THE EARTH'S CRUST:
PETROLOGY
AND MINERALOGY

◄ Exposed rocks. (Courtesy of Norwegian National Travel Office.)

The preceding chapters have discussed such topics as the size, the shape, and the weight of the earth. They have described such major features as the distribution of continents and ocean basins, the densities of continental and oceanic rocks, and the inferences which geochemical and cosmochemical studies provide concerning the composition of the earth. It is now time to take a somewhat more detailed look at those portions of the earth that are specifically available for our examination. By careful examination of the rocks and features exposed on the earth's surface, we shall be able to draw conclusions concerning the overall history of formation of the earth. Our knowledge of this history is, of course, still incomplete, partly because the record is obscured in many places, and partly because for each active geologist there are several thousand square miles of land surface. One of the major problems to be discussed in the latter part of this book is an outline of those portions of the earth's history particularly deserving of further work.

In addition to the rocks exposed at the earth's surface, geologists have available for their examination a number of samples obtained from oil wells and other wells. The deepest of these wells, however, is only approximately five miles, and it is a source of major concern that we have been able to penetrate less than 1 percent of the distance to the center of the earth. We are also concerned by the fact that the rocks which we are studying at the earth's surface are obviously quite dissimilar to those that occur at depth. This dissimilarity has been pointed out in the preceding chapters on the basis of geophysical evidence.

The size, complexity, and long evolution of the earth make it difficult to apply simple classifications and physical concepts to rocks. Indeed, the only simple rock units are those that have not been studied in detail. Just as human fingerprint patterns can be classified into useful (but not genetic) categories, so it is possible to group rocks into a relatively few categories. However, no two granites will be exactly alike in age, composition, grain size, or even origin. In other words, most major geologic systems are multivariant, and exact, quantitative concepts are obtained rarely and with difficulty. Multivariance of causes and factors contribute much to the uncertainty of geological analysis, just as they do for weather forecasting, medical diagnosis, and the determination of legal guilt. Yet clear-cut cases do exist, and it is possible to use the variability in nature to reconstruct the "experiments" that natural processes have run on a time-space scale far beyond man's duplication.

GENERAL CHARACTERISTICS OF ROCK FORMATIONS

If you stand upon the earth's surface the chances are that you will not be standing upon rock. Rocks exposed for any considerable period of time to the action of the atmosphere are generally converted into soils by a process called *weathering*, which will be discussed in Chapter 9. This weathering is generally most intense in areas where the rainfall is highest. Thus, soils are generally thicker and better developed in the eastern part of the United States than in the west, and exposures, called *outcrops*, of bedrock are less common in the east than in the west. There are a number of places where you might look to find outcrops of un-weathered rocks. Sharp cliffs, for example, or stream beds, particularly those with steep banks, generally expose the rock behind them. One of the best places to find fresh, unweathered rocks is in recent road cuts. In general, though not always, you will distinguish bedrock from soil by its hardness and the absence of plant or other organic matter. Whereas many soils can be crumbled in the hands, the fresh rock must generally be broken with a hammer. There are, of course, hard soils and soft rocks, but these are the exceptions.

Layering and sedimentation

Let us assume now that we have found a sizable outcrop of fresh rock and that we can observe in it the following easily defined properties:

1. The rocks have a distinct layering, in the sense that tabular bands of generally different appearance are parallel to each other. If we could investigate the third dimension, perhaps in a small gully on the face of the cliff, we would find that these bands are really tabular. The thickness of the layers probably varies from a fraction of an inch to many feet. We shall call these layers *beds* or *strata* (Fig. 6-1).

Fig. 6-1. Sedimentary rocks exposed at Bryce Canyon, Utah. Note that individual beds in the three pillars in the foreground were obviously continuous until the intervening areas were removed by erosion. (Photo by J. J. W. Rogers.)

Fig. 6-2. Layering in modern beach sands, Galveston Island, Texas. (Photo courtesy of Esso Production Research.)

2. From some of the beds we may scrape away material that, upon close examination, looks just like the sand of a beach or lake shore or river bank. The individual fragments seem to be small, smooth, rounded particles, and we shall call these particles *grains*.

3. Some of the beds may contain the shells of organisms. These shells (fossils) generally consist of calcium carbonate ($CaCO_3$) or silica (SiO_2). In general they are broadly similar, though not identical, to the shells of organisms living today.

Now if we leave the outcrop and look at a modern beach or a modern river bank or a sand dune in the desert, we will see striking similarities between the materials which compose these modern deposits (Fig. 6-2) and the materials which compose the rocks of the outcrop (Fig. 6-3). We can, furthermore, observe a sand dune moving and accumulating material. We can observe, over a period of time, a beach building forward into the ocean. In short, we may see materials being deposited today, and we can infer that such deposition occurred in the past (Fig. 6-4). This is the principle of *uniformitarianism,* which has already been briefly discussed, and indeed modern sedimentation is one of the major pieces of evidence in favor of the concept of uniformitarianism. The inference, then, is that the rocks of the outcrop which we were investigating were formed in a fashion broadly similar to the manner in which modern materials are being deposited. It is possible, then, for us to determine and identify a large class of rocks as having formed at the earth's surface by deposition from water or wind. We shall call these rocks *sedimentary*. To be more precise, a *sedimentary rock* is a hardened (lithified) equivalent of a deposited *sediment.* Approximately 75 percent of the land area of the earth is covered by these sedimentary rocks.

Many of the individual grains which compose sedimentary or other rocks consist of individual chemical compounds. Such naturally occurring compounds are called *minerals.* In fact, the term *rock* is generally applied to a collection of individual minerals. In many types of sedimentary rocks the individual minerals occur as easily separable grains. In other

Fig. 6-3. Layering in ancient beach sands, Dakota formation, Colorado. Features are similar to those shown in Fig. 6-2 but have been tilted by later ground movement after deposition. (Photo by Donald W. Lane, from *American Association of Petroleum Geologists Bulletin*, vol. 47, n. 2, February 1963.)

types of rocks, however, the minerals are so complexly intergrown that it would be difficult to separate one from another.

Volcanic material and rocks of igneous origin

Not all of the rocks that form on the earth's surface can be considered sedimentary. If we go to certain parts of the earth such as Central America, Iceland, or Japan, we can see volcanoes in action and study the materials erupted from them and deposited on the surface. A volcano is simply a mound or hill built around one or more vents and from which subterranean materials are erupted at high temperature and pressure. The erupted material may be a sticky liquid called *lava*, or it may be in the form of broken solid fragments which we shall call *pyroclastic* (meaning "fire-broken"), or it may simply consist of a vapor. In some cases vents may give forth volcanic erupted material without the construction of a true volcanic hill.

The immediate question, of course, is whether or not there are ancient equivalents for these recent volcanic rocks. Intuitively, we feel that there must be some if uniformitarianism is at all valid. It remains, however, for us to prove the existence of such ancient volcanic deposits. In order to do so, it is necessary to know the properties which characterize modern volcanic rocks. From the standpoint of simple inspection of outcrops, the more diagnostic properties of volcanic rocks may be listed as follows:

1. The rocks in many cases are layered, though the layering in general is not as regular as it is in sedimentary rocks.

2. The congealed products of lavas are invariably hard; many of the rocks contain small cavities up to an inch in diameter, apparently once filled by a fluid that escaped after the rock solidified.

3. Close inspection with a magnifying lens indicates that the rocks consist largely of homogeneous material in which there may or may not be detectable crystals of individual minerals.

4. The density of volcanic rocks is generally higher than that of sediments.

From these characteristic properties, it is easily possible to recognize ancient equivalents (Fig. 6-5) of modern congealed lavas (Fig. 6-6). The recognition of pyroclastic rocks is commonly very difficult and may be impossible even for an experienced geologist.

We have now discovered that rocks may be formed at the earth's surface in a variety of ways. Those rocks which have been deposited from water or wind at temperatures and pressures normal to the surface are generally called sedimentary. Rocks which have been deposited after eruption from a volcanic vent may be called volcanic rocks if they have been congealed from a lava, or they may be termed pyroclastic if they represent debris which has been blown as particles through the air. It should be obvious, however, that not all of the rocks currently exposed

Fig. 6-4. Contact between two sedimentary formations in Alabama. (Photo by H. B. Stenzel.)

Fig. 6-5. Layered volcanic rocks on the Columbia River, Oregon and Washington. The conical features at the base consist of fragments which have fallen from the overlying cliffs. (Photo by J. J. W. Rogers.)

at the earth's surface have formed there. We know that in many areas running water and other agents are continually removing surficial materials and exposing rocks underneath. In many cases these rocks have been formed at the earth's surface originally and later buried. In some cases, however, we can demonstrate that the rocks so exposed are at the surface of the earth for the first time. The evidence we might use for such a demonstration might be as follows: A lava flowing over the earth's surface may have a profound effect on the materials which compose that surface. In places these materials may be broken and moved slightly. In other places a soft mud or other sediment may be baked hard by the high temperature of the lava. Along with the baking and hardening, the high temperatures may cause mineralogical changes, such as may result from the effect of oxidation. Such effects of a lava will be seen only on rocks underlying it, and except in rare instances, rocks deposited

Fig. 6-6. Layering of volcanic rocks in a modern volcano, Guatemala. The depression which reveals the layering is caused by collapse of the loose material after eruption of underground support. (Photo by O. Bohnenberger.)

on top of the volcanic material will not be affected by its heat. It is common, however, to find rocks of apparent volcanic origin situated between sediments in which these contact effects are seen both below and above the lava. The only possible conclusion in such cases is that the lava was erupted *into* a sequence of sedimentary rocks rather than *on* its surface. Such rocks which are formed below the earth's surface will be called *intrusive* rocks, as opposed to the *extrusive* ones erupted onto the surface.

SILLS AND DIKES. Another undoubted demonstration of the intrusive nature of certain types of volcanic rocks is shown by the fact that some tabular bodies cut across the bedding formed by sedimentary rocks (Fig. 6-7). In addition to this cross-cutting relationship, it may be possible to find evidence of oxidation, baking, and disruption on both sides of the intrusive body. Intruded volcanic rocks that are parallel to sedimentary bedding and thus lie between two sedimentary units are called *sills* (Fig. 6-8). Rocks which cut across the bedding and thus come into contact with a large number of different beds are called *dikes* (Fig. 6-7). A simple geologic history for an outcrop as is shown in Fig. 6-8 would be: (1) deposition of sediments; (2) a possible lithification to form sedimentary rocks; (3) an injection of the volcanic liquid to form the sill and dikes and their contact features; and (4) uplift and erosion to expose the entire sequence.

Fig. 6-7. Dike of igneous rock cutting horizontally layered sediments. (Photo by T. W. Donnelly.)

THE PLUTONIC OR IGNEOUS ROCKS. It is now necessary for us to extrapolate somewhat beyond the evidence shown by intrusive dikes and sills. The object will be to discuss the mode of formation of a type of rock which constitutes a major portion of the earth's crust. The rocks referred to are characterized by the following features:

1. They occur as large bodies, in places underlying many hundreds of square miles of the earth's surface.

2. They are commonly massive, or at least only rarely show evidence of the layering which is characteristic of the sedimentary and volcanic rocks.

3. They have, in most cases, easily distinguishable individual mineral grains; the rocks are thus quite different from volcanic rocks in which individual minerals are difficult or impossible to recognize. In geological

Fig. 6-8. Sills and dikes in west Texas. Dark patches on the cliff in the background are sills (somewhat irregular masses) with dikes projecting above them (elongate, near-vertical, masses). General history is described in the text. (Photo by T. H. Foss.)

terminology these unlayered rocks are "coarser grained" than the volcanic rocks.

4. In places it is possible to find these coarse-grained rocks in contact with sediments, and the contact features are similar to those found around sills and dikes.

5. Although many of these bodies of coarse-grained rock occur in mountainous regions in which there is considerable vertical exposure, it has not been possible to find a bottom contact for them. In other words, the rocks are not floored in the sense of a sill, which has a different type of rock at its base.

In trying to determine the general mode of formation of these coarse-grained rocks we may notice an interesting feature concerning dikes and sills. A lava erupted on the surface or intruded as a dike obviously forms a solid rock by cooling. We can, if we wish, reverse the process and heat the rock in the laboratory to form a melt similar to the original lava. Furthermore, it is also obvious that the outer margin of a sill or dike must cool more rapidly than the interior when the lava is intruded into rocks colder than itself. An interesting observation in a number of sills and dikes, and indeed even in thick lava flows, is that the number and size of the distinctly recognizable minerals increases from the margin of the body towards the center. The conclusion is that such minerals form and grow most readily where cooling is slowest. This conclusion may easily be verified by simple laboratory experiments, though it is clear in laboratory experiments that other factors, such as the water content of a melt, also affect crystal size. A comparable observation may also be made in some bodies of wholly coarse-grained rock. In places, as the contact is approached, the sizes of individual minerals may be seen to decrease. From this admittedly tenuous line of reasoning, we may conclude that the coarse-grained, massive rocks are simply representatives of lava which has been intruded into the earth's crust and has cooled more slowly than the typical dikes, sills, and lava flows. This conclusion can be reinforced by comparison of the chemical compositions of extruded volcanic rock with the compositions of the coarse-grained bodies. With some exceptions, there are volcanic rocks having all of the compositions that we find in the coarse-grained intrusive rocks. The conclusion that the coarse-grained intrusive bodies have formed by injection and solidification of a melt has been challenged by a number of geologists, and we shall discuss this problem in more detail in Chapter 8.

Once we have decided that coarseness of grain size indicates a comparatively long period of cooling and solidification, it is possible to make other inferences concerning the origin of large bodies of rock. Obviously, a body will cool more rapidly on the earth's surface than it will if buried at some depth and thus surrounded by relatively insulating rock. We can, therefore, say that coarse-grained rocks have probably solidified at some depth within the earth, but the fact that grain size is controlled by a variety of factors in addition to rate of cooling prevents the establishment of any direct relationship between sizes of minerals and depth of formation. We have already seen that geophysical studies have indicated an average thickness of some 20 to 30 miles for the continental crust of the earth, and we may presume that the typical coarse-grained, massive rock body has probably formed somewhere at depths within this range. Rocks which have formed at depth, whether by solidification from a melt or by other processes, are generally given the term *plutonic*.

It is now useful to define the term *igneous*. Strictly speaking, an igneous rock is one which has solidified from a melt such as a lava. As already mentioned, however, there is some controversy concerning the origin of the plutonic bodies which we have been discussing, and the evidence for solidification from a pre-existing melt is simply not conclusive. The practice has persisted in geology to apply the term "igneous," regardless of mode of formation, to most coarse-grained massive plutonic bodies, and we shall henceforth call them *igneous rocks*. Thus, igneous rocks include plutonic coarse-grained bodies and volcanic rocks which have clearly formed by solidification of a melt. The terminological problem arises from the fact that the term "igneous" was originally a genetic term—that is, it implied a particular mode of formation. In general, we shall find that genetic terms are extremely awkward to use for purely descriptive purposes.

Metamorphism

Certain widely distributed types of plutonic rocks have obviously not formed by solidification from a melt. Simple logic, plus a few measurements in deep wells, will demonstrate that the temperature must increase downward in the earth's crust (Chapter 4). It is also apparent that pressures must increase downward because of the weight of overlying rocks. Under these conditions it seems likely, therefore, that sediments once deposited at the earth's surface and later buried under additional material would be changed as they are pushed farther downward into the earth. Indeed, it is possible in many areas such as Scotland or the eastern side of the Appalachian Mountains in the United States to trace sediments from rocks having nearly unaltered original depositional properties into rocks that have obviously been greatly altered. The correspondence of altered and unaltered forms is clear, particularly where the altered rocks preserve the original bedding and compositional variations characteristic of freshly deposited sediments. This process of alteration is called *metamorphism*.

Owing to their formation at considerable depth within the earth, the metamorphic rocks thus formed are commonly closely intermixed with intrusive igneous rocks. In fact, in many places intrusive igneous rocks have apparently raised temperatures in the neighborhood of their contacts above those of the surrounding rocks and have caused a higher degree of metamorphism than is characteristic of the area away from the contact. Even the relatively minor baking and hardening which we have described in connection with sills and dikes intruded into sediments is a form of metamorphism.

The relationships between plutonic igneous and metamorphic rocks are complex, and we shall discuss some of these in a later chapter. In particular, it will be necessary to answer questions such as whether or not a metamorphic process can convert a sediment into a rock that is indistinguishable from one which has solidified from a melt. Another difficult question is whether or not major metamorphism can occur in areas in which the temperature has not been elevated by intrusion of igneous bodies.

In most cases metamorphic rocks can be recognized by a rather simple set of properties:

1. The rocks are almost invariably layered (Fig. 6-9). In some cases the layering is probably inherited from sedimentary bedding, and in some cases the layering is probably developed by the metamorphic process.
2. Most metamorphic rocks are sufficiently coarse-grained to permit individual minerals to be recognized.
3. Metamorphic rocks are considerably harder than equivalent sedimentary rocks, and the grains are generally quite intergrown with each other.

4. Certain special minerals (which will be discussed later) occur only in metamorphic rocks and may be considered diagnostic of a metamorphic origin.
5. Some rocks contain features, such as fossils, that have been greatly distorted out of their original shapes.

ROCK CYCLES

We have now identified the major rock types of the earth's crust, and it is possible to speculate rather broadly on the relationships between them. It is apparent that sediments are formed by the breakdown, removal, movement, and accumulation of some pre-existing material. In geologic terminology these processes are:

1. *Weathering*—chemical and physical alteration of rock material at the earth's surface
2. *Erosion*—removal of weathered or fresh rock from its original location by means of moving water, wind, etc.
3. *Transportation*—carrying of eroded material to another location
4. *Deposition*—accumulation of material as a sediment

Fig. 6-9. Intricately contorted metamorphic rocks in Nevada. (Photo by R. B. Scott.)

Although it is obvious that one sediment may be formed by the erosion of another sediment, it is also apparent that the first sediment must have come from somewhere. In short, the original source of sedimentary material must be some type of igneous or metamorphic rock. A certain cyclical nature of the process is obvious, however, from the fact that metamorphic rocks are in large part formed by the alteration of sediments. Thus, ultimately the source of sediments must be igneous rocks, but even here the problem is complicated by the fact that it is distinctly possible that sediments upon burial are remelted and may then form an igneous melt. If we wish, therefore, we can establish a cycle such as is shown in Fig. 6-10. This is a simplified version of what is commonly called a *geochemical* or *rock cycle*. Unless we wish to assume, however, that the total amount of continental material has always been exactly as much as it is now, it is obvious that, somewhere along the line, material must be added to this cycle from somewhere else in the earth, presumably the mantle. This addition may take the form of molten material, either intruded to form plutonic igneous rocks or extruded in the form of lavas and pyroclastic material.

If all of the material added to the crust from the mantle is in the form of igneous melts, then we may construct a geochemical balance such as

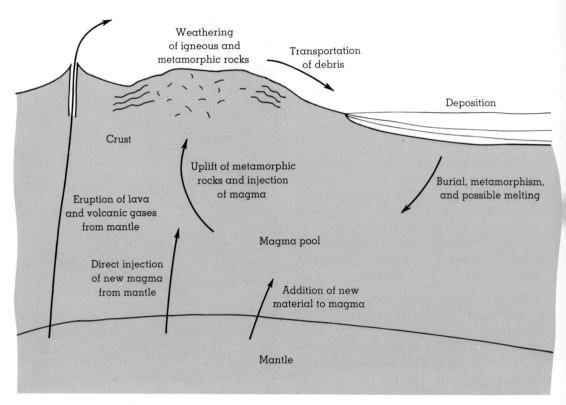

Fig. 6-10. Diagrammatic geochemical (rock) cycle.

is shown in Table 6-1. This table is constructed on the assumption that the total mass of an element now occurring in sediments and in sea water must equal the total mass of the element that has been removed from igneous rock to form the sediment. In order to check this assumption it is simply necessary to estimate the total mass of sediments, of sea water, and of weathered igneous rock and to determine the average abundance of various elements in each of the three materials. The total mass of sediments can be estimated reasonably well from maps of surface outcrops, from records of deep wells, and from geophysical studies. The total mass of the ocean is easily calculated from depth measurements and a knowledge of the surface area. The average abundance of elements in the various rocks is difficult to obtain. Here we may simply indicate that reasonable estimates can be made from large numbers of chemical analyses in which each number is weighted in accordance with the apparent abundance of the rock type it represents. The major problem in the construction of Table 6-1 is the figure for the total mass of weathered igneous rock. This figure may be best estimated as simply the number most closely balancing the abundances of several different elements in weathered igneous rock and in sediments.

On the basis of figures given in Table 6-1 we can see that sodium balances rather well, and we can assume that sodium in sediments and sea

TABLE 6-1.   MASS BALANCE OF SODIUM IN SEDIMENTARY AND IGNEOUS ROCKS

	mass of material	percent of sodium	mass of sodium
sedimentary rocks	$20{,}410 \cdot 10^{20}$ grams	2.0 %	$408 \cdot 10^{20}$ grams
water in rock pores	$3{,}350 \cdot 10^{20}$	0.45	$15 \cdot 10^{20}$
sea water	$14{,}250 \cdot 10^{20}$	1.5	$150 \cdot 10^{20}$
weathered igneous rock	$20{,}410 \cdot 10^{20}$	2.8	$573 \cdot 10^{20}$

water has been obtained largely by the weathering of igneous rock. The abundances of some elements, however, are so much larger in sediments and in sea water than they are in igneous rock that a balance, as in the case of sodium, is virtually impossible. These elements, which include sulfur and chlorine, have undoubtedly been added to the geochemical cycle in some fashion other than in a normal igneous melt. At present this exact mode of addition is not clear, though it is likely that they are emitted on the surface in volcanic gases.

MINERALOGY

Having identified the major rock components of the earth's crust and discussed briefly the relationships between them, we now proceed to take a somewhat closer look at the details of the composition and mineralogy of the rocks. From such a detailed investigation it will be possible for us to draw more precise inferences concerning such problems as the evolution of large suites of plutonic igneous rocks, the mechanism of eruption of volcanic rocks, and the origin and transportation processes of sediments. For such purposes it is first necessary to be acquainted with the field of mineralogy.

Minerals have already been defined as naturally occurring chemical compounds, generally inorganic. The term "chemical compound" implies a fixed composition, or at least a composition varying within certain prescribed limits, and it also implies that most minerals have a distinct crystalline structure. Compounds of the same chemical composition but different crystalline structure—that is, crystalline polymorphs—generally have distinct mineral names. Over a thousand different and distinct minerals have been described. The practicing geologist, however, will rarely encounter more than a hundred of these minerals, and most geologists can operate satisfactorily with a knowledge of a few dozen. In this book we shall mention only a few of the more important minerals.

Identification

The ultimate basis for the identification of a mineral is a complete chemical analysis and a structural determination by X-ray methods.

These techniques, of course, are hardly usable by geologists in the field, and it is necessary for all students of geology to be able to recognize minerals on the basis of certain easily determinable physical properties. The major properties which are used for identification purposes are:

1. Color
2. Crystal form, where available, although most minerals do not show well-developed crystals
3. Cleavage, which is the property of a mineral to split along one or more series of parallel planes
4. Specific gravity
5. Hardness, which refers to the ability of a mineral to scratch or be scratched
6. Luster, which is the external "look" of a mineral and is described in such terms as metallic, glassy, etc.

Of these diagnostic properties, color is perhaps the least useful. The mineral quartz (SiO_2), for example, may have colors ranging from dark gray to white to colorless to rose-red to green. These color variations are apparently caused by the presence of minor amounts of materials other than SiO_2. For example, rose-colored quartz apparently contains a small amount of manganese. Despite these variations, however, most quartz is recognizable by its light gray to colorless appearance, and in general the colors of minerals are moderately diagnostic.

Most naturally occurring minerals crystallize in media that contain other materials, either previously formed or simultaneously growing. In such cases the normal crystal form a particular crystal lattice would assume externally cannot be developed, and the borders between two mineral grains are irregular or represent some sort of a mutual adjustment of the two lattices. In a few cases, however, such as the crystallization of minerals in open cavities, as in Fig. 6-11, the crystal form characteristic of the particular mineral can be developed. Some of these forms are quite spectacular, and they can provide information on the internal crystalline structure that gives rise to them. As a diagnostic property, however, definite crystal form is too rare to be particularly useful.

Cleavage is one of the most diagnostically useful mineralogical properties (Fig. 6-12). A mineral cleaves along planes across which the bonding between layers of ions is comparatively weak. Thus, cleavage is a property that is repeated throughout the mineral. This repetitive property is one good method by which a beginning student may make the initially difficult distinction between

Fig. 6-11. Crystals growing into a cavity. The mineral is an uncommon silicate known as apophyllite. (Courtesy of Ward's Natural Science Establishment, Inc., Rochester, N.Y.)

cleavage and crystal surfaces, for a true external crystal surface will not be duplicated by fracturing. Furthermore, cleavage surfaces, being freshly formed by fracturing, are invariably shiny and unaltered; conversely, crystal surfaces may be dull, somewhat pitted or etched, and will in general show the effects of having been in contact with other materials for a long period of time. A mineral may have from 0 to 6 directions of cleavage. A few minerals have a tendency to break along a small number of reasonably flat surfaces which are not cleavage surfaces, owing to the fact that they are not capable of being repeated by further fracturing. Such surfaces are called *partings* and may be difficult for a beginning geologist or even a practicing one to distinguish from true cleavage.

Specific gravity can be measured accurately only by some kind of immersion method. It is easily possible, however, for a geologist to develop the ability to estimate roughly whether a mineral is heavy or light by simply hefting it in his hand.

Fig. 6-12. Cleavage fragments of ordinary calcite. Some of the pieces are opaque because of imperfections in the lattice. (Photo by J. J. W. Rogers.)

No precise determinations can be made in this fashion, but the property is useful in some cases.

Scratch hardness is a useful diagnostic property for some minerals. If you take two minerals at random and rub them against each other, one generally will tend to scratch the other. The mineral which does the scratching is said to be harder than the one which is scratched. In this very empirical manner an arbitrary hardness scale called the *Mohs' hardness scale* has been established. On this scale a mineral will scratch any other mineral below it, and the standard reference minerals are as follows: (1) talc; (2) gypsum; (3) calcite; (4) fluorite; (5) apatite; (6) orthoclase; (7) quartz; (8) topaz; (9) corundum; (10) diamond. Other minerals may be placed in this scale by direct comparison. Unfortunately, most of the major minerals in normal rocks have hardnesses in the range of 5 to 7, and the differences between them are not easily apparent. For comparison purposes, a piece of glass or an ordinary penknife blade have hardnesses of approximately 5. Your fingernail has a hardness between 2 and 3.

The luster of a mineral is a diagnostic property in a few cases. It is generally easy to distinguish between metallic and nonmetallic minerals, and certain highly glassy minerals are readily recognized. Most minerals, however, particularly those occurring in common rocks, have a generally dull appearance, and the differences in luster are not sufficiently large to be usable for recognition.

In addition to the diagnostic properties listed above, some minerals tend to occur in rather definite shapes. Mica, for example, is generally in the form of thin plates. These plates are formed not as individual crystals but by virtue of the pronounced tendency for mica to cleave in one direction. Similarly, hornblende grains tend to be elongate (somewhat pencil shaped), in part because this is their normal growth shape and in part because of two directions of cleavage.

A list of the important minerals for the beginning student to know is given in the Appendix along with the most obvious diagnostic properties and a few comments concerning the occurrence and importance of the minerals.

Composition

The science of mineralogy has made numerous contributions in addition to the simple description and recognition of minerals, important as that may be. Detailed investigations of both the composition and the atomic structure of minerals have led to a number of highly interesting results, some of which are discussed below.

As described briefly in Chapter 5, the earth's crust consists predominantly of oxygen, silicon, and aluminum. In fact, owing to the large size of the oxygen ion (radius of 1.40 Å) and the small size of silicon (0.41 Å) and aluminum (0.50 Å), the earth's crust may be viewed almost exclusively as a vast accumulation of oxygen ions with interstitial cations (Table 6-2). Simple calculations from various ionic radii will demonstrate that approximately 90 to 95 percent of the earth's crust is occupied by oxygen. Owing to the abundance of silicon and aluminum ions in the earth's crust, virtually all of the oxygen ions have at least a part, and in some cases all, of their negative valence balanced by silicon and aluminum. The size of the silicon ion is such that it forms tetrahedral SiO_4 groups. The aluminum ion has a size which permits it to form either tetrahedral AlO_4 groups or octahedral AlO_6 groups. The oxygen valences which are not satisfied by silicon and aluminum are neutralized by the other cations, predominantly calcium, magnesium, iron, potassium, and sodium. For these reasons the major rock-forming minerals are generally referred to as silicates or silicate aluminates.

The principal minerals of igneous and metamorphic rocks are quartz, potassium feldspar (orthoclase or microcline), plagioclase, biotite, augite, and hornblende. As can be seen from the formulas in the Appendix, all of these minerals are silicates with different amounts of the various major cations.

A glance at the mineral formulas listed in the Appendix indicates that many minerals are chemically very complex. This complexity is particularly characteristic of the major rock-forming silicates. Fortunately, however, it is possible to express the formulas of many complex minerals in terms of proportions of rather simple compounds. These simple, perhaps ideal, compounds are commonly referred to as *end members*. Minerals which consist of a chemically homogeneous admixture of these end members are commonly termed *solid solutions*. X-ray analysis shows

TABLE 6-2. RADII OF VARIOUS IONS

Na^+	$0.97\overset{\circ}{A}$
K^+	1.42
Rb^+	1.57
Mg^{++}	0.66
Fe^{++}	0.74
Ca^{++}	0.99
Sr^{++}	1.16
Pb^{++}	1.24
Ba^{++}	1.43
Al^{3+}	0.49
Ga^{3+}	0.59
Fe^{3+}	0.64
Si^{4+}	0.40
O^{--}	1.40
S^{--}	1.85

SOURCE: From Green, Geochemical Table of the Elements for 1959, *Geological Society of America Bulletin.*

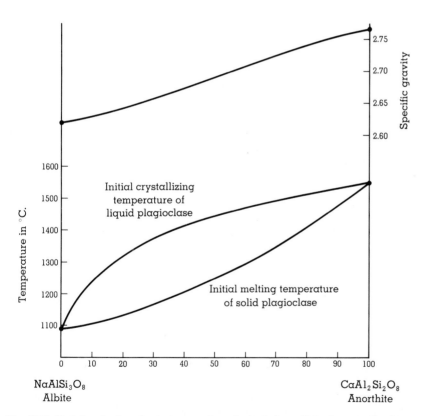

Fig. 6-13. Variation in the physical properties of plagioclase. Note the smooth changes in all properties, indicating complete isomorphism and solid solution. Note also that initial melting and initial crystallization temperatures in such series are not identical.

that these solid solutions are generally true single compounds rather than mixtures of small separate particles of each end member.

The nature of these solid solutions can be best illustrated by reference to the plagioclase series (Fig. 6-13). It is extremely rare to find either pure albite or pure anorthite in nature, and practically all plagioclase in normal rocks has an intermediate composition. In typical igneous rocks the composition of the plagioclase varies from approximately 20 percent to approximately 50 percent anorthite. As shown by Fig. 6-13, the physical properties of the various plagioclases vary in a smooth manner between the properties of the pure end members. The density, for example, increases slowly from albite to anorthite. Furthermore, the optical properties, including primarily the various indices of refraction, also show smooth variations between the extreme values, though we are not in a position to study these properties here. The construction of figures such as Fig. 6-13 is a simple matter of comparing measured physical properties with analyzed chemical compositions, and a great deal of effort by mineralogists has gone into the preparation of such summaries for a wide variety of minerals which exhibit solid solutions. Notice that a solid solution does not have a single melting point but rather melts over a fairly broad range of temperatures.

Two or more end members which form such a smooth solid solution as is shown for the plagioclases are said to form an *isomorphous series.* The term implies that the two components have similar structures and can thus interchange for each other freely within the crystal lattice. In some cases two components will mix freely only over part of the possible compositional range. For example, ferrous ion can substitute isomorphically for zinc ion in the mineral sphalerite (ZnS) only to the extent of about 20 percent of the zinc ion positions. Higher proportions of ferrous ion are not found nor are they to be expected on the basis of laboratory and theoretical studies. We may refer to relationships of this type as "partial isomorphism" or "limited solid solution."

Whether or not two materials will form an isomorphous series is determined largely by the sizes and partly by the charges of the various cations involved. The common ionic radii of the various elements are listed in Table 6-2. From this table the reason for isomorphism in the plagioclase series is quite apparent. Both sodium and calcium have approximately equal sizes, although the sodium has a valence less than that of calcium. As a rough and highly empirical rule of thumb, it has been found that two ions will substitute for each other in an isomorphous series if their radii are within approximately 15 percent of each other, providing that their valences do not differ enormously. In plagioclase, a substitution of calcium for sodium requires concurrent substitution of aluminum for silicon in order to maintain charge balance.

By reasoning similar to the above, we may predict an almost complete isomorphism between iron and magnesium and between silicon and aluminum. Calcium and magnesium, however, are obviously not isomorphous with each other. Consequently, in minerals containing both calcium and magnesium there must be a separate structural position for calcium distinct from the structural position occupied by magnesium.

Hence, the structure of dolomite $(CaMg(CO_3)_2)$ is quite distinct from that of calcite $(CaCO_3)$, whereas the structure of albite $(NaAlSi_3O_8)$ is very similar to that of anorthite $(CaAl_2Si_2O_8)$.

Considerations similar to those which we have been discussing enable us to predict the location of a number of the minor elements that occur in the earth's crust. For example, the element rubidium has an ionic radius of 1.5 Å and a valence of 1. We would expect, therefore, that it would occupy the same position as potassium in a silicate structure. It turns out that the isomorphism between rubidium and potassium is so perfect that the two elements are separated only with great difficulty in geological processes. For example, no mineral consisting purely of rubidium and anion groups has ever been discovered. By the same token, practically every potassium mineral contains a small amount of rubidium. In fact, the ratio of potassium to rubidium is nearly constant in all minerals and all rocks that have been investigated in the earth. As an additional example, the divalent ion barium with an ionic radius of 1.35 Å is in part substituted for potassium in a variety of minerals. The isomorphism between barium and potassium, however, is less perfect than that of rubidium and potassium, and consequently there are a number of pure barium minerals.

Geologic processes which separate two potentially isomorphous ions are said to *fractionate* the ions. Studies of the fractionation of elements represent an important field of modern geologic research. Some major fractionation processes have already been discussed in Chapter 5, and in our discussion of the evolution of igneous rocks in Chapter 8 we shall discuss in some detail a few of the more important compositional variations. An important point which should be mentioned here, however, is that isomorphous cations are not attracted with equal strength to anion lattices. We might expect *a priori* that small ions of high charge are more strongly bonded to anions than large ions of small charge. Thus, the calcic plagioclase (anorthite) should exhibit somewhat stronger interionic bonding than the sodium plagioclase (albite), and we might expect that anorthite would melt at a higher temperature than pure albite (Fig. 6-13). Similar relationships can be found for the slightly smaller magnesium ion in comparison with the somewhat larger iron ion.

Mineral groups

The construction of an orderly classification of more than a thousand separate minerals is a very difficult task. The classification invariably used by modern geologists is based on the nature of the anion which comprises the mineral. Thus, minerals are separated into such groups as sulfides, oxides, carbonates, sulfates, silicates, etc. Further subdivisions may be based on the nature of the attached cations or, in the case of silicates, may be based on the mode of cross-linkage between various silica and alumina groups. This essentially structural classification is discussed in the last section of this chapter.

We have already noted that a rather small number of silicate minerals constitute most of the earth's crust. Other groups of minerals occupy subordinate but highly interesting positions, and a brief description of some of these groups seems appropriate here.

Metallic ores generally contain large quantities of sulfide minerals. Most of the lead and zinc obtained in mines throughout the world are derived from sulfides, the major lead mineral being the simple lead sulfide, galena, and virtually the only zinc mineral being the simple zinc sulfide, sphalerite. Most copper deposits consist of various types of copper sulfides, such as chalcopyrite, though in a few mines other types of copper minerals are important economic materials. A ubiquitous associate of ore deposits is the iron sulfide, pyrite. The presence of pyrite (FeS_2) in sulfide metal deposits of almost all elements has led some geologists to propose that the iron for the pyrite is derived from the rocks surrounding the metallic deposits, though other geologists feel that the iron is introduced along with the sulfur in some type of ore-carrying fluid.

Oxides can develop in a variety of ways. Magnetite occurs in small amounts in almost all igneous rocks. The oxidized iron minerals such as hematite (Fe_2O_3) and limonite are restricted largely to deposits formed in contact with the atmosphere of the earth's surface. The yellow staining common in many weathered rocks is generally limonite or some related mineral. For classification purposes, it is a moot point whether quartz should be considered an oxide or a silicate.

The two major carbonate minerals are calcite and dolomite, which occur almost exclusively in sedimentary rocks though they are present in some metallic ore deposits. In rock form, calcite is referred to as *limestone* and is one of the very common types of sedimentary rocks. A large number of shell-secreting organisms build their shells from calcite. Dolomite is considerably less common than calcite, and its origin poses a problem which we shall discuss in Chapter 7.

Water-soluble salts such as halite are, of course, extremely rare. They are formed by extreme evaporation of bodies of water, and their preservation naturally requires either extremely dry climate or burial and protection fom the action of rain water and rivers. A few desert areas, such as the Atacama region of northern Chile, contain such exceptionally soluble salts as sodium nitrate, but their occurrence is very limited.

This brief list by no means exhausts the types of minerals or their occurrence. For example, the phosphate mineral apatite ($Ca_5(PO_4)_3Cl$) is extremely common in small amounts in most igneous rocks. Similarly, one of the main ores of uranium is a complex calcium uranium vanadate known as carnotite. The major rock-forming minerals, however, comprise well over 99 percent of the earth's crust.

Crystal structure

The structures of minerals can be studied in two principal ways. Probably the most significant data are obtained from X-ray investigations, which are capable of determining the positions of the various ions within the crystal. The classical and original method of investigating the structures of crystals, however, was based solely on the external shape, which we will call *morphology,* of well-formed crystals. Careful work, in fact, enabled students of external crystal form to anticipate a good many of the results that were later obtained more exactly by X-ray studies. Consequently, we shall begin our discussion of structures with the concept of morphology.

A well-formed crystal is bounded by a number of faces. The minimum number, of course, is four, and some crystals have been found with fifty or more faces. One of the earliest tasks facing students of crystals (crystallographers) was to develop a system of describing and referring to all of these various faces in some easily visualized manner. For this purpose, the concept of symmetry is of the greatest importance.

Consider, for example, a simple equilateral triangle. The three sides of this triangle can be visualized in terms of one side and a three-fold rotation about an axis through the center of the triangle and perpendicular to the plane of the triangle, as is indicated in Fig. 6-14. A rotational axis of this type is said to be a "three-fold symmetry axis," and each one of the sides of the triangle can be considered as "equivalent." Another type of symmetry operation is simple reflection across a plane as is shown in Fig. 6-15. It is also possible to conceive of centers of symmetry, such that equivalent points occur opposite each other on a line through the center; thus a square has a center of symmetry, and a triangle does not. Both geometric and algebraic proofs are available to demonstrate that the total number of possible symmetry operations consists of a center, a set of reflection planes, and two-, three-, four-, or six-fold rotation axes. Now consider a crystal characterized by one plane of symmetry and the two-fold rotation axis perpendicular to this plane. If, as in Fig. 6-16, we place a point randomly in the crystal, the various symmetry operations will cause this point to be multiplied into four equivalent points. The more equivalent points that are generated by the various symmetry operations for a particular crystal, the more symmetrical the crystal is said to be.

It is possible, though a bit tedious, to show that all of the various permitted symmetry operations can be combined to form exactly 32 different types of crystal symmetries. These 32 types are called *point groups,* and Fig. 6-16 shows a rather simple example of such a group. On the basis of these point groups, crystallographers can now place any natural crystal into one of 32 *classes.* All that is necessary for this purpose is to identify all of the symmetry operations that are required to develop the positions of the various faces on the crystal. The actual process is, of course, more complicated than implied here. In fact, a number of rather complex projection techniques are needed, and a person who does not understand his spherical trigonometry need not apply for a position as a crystallographer. You may find it interesting, for example, to demonstrate that a cube has 6 two-fold axes of symmetry, 4 three-fold axes, 3 four-fold axes, 9 planes, and 1 center.

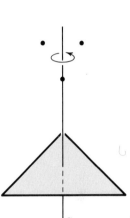

Symmetry axis

Fig. 6-14. Three-fold symmetry axis through the center of an equilateral triangle. The axis generates three "equivalent points."

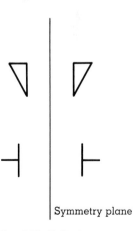

Symmetry plane

Fig. 6-15. Reflection across a symmetry plane. How would the effects of a two-fold symmetry axis be distinguished?

It is possible to simplify these 32 crystal point groups even further. In normal geometric studies, we are accustomed to referring to the positions of points in a three-dimensional space in terms of their relationship to 3 mutually perpendicular axes of reference. In dealing with crystals such as cubes and octahedrons, this coordinate system is obviously still useful. Is such a coordinate system useful, however, in describing a crystal such as a 6-sided pyramid on a base? For such a crystal, the position of the various faces might more easily be referred to in terms of an axis perpendicular to a plane containing 3 axes at 60° from each other. Similarly, in regard to the point group earlier illustrated in Fig. 6-16, we might wish to refer to the position of the various points in terms of 2 mutually perpendicular axes and 1 inclined at an angle to them. A total of 6 coordinate systems may be evolved in this fashion. Minerals may then be classified in terms of the *crystal system* which best describes their symmetry.

X-ray studies of minerals proceed essentially from this base of morphologic crystallography. The purpose of X-ray investigation is twofold. First, and simplest, is the opportunity which X-ray study provides for the identification of minerals. Second, and very important, is the opportunity that X rays provide to determine the precise location of atoms in crystal lattices and thus to specify exactly the crystal structure.

X rays are produced by bombarding a metal target with high-voltage electrons (Fig. 6-17). The bombardment causes electrons in the metallic target to be "excited" above their normal energy, and the process may

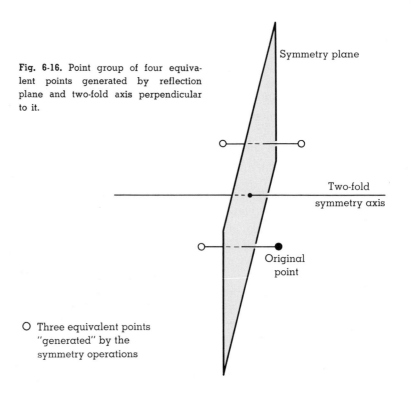

Fig. 6-16. Point group of four equivalent points generated by reflection plane and two-fold axis perpendicular to it.

Symmetry plane

Two-fold
symmetry axis

Original
point

O Three equivalent points
"generated" by the
symmetry operations

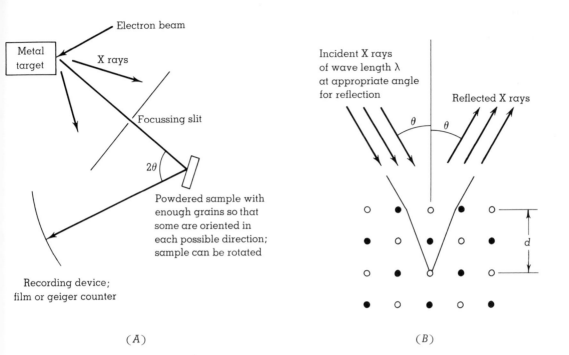

Electron beam

Metal target

X rays

Focussing slit

2θ

Powdered sample with enough grains so that some are oriented in each possible direction; sample can be rotated

Recording device; film or geiger counter

Incident X rays of wave length λ at appropriate angle for reflection

θ θ

Reflected X rays

d

(A)   (B)

Fig. 6-17. Diagrammatic illustration of X-ray procedure. The upper part (A) shows the basic process of emission of X rays from a target, selection of a single "beam" by means of a small focussing slit, reflection from a powdered sample, and recording on film or radiometrically. The lower part (B) shows incident rays penetrating a crystal and being reflected at the same angle Θ. Only those crystals in the powder which have this orientation to the X rays will show reflections at Θ. The total angle between incident and reflected beams is 2Θ and is shown in part A. The reflected rays must satisfy the equation $N\lambda = 2\,d\,\sin\,\Theta$.

be visualized in terms of knocking the metallic electrons out of their normal orbits around the nuclei to higher energy positions further from the nuclei. The excited electrons later return (drop) to their original energy levels, and the difference in energy between the excited and original states is emitted in the form of X rays. The electrons in the metallic structure are said to be "quantized" to the extent that they may assume energies of only certain particular values. Thus the transition from an excited to an original state takes place in a pattern of discrete energy jumps, and the energies of the emitted X rays correspondingly have certain fixed values. The various permissible energy levels in atoms and ions differ from one element to another, and thus the X radiations from different targets have energy levels characteristic of the particular metal used in the target. A commonly used target is copper, which emits its primary radiation with an energy of 7350 electron volts. The energy of electromagnetic radiation, such as X rays, is inversely proportional to the wave length of the radiation, and the energy of the copper X rays corresponds to a wave length of 1.54 Å ($1.54 \cdot 10^{-8}$ cm).

When energy (X rays) with a particular wave length is passed through a crystal, the various waves interact with the ions which comprise the crystal. Each ion or atom in the crystal lattice takes the little packets of radiation energy coming from the target and "bounces" them off in all directions, a process which is known as "diffraction." These diffracted X rays then pass back out of the crystal, and in most directions the emitted radiation is extremely small. In a few directions, however, the crystal lattice and the X rays will interact in such a way that the radiation passing back out of the crystal will be very intense (see Fig. 6-17). This reinforcement occurs where the emitted X-ray beam has been rotated through an angle (2Θ in Fig. 6-17), such that the rays diffracted by each ion in the crystal arrive at the surface of the crystal "in phase." By "in phase" we mean that the high and low points of two adjacent rays of the same wave length are opposite each other, and under these circumstances the rays reinforce each other and generate a strong radiation beam at the angle shown. These positions of most intense diffraction are recorded as X-ray peaks.

The positions of X-ray peaks are related to the crystal lattice and the incident radiation by the Bragg equation (whose derivation we shall not give here but which is available in most standard texts in physics and chemistry). The equation is

$$N\lambda = 2\,d\,\sin\Theta$$

where N = order of diffraction (a small integer); orders above the second or third generally contain very little energy

λ = wave length of X-ray beam from target

d = space between equivalent planes in the crystal

Θ = one-half of the total angle between emitted and incident radiation.

As indicated, the symbol d refers to the distance between equivalent planes in the lattice. Equivalent planes are simply planes that contain two-dimensional arrangements of atoms identical to those of other parallel planes, and the distance between these repeated, identical planes is referred to as a "d space" (see Fig. 6-17). In a three-dimensional crystal, parallel equivalent planes may be drawn in a variety of orientations, and thus crystals have a large number of characteristic d spaces. Every compound has a set of d spaces characteristic of its own crystal structure and presumably at least slightly different from the set of d spaces of every other compound. In simple structures such as the mineral halite (NaCl), the total number of possible equivalent diffraction planes is small, and the number of measurable d spaces is consequently small. In complex materials such as a plagioclase, the number of possible d spaces is enormous.

The measurement of d spaces is the simplest of all X-ray measurements. In many cases such measurements are used solely for the purpose of identifying an unknown mineral. Simple measurements, however, can also yield very interesting geological results. Suppose, for example, that we have available the potassium feldspar crystals from a typical volcanic rock and also from a typical plutonic rock. Chemical analysis may indicate that the two minerals are identical. On an X-ray machine, however, we will find a large number of additional diffraction peaks appearing in the X-ray pattern of the plutonic feldspar that do not appear in the X-ray pattern of the volcanic mineral. If we subtract the peaks of the volcanic feldspar from those of the plutonic one, we will then have a residue of peaks which can be identified on the basis of the *d* spaces indicated. It will turn out that these peaks represent the mineral albite (sodic plagioclase). If we now take the plutonic feldspar and heat it to a temperature slightly below its melting point, approximately 1150° C., we will find, upon re-X-raying it, that the albite peaks have now disappeared, and the X-ray pattern looks exactly like that of the volcanic feldspar.

What we have observed in this series of experiments is a very interesting geological phenomenon which can be at least partially duplicated in the laboratory. The phenomenon is generally given the term *exsolution* or *unmixing*. It seems that at high temperatures albite and potassium feldspar are completely isomorphous despite the large difference in the size of the sodium and potassium ions. This isomorphism, however, is not possible at low temperatures. Consequently, if a feldspar crystallizes at high temperature and then cools very slowly, the two separate sodium and potassium feldspar phases tend to unmix from each other and form a complex intergrowth. If, as in volcanic rocks, however, the feldspar is chilled very quickly to very low temperature, the unmixing is such a sluggish process that it may not occur at all. Thus, by a series of very simple X-ray measurements and equally simple laboratory experiments, we have arrived at an extremely fundamental relationship between the rates of cooling, and thus the modes of formation, of volcanic and plutonic rocks.

If we combine measurements of the position of diffracted X-ray beams with measurements of the intensity of these beams, we can begin to locate the positions of individual ions in the crystal lattice. This process of complete structural analysis is quite involved, and computations for complex crystals must generally be made on a computer. Some minerals, in fact, are so complicated that their structures are not yet known. The structure of the complicated and rare mineral carminite is reproduced in Fig. 6-18 just as an indication of the types of problems which may be encountered by crystallographers.

One of the interesting results of X-ray structural

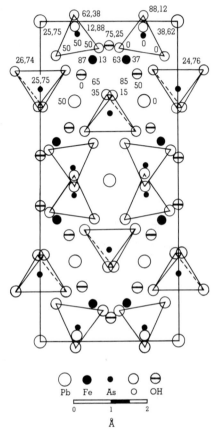

Fig. 6-18. Crystal structure of the rare mineral carminite (a lead-iron arsenate) as projected on one crystal plane. The numbers next to some of the ions indicate the distance above and below the reference plane; e.g., 62, 38 shows that this atom occurs at .62 units above the plane and is repeated at .38 units below the plane, which is then .62 units above the next reference plane. The distance (1 unit) between reference planes is the dimension of the "unit cell" of the crystal. (From J. J. Finney, Colorado School of Mines, in the *American Mineralogist*, vol. 48, 1963, p. 11.)

analysis is the recognition of different characteristic types of silicates. In most silicates, the ratio of the tetrahedrally arranged silicon and aluminum ions to other cations is sufficiently large for at least some of the oxygen ions to have all of their valences satisfied by silicon and aluminum. Such oxygens are effectively shared between silicate tetrahedra and form cross-linked structures of various types. In quartz, of course, all oxygens are shared between two tetrahedra, and a rigid framework structure is developed. A similar structure is characteristic also of the feldspars. The potassium, sodium, or calcium of feldspars is in the lattice only to compensate for the charge deficiency caused by insertion of aluminum in place of one of the silicon ions. The excellent cleavage of the micas (biotite and muscovite) results from the fact that the silicon, aluminum, oxygen, and hydroxyl ions in micas are complexly coordinated in extensive parallel sheets. Bonding between the sheets is rather weakly provided by potassium ions, and hence the mineral cleaves along these planes of weak bonds. In amphiboles and pyroxenes the silica tetrahedra are linked together in long chains, leaving, in general, two of the oxygen ions in each tetrahedron to have part of their valences satisfied by other cations. The only common rock-forming silicate in which there is no cross-linkage of the silica groups is olivine $(Mg,Fe)_2SiO_4$. A glance at the olivine formula will show that the ratio of silicon to other cations, in this case magnesium and iron, is much smaller than in the other silicate structures. Consequently, the SiO_4 tetrahedra are simply surrounded by magnesium or iron ions.

The discovery of these basic types of silicate structures has led to some extremely important conclusions concerning the mode of evolution of igneous rocks. We shall discuss in more detail in Chapter 8 the fact that the more complexly cross-linked minerals generally have lower temperatures of formation. The subjects of morphologic and X-ray crystallography are rewarding studies in themselves, but part of their importance arises from the light which they shed on related fields.

CHAPTER 7

SEDIMENTARY

ROCKS

◀ Bryce Canyon. (Photo by J. J. W. Rogers.)

$\mathbf{M}$ost of the geologists of the world are concerned in one way or another with the study of sedimentary rocks. The reasons for this concentration are easy to find. First, over three-fourths of the earth's land surface is covered by sedimentary rocks. Second, all fossils occur in sedimentary rocks, and persons studying paleontology must of necessity know something about the rocks which contain their objects of interest. And third, the restriction of petroleum to sediments provides a distinct economic motive for the study of these rocks. This last fact alone would be sufficient to account for the exceptional interest of geologists in sedimentary rocks, since the petroleum industry employs about two-thirds of the practicing geologists in the United States.

DESCRIPTION OF SEDIMENTARY ROCKS

Our study of sedimentary rocks requires a classification and description of the different types of sediments which have been found to occur in nature. The immensity of the earth's surface and the vast number of things which occur on it have caused both geologists and biologists to become much involved in classification. The human mind simply cannot grasp the various diverse objects which it encounters in nature unless some order is supplied by means of classification schemes. All methods of classification are to a certain extent arbitrary. The ultimate test of a classification is simply its utility. Does it or does it not supply the investigator with a simplified framework in which he can consider his subject material? Ideally a classification scheme should have genetic significance by having each category directly related to a distinct mode of origin.

In the case of sedimentary rocks we can start with a broad two-fold classification. The first group consists of those rocks in which the component materials have been derived elsewhere, from preexisting rocks, and have been moved—perhaps great distances—to the ultimate site of deposition. Rocks of this type are commonly referred to as *clastic* or *detrital*. A sediment containing small pieces of the igneous rock granite has obviously been, at least in part, derived from the breakdown, movement, and accumulation of pieces of original granite (Fig. 7-1). A second broad group of sedimentary rocks consists of those rocks whose component materials have been formed either in or very close to the ultimate site of deposition. Such rocks include chemical precipitates and certain types of sediments which consist largely of the broken shells of organisms that lived in or near the depositional environment. This second group of rocks includes the limestones and dolomites and is commonly referred to as *chemical*. This broad subdivision is useful but not wholly satisfactory. We shall find it necessary to subdivide further both categories of rocks.

Clastic rocks are generally subdivided largely on the basis of the grain size of the component material. One of the earliest, and still the most

TABLE 7-1. **WENTWORTH SIZE SCALE**

material	size in mm
Gravel, pebbles, cobbles, etc.	
	2
Sand	
	1/16
Silt	
	1/256
Clay	

widely used, classifications of grain size is the Wentworth size scale (Table 7-1), which categorizes the sizes of the various sedimentary particles into a geometric scale. On the basis of this size scale, clastic sediments are simply named for the average size of their included particles. The commonly used terms are:

CONGLOMERATES AND BRECCIAS. These are rocks which consist of pebble- and cobble-sized material. In a conglomerate the grains are reasonably smooth and rounded. In a breccia the grains are irregular and

Fig. 7-1. Photomicrograph of a thin section of a typical sandstone. This rock has been cut to a thickness of 1/1000 inch, and the minerals are transluscent. The grains shown here consist of quartz, potassium feldspar, and plagioclase, and the different materials are essentially identical to those found in granites. Magnification 100 times. (Photo by J. J. W. Rogers.)

Fig. 7-2. Contorted beds. These represent layers of sediment which were deposited horizontally and then shifted about before they became hardened. (Photo by H. B. Stenzel.)

angular. Conglomerates and breccias generally develop in areas quite close to their source rocks, and the reasons for this proximity are easy to find: (1) it is obviously more difficult for transporting agents such as water and wind to move large particles than to move the smaller ones; and (2) during transportation of material, large particles can be broken up into smaller ones. If we wish to be more specific in naming a conglomerate or a breccia we could prefix an adjective describing the nature of the materials which constitute the pebbles and cobbles.

SANDSTONES. (See Fig. 7-2.) Sediments consisting primarily of sand-sized materials constitute approximately one-fourth of the sedimentary rocks exposed on the continents. The predominant minerals of sandstones are quartz and feldspars, and in many sandstones quartz constitutes virtually the entire sediment. Minerals such as biotite, hornblende, and augite, which are common in igneous source rocks, are comparatively unstable in contact with the air and water of the earth's surface. This instability of minerals at the earth's surface is a topic we shall consider later in our discussion of the formation of soil and the weathering of rocks. It should be mentioned here, however, that minerals containing iron and magnesium are generally destroyed during sedimentary processes, and hence the proportion of quartz and feldspar is increased in sedimentary rocks over its percentage in igneous rocks. Geologists commonly subdivide sandstones into three different groups:

1. Orthoquartzites—these sediments are defined as consisting almost entirely of quartz. They are widespread in occurrence and are the common sandstones in the midwestern part of the United States, and thin beds of orthoquartzite have, in places, been traced for many hundreds of miles.

2. Arkoses—arkoses are distinguished from orthoquartzites by their content of feldspar, predominantly orthoclase or microcline. Arkoses

are developed in a variety of sedimentary environments, and in particular they may be found near the base of a sedimentary column where it lies directly on igneous rocks.

3. Graywackes—these rocks are characterized by an abundance of fragments of preexisting rocks. Many graywackes, in fact, contain small fragments of volcanic and metamorphic rock in addition to moderate amounts of quartz, plagioclase, and perhaps orthoclase or microcline. In addition, some graywackes contain large quantities of the normally unstable iron- and magnesium-bearing minerals. Graywackes are found in only a few areas in the country, but where present they commonly form immensely thick sequences measured in terms of tens or even hundreds of thousands of feet. When we discuss the evolution of continents, we shall find that graywackes are characteristic of deep and rapidly subsiding depositional basins referred to as *geosynclines*.

SILTSTONES.   These are rocks that are composed of hardened silt.

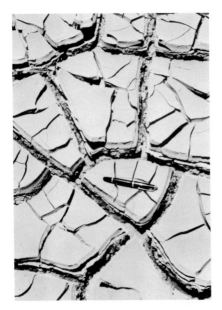

Fig. 7-3. Mud which will harden to form shale. The cracks developed in this mud are caused by shrinkage as the upper surface dries. (Photo by U. Clanton.)

SHALE.   (See Fig. 7-3.) Shale is best defined as consisting of extremely fine-grained minerals in the size range designated as clay. In addition to this size definition for shale particles, many of the minerals that are found in the shale are commonly referred to as clay minerals. A clay mineral is a particular type of hydrated aluminum silicate having a sheet structure similar to that of the micas. In fact, fine-grained muscovite is one of the major clay minerals and is probably the most common component of the ordinary shale. The term clay unfortunately has both a chemical and a size significance. Nearly two-thirds of all sedimentary rocks are shale.

The distinction between the various types of clastic sedimentary rocks is generally not too difficult. Some difficulty, of course, is encountered in distinguishing between shales and siltstones or coarse siltstones and fine sandstones, but small mistakes in this range are not serious and are made every day by experienced geologists. Naturally, a number of questions can be raised. What, for example, should we call a sediment in which half of the grains are in the size range of sand and half of the grains are in the size range of silt? Is this rock a silty sandstone or a sandy siltstone? The answer to this question is certainly not clear. Perhaps the best procedure is to keep on making measurements until one obtains 51 percent of one component or the other and then name the rock accordingly. We have encountered here, on a minor but vexing problem, the general question of what to do about gradations when we place objects in a classification scheme. Classifications must, of necessity, have sharp boundaries, but natural materials do not have such sharp differences in kind. Ideally, in any type of classification scheme, the boundary should be drawn through those areas which contain the smallest number of samples, though this is not easy to do.

Sedimentary grains, being roughly spherical, do not generally pack together so as to eliminate all of the empty space between them. In consequence, virtually all sandstones, conglomerates, and other similar rocks contain small amounts of materials interstitial to the sand grains. These materials are commonly referred to as *matrix* or *cement*. In some cases the matrix material consists of calcite and dolomite, or other possible chemical precipitates. In other cases the matrix consists of small amounts of clay minerals which have, perhaps, been transported to the site of deposition and incorporated among the sand grains. In some rocks the spaces between sand grains are not filled, and the resulting openings are called voids or *pores*. The total percentage of open space in a rock is referred to as the *porosity*.

The chemical rocks are primarily limestones, consisting of the mineral calcite, and dolomites. Some geologists, in order to avoid confusion between the mineral and rock names, refer to a rock containing dolomite as *dolostone*. Carbonate rocks comprise approximately five percent of all of the known sediments. Limestones are classified as *chemical* largely by a terminological convention, and because it is felt that the material constituting limestones has generally been deposited by some type of chemical precipitation from water.

Apparently almost all limestones were originally deposited in the ocean, and limestones now occurring in the center of continents constitute one of the best lines of evidence that continental areas were at one time at least slightly submerged. One of the best pieces of evidence for a marine origin for the average limestone is the fact that the bulk of the calcite in most limestones consists of small pieces of shells of marine invertebrates (Fig. 7-4). Many limestones, in fact, consist almost exclusively of pieces of brachiopods, mollusks, corals, or other organisms. In a sense, a limestone consisting of pieces of mollusks having a size range within the limits of sand could be called a type of sandstone, because, strictly speaking, the term sand implies nothing about the nature of the material and refers only to the size. By convention, however, sandstones consisting wholly of calcium carbonates are generally referred to as lime-

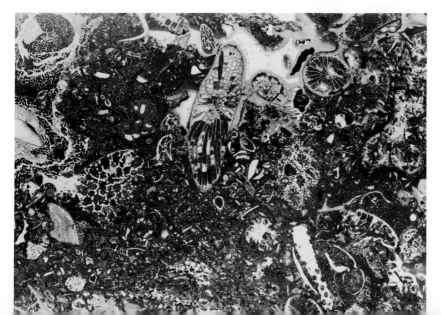

Fig. 7-4. Photomicrograph of thin section of limestone. Most of the rock consists of fragments of shells of various marine animals, such as corals. Magnification 25 times. (Photo by E. G. Purdy.)

stones. The removal of these sediments from the clastic category is not wholly illogical, because in most cases the shell fragments which comprise the limestone have probably been derived from organisms living very close to the site in which the final accumulation occurred—instead of being transported great distances, as are the quartz and feldspars of many sands.

In addition to shell fragments, limestones contain a large variety of other types of material. *Oolites*, for example, are small, generally highly polished, spherical aggregates of calcium carbonate. In our discussion of the geology of the Recent carbonate deposits of the Bahama Bank, we shall mention oolites briefly again (p. 138). The mode of formation of these small spheres has not been definitely established. Some carbonate rocks consist exclusively of extremely fine-grained calcite. It is possible that such fine-grained calcite represents a direct chemical precipitation from sea water. It has also been proposed, however, that this material is simply the product of a very fine grinding of shell fragments or, perhaps, is the product of the breakdown of organisms containing exceptionally fine-grained calcite as part of their organic structure. The fact that current geologic opinion is roughly evenly divided on these alternatives indicates that no particularly conclusive evidence has yet been obtained as to the precise mode of formation of this material.

Dolomites are less common than limestones, although they are extremely abundant in deposits of certain periods. There appear to be two major types of dolomites. The first occurs as broad extensive beds of relatively fine-grained, homogeneous material. It looks almost identical to fine-grained limestone and can be distinguished only by simple chemical tests, as is discussed in the list of identifying properties of minerals in the Appendix. The other type of dolomite consists generally of more coarsely crystalline material. This type of dolomite generally does not form extensive beds but may occur as irregular patches within a sequence of limestones (Fig. 7.5). In many cases these patches cut across the bedding or other original features of the limestones, and the dolomite quite clearly has formed after deposition of limestone. In a later section of this chapter we shall discuss in more detail some of the chemical problems involved in the formation of dolomites.

Halite, gypsum, and related materials constitute a very small portion of the geologic record and occur in only a few places on the earth's surface. These minerals are generally grouped together under the term *evaporites*. The name is chosen because the rocks have apparently formed by evaporation and consequent precipitation of the dissolved materials

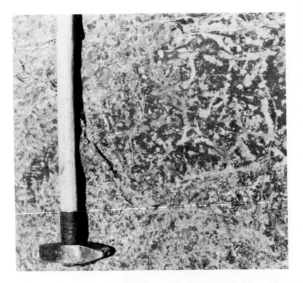

Fig. 7-5. Irregular distribution of dolomite in limestone. The white dolomite is scattered in patches through the original limestone. (Photo by F. Beales.)

in sea water. A modern example of this unlikely extreme evaporation can be found in the Gulf of Karabogaz, on the eastern side of the Caspian Sea. Here, soluble salts (e.g., sodium sulfate) are being precipitated under an atmosphere of extreme dryness and exceptionally high temperatures. Repeated influx of water from the sea replenishes the supply of materials for precipitation in this Gulf, and a considerable thickness of soluble salt is being accumulated. Apparently, evaporating environments roughly similar to this have existed in a few places in the geologic past; it was in such environments that the evaporites, predominantly consisting of halite, gypsum, or the anhydrous form of gypsum known as anhydrite, were formed.

Two other sediments of extremely restricted occurrence should also be mentioned. One of these is a rock which consists exclusively of fine-grained SiO_2 and is called *chert*. In most cases, this SiO_2 is not in the crystalline form of quartz, and in some rocks the material is completely amorphous. Chert occurs in a few places in thick and extensive beds intermingled with other sediments. In most occurrences, however, the chert forms small streaks or patches incorporated in other sediments, predominantly limestones. The origin of chert is not fully resolved. Chemical and biological precipitation, as well as mechanical accumulation, have been suggested, with the evidence for each theory about equally convincing.

Another minor but highly important type of sediment is referred to as *iron formation*. Iron formation generally consists of iron oxides, such as magnetite and hematite, interbedded with chert. The importance of these rocks is that a small amount of chemical alteration converts them into highly concentrated hematite rock, generally by a partial removal of the chert, and the resulting hematite rock forms the major iron ore deposits of the world. It is difficult to imagine an environment in which chert and magnetite could have been deposited from sea water. The problem is slightly simplified by the fact that all of the iron formation deposits of the world are exceptionally old and may have been formed at a time when the sea water and atmosphere were different from those observed today.

RECENT SEDIMENTS

The study of recent sedimentary environments affords virtually the only opportunity for interpreting the origin of ancient sediments. There are two approaches to such study. One is highly pragmatic, and the other is more theoretical and, in the long run, potentially more fruitful. As an example of the practical approach, let us say that we would like to be able to recognize beach sands in ancient rocks. For this purpose we would go to a large number of modern beaches, describe as many of the properties of their sediments as we could find, and prepare a list of criteria in which beach sands differed from other types of sands. Hopefully, we could prepare a list of features which would be characteristic only of beach sands and would prevent our confusing other types of sand deposits with the beach sands. This approach has proved extremely useful and is widely utilized for both academic and industrial problems.

The drawbacks to this pragmatic method are, however, two-fold. First, it may not be possible to find a group of easily measured properties which will provide an absolute distinction from the rocks of all other types of environments. We might, for example, discover that beach sands and sands deposited in the centers of small lakes are indistinguishable from each other in regard to the properties which we have chosen to measure. The second drawback is that no two sediments are absolutely identical. Though we might determine the properties of the sand on one beach or one part of one beach, if we move down shore perhaps only a few miles, we shall find that the properties may be quite different from those we have found previously. Our list of distinguishing criteria, therefore, must represent rather broad averages or ranges of characteristics.

The other, and more theoretical, approach to the study of modern environments is based on a determination of exactly what factors in the modern environment are responsible for the development of measurable properties of the sediment. We might, for example, try to relate the average sizes of grains in a river sand to the velocity of the river. As a further example, we might try to relate the type of calcium carbonate deposited in a certain area to the temperature and salinity of the surrounding water and, in consequence, to the type of organic activity which may have produced the carbonate.

General observations of recent sedimentary environments are obviously not new. As mentioned in the first chapter, such observations constitute a major part of the evidence which has led to the formulation of the concept of uniformitarianism. The fact that we can find rocks forming today which are similar or identical to rocks which occur in the geologic record leads strongly to the conclusion that the nature of geologic processes has not undergone any radical change during the portion of the history of the earth which we are able to examine (Figs. 7-6 and 7-7). Without this type of proof of uniformitarianism it would be virtually impossible for geologists to interpret the history of the earth.

Let us turn now to two examples of a detailed study of a modern sedimentary environment. The Mississippi River is the largest river in North America. Each year it carries about 500 million tons of sediment from the mid-continent of the United States out into the Gulf of Mexico. The material which is delivered to the Gulf of Mexico is distributed to a variety of places. Part of it simply is washed out into deep water and ultimately settles in the deeper parts of the Gulf. A part of the sediment is carried westward along the coast of the Gulf by currents and is deposited either in shallow water or is, perhaps, washed up on beaches. A fair portion of the sediment, however, accumulates very close to the mouth of the river and has, in part, formed within the river mouth. This accumulation of material near the mouth of the river has formed a broad wedge of sediments amounting to a total accumulation of 8000 cubic miles in the last approximately 60,000 years. As a result of this deposition, the shore line has moved outward, and in the last 60,000 years a total outward growth of 50 miles has been attained (Fig. 7-8).

A thick accumulation of sediments at the mouth of a river is commonly referred to as a *delta* (Fig. 7-9), and the deltaic sediments of the

Fig. 7-6. Ripple marks in sediments of the Smithwick formation, central Texas. (Photo by U. Clanton.)

Mississippi River have a complex and interesting history. As the shoreline has built outward, the river has shifted from one position to another. In fact, this deposition has made the area so flat that the river has commonly split into a number of channels, each of which carries a part of the river water out into the Gulf. These separate channels, similar to those shown for the modern river in Fig. 7-10, are called *distributaries*.

The deposition of sediments at any one time in such a river-and-marine complex takes place in a variety of ways. Along the individual distributary channels there are, of course, simply normal river sediments. During flood periods, the distributaries may overflow their low banks and wash some sediment out into the interdistributary areas. During normal nonflood periods, the interdistribu-

Fig. 7-7. Ripple marks in modern sediments in the Bay of Fundy, Nova Scotia, and New Brunswick. Compare with Fig. 7-6. (Photo by G. DeV. Klein.)

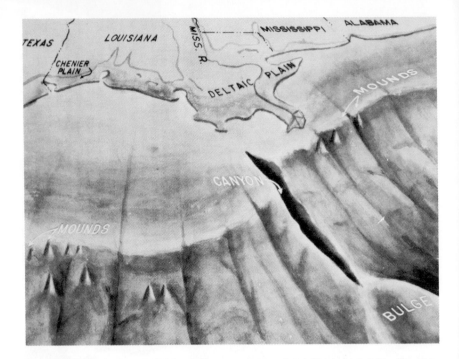

Fig. 7-8. Schematic representation of the environment of the Mississippi delta. The state names are lettered on the comparatively high ground consisting of older rocks whose southern margin is the gray line landward of the coast. The Mississippi River Valley is marked by lower, recent sediments, and these sediments have extended out into the Gulf of Mexico as a deltaic plain. The chenier plain is a low coastal plain formed by modern sediments away from the river mouth. The most recent portion of the delta is the one along which the modern river has extended its course. The submarine canyon in the steep portion offshore was cut when the Mississippi River extended out over the shallow submarine shelf during recent lowering of sea level by the incorporation of water into glacial ice. The sea level was lowered to approximately the point marked by the head of the canyon. The bulge (lower right) consists of sediments swept down the canyon and deposited at the foot. The origin of the scattered mounds is not certain. (Courtesy of Esso Production Research.)

tary areas catch small portions of fine-grained sediments that are washed back landward after being delivered to the Gulf from the distributaries; in part, these interdistributary areas may simply accumulate very fine clays that settle slowly out of flood waters. Deposition along the distributary banks and in the interdistributary areas is at least partly subaerial, to the extent that portions of the area are above sea level.

Most of the sediment which is carried out into the open Gulf is deposited in a broad arc around the distributary mouths and consists largely of a mixture of sands, silts, and clays. Part of the sandy sediment brought down by the distributaries is accumulated in the form of offshore islands (sand bars). These islands are built in large part by wave activity and represent an accumulation of the coarser and generally sandy material left behind by rather thorough washing out of the fine clays.

If we could expose a vertical section through the most recent portion of the entire Mississiippi Delta, we would see sediments having the configuration shown in Fig. 7–11. Such a vertical slice is referred to as a "cross section" and is constructed from a large number of drillings made in the deltaic material. The pattern of distributary sands (bar fingers), interdistributary clays (clay wedges), and other materials is quite characteristic of deltas elsewhere.

A sedimentological study, such as the one which we have just described of the Mississippi Delta, contributes geologic information on a variety of topics. First, we now know more about the geology of the Mississippi Delta itself. Second, owing to the similarity of this and other deltas, we now know something concerning the nature of the formation of deltas and deltaic sediments. And third, by relating the nature of the sediments formed in specific environments to the processes by which these sediments have formed, we have now learned something concerning the general processes of formation of different types of sediments.

Similar studies can be made in the areas of deposition of carbonate rocks. One such investigation has been in the Bahama Banks, east of the Florida peninsula (Fig. 7-12). The Bahama Banks are a broad and very shallow (water depth less than twenty feet in many places) part of the sea floor on which certain areas have been built up as islands above the present sea level. The banks are separated from the mainland of North

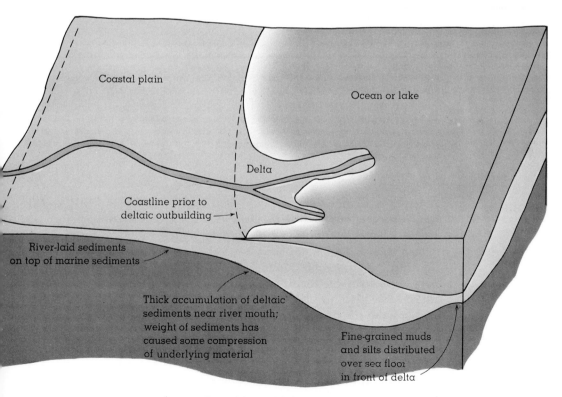

Fig. 7-9. Typical large delta.

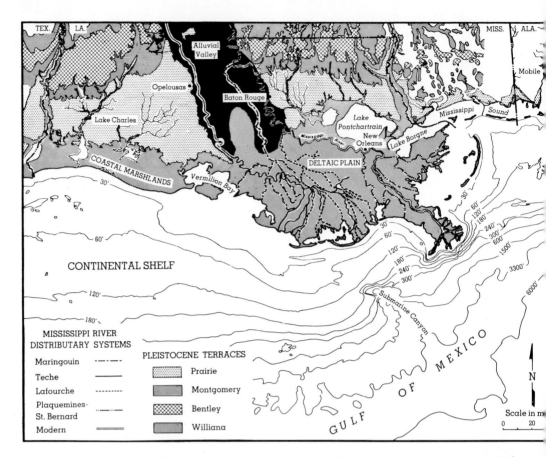

Fig. 7-10. Mississippi Delta and surroundings. The various terraces are comparatively elevated surfaces cut on older rocks. The river runs in an alluvium-filled valley (alluvium is soft, recently deposited sediment on land), and the delta extends out from the mouth. The river has changed its course many times in the past, and the paths of the major former distributary systems are shown. Both distributary systems and terraces are given special names for easy reference. Compare with Fig. 7-8. (From H. N. Fisk, Esso Production Research.)

America by channels of extremely deep water, and consequently no silicate sediments are washed in. As a result, all of the sediments of the Bahama Banks consist of calcium carbonate in a variety of forms.

In warm, shallow water such as occurs on the Bahama Banks, conditions are very favorable for the precipitation of calcium carbonate. In part, these favorable conditions result from the intensive organic activity which takes place in such climates. In some places the calcareous organisms grow so closely together that they form communities which develop accumulations of calcium carbonate. These accumulations are gradually built upward by the growth of new organisms on the skeletal remains of former ones. Such accumulations are commonly referred to as *reefs*. The reefs grow upward from the shallow ocean floor until they reach sea level, and later small changes in sea level or uplift of the underlying rock

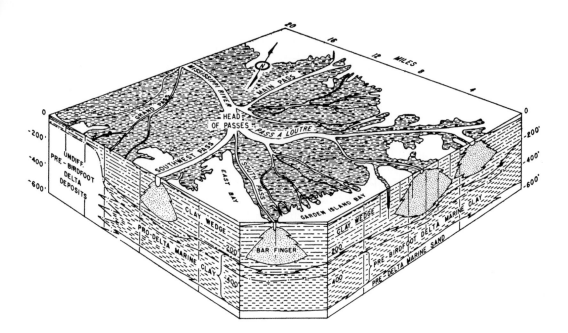

Fig. 7-11. Map and section of most recent ("birdfoot") portion of the Mississippi Delta. Note that "bar fingers" of sand are built by the shifting distributaries, and the coastline is extended outward along these river courses. Clays are deposited in quiet water between the distributaries, and the whole complex lies on predeltaic sediments. (From H. N. Fisk, *et al.*, *Journal of Sedimentary Petrology*, vol. 24, 1954.)

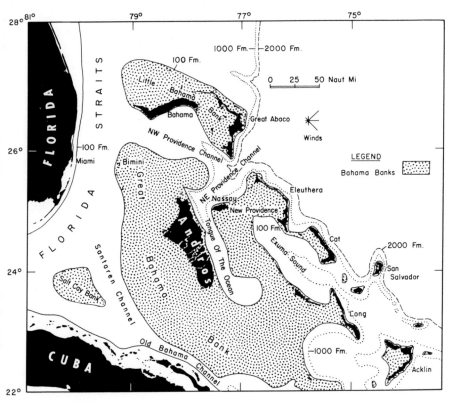

Fig. 7-12. Bahama Banks. Contours are water depths in fathoms (six feet). Depths on the banks are in the range of ten feet. (From E. G. Purdy.)

may cause the reefs to be exposed in the form of islands. A number of calcium carbonate-secreting organisms contribute to the formation of reefs, and among these organisms are corals, from which the term "coral reef" is derived. In most coral reefs, however, much of the skeletal calcium carbonate has actually been secreted by algae.

In addition to the small and scattered reefs, a variety of other sediments are distributed over the Bahama Banks. One of the most widespread types of sediment is the fine-grained calcium carbonate commonly referred to as *lime mud*. This material as originally deposited is not in the form of calcite; rather, it is a mineral with the same formula but slightly different crystal structure known as aragonite. (Much of the calcite now found in ancient sedimentary rocks was probably at one time aragonite, which is unstable and tends to invert to calcite in a relatively short period of time.) Different theories for the precipitation of the calcium

Fig. 7-13. "Dunes" of oolite sands. These accumulations of calcium carbonate in the form of spherical grains behave under water just as sand dunes in deserts. (Photo by E. G. Purdy.)

carbonate in lime muds propose either a simple chemical precipitation from the supersaturated waters over the bank or an accumulation from the breakdown of parts of marine algae. Apparently the types of marine algae which are common in the waters of the Bahama Banks contain very small, rod-like crystals of aragonite, and it is thought that the lime muds may have formed by accumulation of these crystals after the death of the algae.

Water movement over the central portions of the Bahama Banks is comparatively minor owing to the presence of large islands to the windward (east). Around the margins, however, currents from deep water wash in and contribute distinct patterns to the sediments. In areas of extreme water movement and current activity, the oolite accumulations are developed (Fig. 7-13). As we discussed previously, oolites are spherical particles consisting of an aggregate of very tiny calcium carbonate crystals. For reasons which are not entirely clear, oolites develop only in areas where current activity and water movement is pronounced. Probably the grains can form in perfectly spherical shape only if they are rotated from time to time by passing currents. As shown in Fig. 7-13 the overall pattern of these accumulations of oolites in areas of current activity is much like the appearance of sand dunes in deserts, and the water currents have acted upon oolites in much the same way that wind acts upon sand. (We shall discuss the formation of sand dunes in more detail in Chapter 12.)

For the purpose of interpreting ancient sediments, the study of the Bahama Banks and other environments has led to a variety of important conclusions. Now, for example, we have direct criteria for the recognition of ancient reefs, even though the organisms which formed those reefs may be considerably different from those which occur in modern marine waters. We also know something about the conditions which lead to the formation of fine-grained lime mud even though the exact mode of formation may be in doubt. Similarly, we can equate the formation of large deposits of oolitic limestone with the presence of marked current activity. These conclusions, naturally, are not drawn simply from the study of one area of limestone deposition. Results obtained from the study of a variety of areas must generally be correlated and the differences resolved before some conclusion can be drawn concerning the conditions of formation of any particular type of rock. A large portion of modern geologic research on sedimentary rocks is currently being devoted to the study of recent sediments of all types. Economic incentives for such studies arise from the observations that buried sand bodies in the Mississippi Delta and other deltas and buried reefs in western Canada and other areas are prolific petroleum producers.

LABORATORY STUDIES

In addition to the study of naturally occurring recent sediments, it is possible for sedimentary petrologists to derive a great deal of information from experiments conducted in the laboratory (see Fig. 7-14, *A–C*). Some of the experiments are concerned with the transportation of sedimentary

Fig. 7-14. *A–C.* Progressive destruction of original sedimentary bedding by boring clams. Time lapse is one month between *B* and *C.* Many presently structureless sediments may simply have been altered by organisms in this fashion. (Photos by P. Scruton and D. G. Moore.)

particles. The process consists simply of making a long trough, or flume, down which sediment-laden water may be flowed. It is possible, of course, to flow this water over bottom materials of various types and to investigate the erosion of the bottom or deposition of the materials on it and to describe the transportation process in general. Another and very important type of laboratory study that has been conducted is in regard to the precipitation of carbonate minerals. We shall want to discuss these experiments in somewhat more detail.

Calcium carbonate has a solubility product of approximately 10^{-8} as calcite. The solubility of the unstable form aragonite is, of course, slightly higher. The total amount of calcium carbonate which can be dissolved in water that is in contact with the earth's atmosphere is somewhat higher than might be predicted from the solubility product alone. This higher solubility is caused by the fact that carbon dioxide from the atmosphere dissolving in sea water causes a reaction which favors the formation of a bicarbonate ion. The equation is

$$CO_2 + H_2O + CaCO_3 \rightleftharpoons Ca^{++} + 2\,HCO_3{}^-$$

The concentration of carbon dioxide in the earth's atmosphere is 0.03 percent and is sufficient to assure that virtually all of the carbonate in any water on the earth is in the form of the bicarbonate ion, which is highly soluble. Precipitation of calcium carbonate can occur in two ways. One is ordinary evaporation. Simple experiments with normal sea water indicate that calcium carbonate generally precipitates when the sea water has been reduced to a volume of approximately one-half its original amount. The other method of precipitation of calcium carbonate is to heat the water. Though higher temperatures generally cause increased solubility of salts, the reverse effect is obtained with calcium carbonate, because the high temperature drives carbon dioxide out of the water and thus causes conversion of bicarbonate to carbonate ion and resultant precipitation of the insoluble calcium carbonate. This lower solubility at higher temperatures is one apparent reason for the restriction of reef growth and other calcium carbonate accumulation to tropical or near-tropical regions.

Although the formation of calcium carbonate is not too difficult to understand, the occurrence of dolomite in sediments is a particularly difficult problem. The problem arises from the fact that laboratory experiments on the precipitation of calcium and magnesium carbonates have failed to synthesize dolomite at temperatures below several hundred degrees centigrade. In general, when calcium, magnesium, and bicarbonate are dissolved in water in the proper proportions and the solution evaporated, the resulting precipitate is simply a mixture of calcium carbonate and poorly crystallized magnesium salts rather than the mineral dolomite.

This inability to form dolomite at low temperatures by direct precipitation correlates reasonably well with observations of dolomite rocks made in the field. We mentioned earlier that one major type of dolomite occurs as irregular patches and bands which cut across the original features of limestone beds. Detailed features such as shown in Fig. 7-15

Fig. 7-15. Crystals of dolomite penetrating calcite oolites. The dolomite is clearly replacing the original limestone. Magnification 100 times. (Photo by R. C. Murray, Shell Development Co.)

demonstrate clearly that dolomite in the rocks shown has formed after the development of an original limestone bed. Most geologists, therefore, believe that dolomite forms by reaction of magnesium- or magnesium carbonate-bearing solutions with a previously deposited limestone. The exact mechanism for such a reaction is not clear, and it has not been satisfactorily duplicated in the laboratory. The fact that it occurs, however, is unquestionable on the basis of the simple evidence found in the rocks. Indeed, we have here an example of the manner in which purely geologic evidence may be used to shed light on a chemical problem. Verification of the formation of dolomite by reaction from limestone has recently been provided by borings made on Pacific atolls in connection with the various nuclear tests performed after the Second World War. In connection with geologic studies of these atolls a number of deep holes were drilled and cores obtained from them. In many of the calcium carbonate rocks formed in these islands the concentration of dolomite is virtually zero at the surface. At depths greater than 1000 feet in the borings, however, many of the limestones have been at least partially converted to dolomites. The source of the magnesium is uncertain, but the fact of the reaction is undoubted.

The explanations given above are satisfactory to account for the formation of coarse-grained dolomite, which obviously replaces, or is secondary to, the original limestone. The origin of fine-grained beds of pure dolomite, however, is less certain. Possibly these, too, have formed by some type of reaction leading to a replacement of the "primary" limestone by a "secondary" dolomite. It is conceivable, however, that these bedded rocks may have formed by some type of direct precipitation, although this reaction has not been duplicated in current chemical experiments. The dolomite problem remains unresolved despite much effort.

One of the difficulties involved in the interpretation of ancient carbonate rocks is the absence of modern counterparts. At the present time, limestones are being deposited in only a very few areas of the world, and this scarcity contrasts very sharply with the abundance and wide distribution of limestones in certain parts of the geologic past. Conditions today are obviously not as conducive to the formation of carbonate rocks as they have been in the past. This is one of many indications that the present condition of the earth's surface differs in some respects from the conditions of the past. We have already encountered other evidence to this effect, namely that marine sediments can be found in the central parts of continents where they are now exposed to the air. Obviously, during many periods of the geologic past the continents were partly, or perhaps completely, flooded by ocean waters. It was largely during these periods of extensive flooding that the carbonate rocks of the past were formed. The absence of modern counterparts makes laboratory evidence and experimentation all the more important.

ANCIENT SEDIMENTS

Having discussed the types of information which we might obtain from a study of recent environments or from laboratory experiments, it is now possible to turn to a brief discussion of the types of investigation which could be made of ancient rocks. The fundamental object of all such investigations is to determine, as accurately as possible, the *history* of formation of the rock and the precise *environment* in which it was developed. By "history of formation" we mean the complete sequence of events leading to the development of the particular rock. To understand such a sequence we would want to know: (1) the source from which the material was derived, if it was transported to the depositional site from a source rock; (2) the mechanism of transportation; and (3) the immediate past and immediate future history of the area in which the rock was formed.

In determining the environment of formation of a rock, it is necessary to investigate a somewhat different set of properties than were utilized in our study of the source and developmental history. The environment must be determined from rock features which were specifically controlled and affected by processes acting within the environment itself. For example, the composition of any mineral precipitated in a rock from sea water at the time of formation of the rock will tell us something about the composition of the sea water and, perhaps, its temperature. The composition of a mineral derived from some source rock outside of the environment, however, obviously tells us nothing about the environment itself.

Similar statements may be made for purely physical features. As an example of such features, we may consider *cross-bedding*. Cross-bedding, as shown in Fig. 7-16, is simply a sequence of thin beds inclined at an angle to the bedding planes which delineate the rock body itself. Such cross beds are formed by deposition of sand from currents, and the mechanism of deposition is merely the addition of a layer of the bed against an already tilted layer and a progression of the deposition in a down-stream or down-current direction. Thus a rock that is cross bedded

Fig. 7-16. Cross-bedded sands in a modern river. A meter stick gives the scale. Cross beds are inclined downstream. (Courtesy of Esso Production Research.)

not only signifies the presence of water, or perhaps wind, currents during its formation but also yields information about the direction from which the current was flowing.

This mode of formation of cross-bedding has been determined by a study of sediments in recent environments. In the study of such sediments, however, it is important to be sure that the environment itself is causing the formation of the feature under investigation. If, for example, a cross-bedded sedimentary rock was suddenly exposed by erosion at the base of a river, the present river flowing over it might have no relationship to the direction of inclination of the cross beds. Therefore, in order to establish that cross beds incline away from the direction of flow of a current, it has been necessary, as in other studies of recent sediments, to find an environment in which the beds are actually forming in an area affected by currents. At first glance, this seems to be an easy task, but actually it may be quite difficult. One really suitable proof of a relationship between sedimentary feature and environmental process is demonstrating that the features of the sediment vary from time to time as the processes change. Thus, in the case of cross beds, the direction and angle of the beds should fluctuate with changes in the controlling current.

Features such as cross beds permit the determination of the direction of transportation of the sedimentary material. It is thus possible to hypothesize the location of the source of a sediment. Extensive studies of this type have been made in a number of areas, including a sequence of rocks approximately 300 million years old in the Appalachian Mountains. One of the results of these studies is the preparation of a map, such as is shown in Fig. 7-17, on which the directional features have been plotted. The sediments are demonstrably marine from their content of fossils and other features, and the map of Fig. 7-17 shows rather clearly that the source of the sediments was some land area to the east of the present deposits. Preparation of maps of this type for each bed in a thick sequence permits a description of the change in source area and position of the depositional basins throughout geologic time. It is interesting to note that the conclusion about an eastward source derived from the study of cross-bedding in Fig. 7-17 is verified by other types of evidence (Fig. 7-18).

We mentioned in the preceding paragraph that fossilized organisms may be used as evidence for the determination of sedimentary environment. If we find, for example, a suite of organisms which could only have lived in the ocean as the dominant fossils in some particular sedimentary rock, then the conclusion is that this rock was formed on the ocean floor (see Fig. 7-19). There are two dangers in such a conclusion. One is that the fossils occurring in a rock may not have lived in the environment in which the rock was deposited. That is, they could have been derived by erosion from some source rock elsewhere and simply been transported to the site of deposition in the same manner as the normal sand grains of a sandstone. The second danger results from the difficulty of knowing exactly what organisms lived in the ocean or other environments in the past. The mere fact, for example, that all corals are marine organisms today does not prove that all corals lived only in the ocean in the past. The presumption is strong in this particular case, but a strong presumption does not constitute a proof.

As another example of the interpretation of the mode of formation of ancient sediments, we can consider the problems of determining the origin of shales. This problem is especially difficult because the fine-grained nature of the shale prevents detailed studies, such as we could make of sand. Furthermore, the problem is exceptionally important because, as already mentioned, shales constitute well over one-half of the entire sedimentary sequence.

Most shales consist of clay minerals, that is, hydrated aluminum silicates with a sheet structure similar to that of mica. Consequently, one of the best methods that has been devised for the study of shales is X-ray analysis, which yields, with fair accuracy, the percentages of the many different types of clay minerals that occur in the rocks. These minerals tend to undergo chemical reactions quite easily. The ease of reaction is caused partly by the small grain size of the clays and partly by the fact that their layered structure permits the ready absorption of cations between the separate silicate layers. It has been hypothesized, therefore, that clays delivered to a sedimentary environment would undergo reaction with the sea water or fresh water of that area and that the resulting composition of the clays would yield evidence concerning the nature of the water. Reactions of this type which occur in freshly deposited sediments are called *diagenetic reactions,* and the general process of alteration of sedimentary material prior to its becoming a hard rock is called *diagenesis.*

The difficulty with the hypothesis of diagenetic alteration is that the clay minerals which occur in shales consist of the same wide variety of minerals also formed in soils and by other weathering processes. In consequence, it is possible to explain the mineralogy of any particular shale simply in terms of the nature of the clays derived from the source materials. Thus, two shales differing in their proportions of different minerals may simply represent: (1) materials derived from different sources; or (2) materials from the same source deposited in different environments.

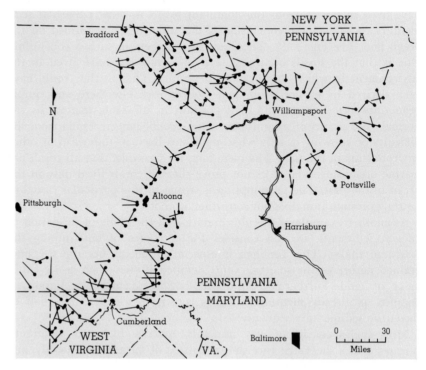

Fig. 7-17. Average directions of currents as indicated by cross-bedding measurements on outcrops of the Pocono formation. Despite fluctuations, currents are clearly directed mainly to the northwest. (From Bernard R. Pelletier, *Geological Society of America Bulletin*, vol. 69, 1958.)

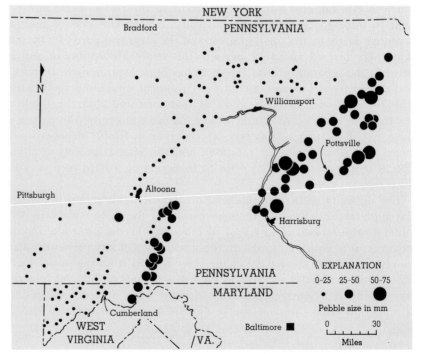

Fig. 7-18. Distribution of sizes of largest pebbles in outcrops of the Pocono formation. Compare with Fig. 7-17. The two figures both indicate a source of sediment to the southeast and transportation toward the northwest. (From Bernard R. Pelletier, *Geological Society of America Bulletin*, vol. 69, 1958.)

The relative importance of these two effects is largely unknown. A general problem connected with all efforts to interpret the origin of ancient sediments is the separation of the effect of source materials and the effect of environment.

Thus far we have considered only the problem of interpreting the origin of one particular sample of sediment. Geologists, however, are generally able to work with sequences of sediments deposited over a long period of time and having great lateral extent. In general, the interpretation of a sequence is somewhat easier than the interpretation of individual rocks. For example, assume that we are investigating two dissimilar rock types which are intimately interbedded; that is, they form alternating layers of one rock type and the other. Some lines of evidence may lead us to the conclusion that one of these rocks has formed in the deep ocean and represents a marine sediment. The other rock, at first glance, may seem to be the type of material that forms in a desert. If the two sediments are closely interbedded, however, these interpretations of their origins are incompatible. One or both of the conclusions are wrong, and the error might not have been recognized in the absence of the association of rock types.

In the interpretation of the history of sedimentary rocks, an effort is continually made to find the most plausible answers. In the preceding paragraph we have used an example of reasoning by association, which is extremely important in all types of geologic studies. For example, although we cannot find dolomites forming in modern oceans, their intimate association with other types of rocks known to be sedimentary convinces us that they are sediments.

Let us consider a specific instance of the interpretation of a sequence of ancient sediments. A study has been made of a group of Dakota sandstones, a formation approximately 75 million years old, in western Colorado. This sequence of rocks ranges from about 100 to 200 feet thick and changes in lithologic character from the base to the top. Most of the rocks show features which seem to be characteristic of deposition from rivers or fairly shallow marine water. The problem is to determine the

Fig. 7-19. Coral reef. The fossils that build the framework of the reef are not easy to see. The radiating structure extending upward from the base of the rock in the lower middle part of the picture is a coral. Irregular patterns elsewhere are generally coralline. Width of view shown is approximately six feet. (Photo by E. G. Purdy.)

TABLE 7-2.   SUMMARY OF ENVIRONMENTAL CRITERIA

	Stratification	Bedding Surface Features
Fluvial	High-angle cross beds in tabular to lenticular sets 1-2 ft. thick. Regular, thin lamination	Parallel and cuspate current ripples; parallel and irregular megaripples. Wood, tracks, trails, and other impressions
Tidal Flat	Thin, irregular bedding; thick, sets of cross beds; ripple cross laminae; burrows of organisms	Many types of wave and current ripples in sand and mud; impressions of many kinds; tracks, trails; flow marks
Beach	Tabular to wedgeshape sets of thin, regular lamination; low-angle cross beds	Wave and current ripples; swash and rill marks; lineation features
Lagoon	Thinly laminated to structureless sand, silt, and clay. Regular and irregular beds. Burrowing structures	Wave ripples. Trails, tracks; algal mats; mud cracks and crystal impressions on margins
Marsh	Thin, irregular beds. Beds disrupted by plant roots	Not known
Marine	Tabular to irregular sets of low-angle cross beds; irregular thin beds	Wave ripples away from shore. Trails and burrows of organisms

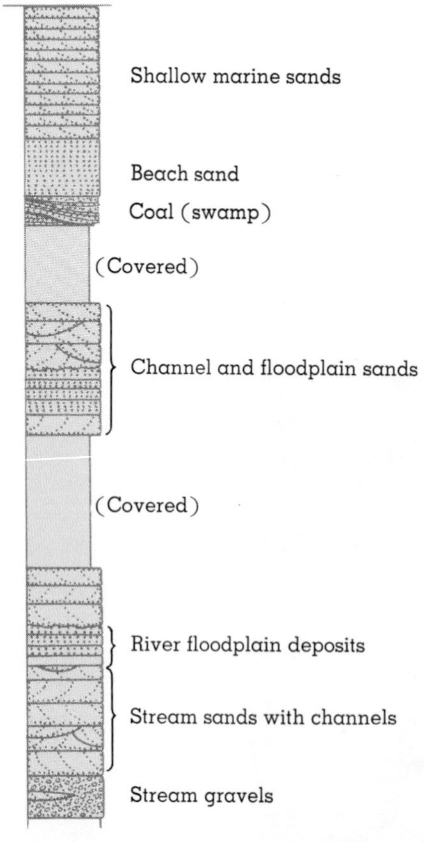

Shallow marine sands

Beach sand

Coal (swamp)

(Covered)

Channel and floodplain sands

(Covered)

River floodplain deposits

Stream sands with channels

Stream gravels

Fig. 7-20. Stratigraphic section of Dakota sandstone showing features that indicate different sedimentary environments. Discussion in the text. (From Donald W. Lane, *American Association of Petroleum Geologists Bulletin*, vol. 47, n. 2, February 1963.)

Lithologic Features	Biota	Other Features
Well to poorly sorted sands and gravels. Wood; clay pebbles; coal	Mainly land plants; rare vertebrate remains	Channels; subaerial erosion and weathering features. Irregular thickness
Shale pebble conglomerates; interbedded sand, silt, and clay; iron oxides and sulphides; fecal pellets	Mollusks; algae; fish; worms; crustaceans	Small channels; irregular thickness and character
Excellent sorting. Coquinas. Sand or coarser in texture	Marine invertebrates. Wood debris. Vertebrate hard parts	Thin, widespread deposits. Small variation in thickness
Fine grained except near rivers and inlets. Iron sulphides; carbonates; evaporites; fecal pellets	Mollusks, algae; worms; crustaceans; fish	Irregular thickness and character
Silt and clay. Iron oxides and sulphides	Mainly plants	Irregular thickness and distribution
Sand, silt	Great variety of plants and animals	Relatively continuous and tabular as a unit

SOURCE: From D. W. Lane, *Bulletin of American Association of Petroleum Geologists,* vol. 47, 1963.

geologic history of the area in terms of movement of the shoreline back and forth across the region. If, for example, the ocean waters were rising and encroaching upon the land during the period of deposition of this formation, there would be a progressive change from river to shoreline to marine sediments. Furthermore, within the sequence of marine sediments there should be evidence at any one location of increase in depth of water in which the sediments were deposited. The first task in reconstruction of the sedimentary history, then, is to assemble a list of criteria that would characterize rocks from any of several environments. A simplified version of such a chart is shown in Table 7-2, which is based on the study of modern sediments.

By following such a chart of criteria, it is possible to prepare a description of the actual variation in characteristics of the Dakota sandstone from the base to the top of the investigated sequence. Since there seems to be no particularly good way to invalidate the assumption that young rocks are deposited on top of older ones, the rocks presumably become progressively younger upward in the section. It is also necessary to investigate sections of the formation in a variety of places. A diagrammatic

TABLE 7-3. SUMMARY OF ENVIRONMENTAL

	Stratification	Bedding Surface Features
Fluvial	High-angle cross beds in sets to 2 ft. thick. Thin, regular lamination	Wood fragments and plants. Current ripple marks. Bedding surfaces rarely exposed
Tidal flat	Thin sets cross lamination; thick sets low-angle cross beds. Abundant burrowing structures	Wave and current ripples of many types, in sandstone and shale. Trails, tracks, wood impressions
Beach	Tabular and wedge-shape sets of thin, regular lamination. Low-angle cross beds	Surfaces not exposed
Lagoon	Thin-bedded and structureless strata, regular and irregular. Possible boring structures	Surfaces not exposed
Marsh	Thin, irregular beds, with possible root traces	Surfaces not exposed
Marine	Tabular to irregular sets of low-angle cross beds	Surfaces not exposed

illustration of properties of some of the rocks in one of the sections is shown in Fig. 7-20. Though the details of this particular study are not important for the student in an introductory course, it is worthwhile to compare the properties shown in Fig. 7-20 with the various criteria of depositional environments listed in Table 7-2. In particular, the presence of stream cross-bedding and small channels in the lower part of the Dakota section is reasonably good evidence of river deposition. The woody and coaly material found somewhat higher in the section is characteristic of swamp or marsh deposits, and the fine lamination characteristic of beach sand is well displayed above the swamp deposits. The uppermost rocks clearly exhibit features of normal marine sand and shale. A complete tabulation of properties of the Dakota sandstone is shown in Table 7-3 and comparing this data with Table 7-2 clearly establishes the nature of the various depositional environments of the sandstone.

No one rock could be taken out of the Dakota section, examined, and placed with any great degree of confidence in any one particular sedi-

Lithologic Features	Biota	Other Features
Clay and chert pebble conglomerates. Poor sorting. Wood, coal. Plant remains	Dinosaur footprints	Channels; erosion and weathering features. Irregular thickness
Shale-pebble conglomerates. Interbedded sandstone and black shale. Organic matter. Wood fragments	Burrows of organisms. Mollusks	Irregular thickness and character
Well-sorted fine to medium standstone, rarely granular. Wood fragments	None seen	Widespread. Uniform thickness and character
Black shale and siltstone. Iron sulphides and organic matter	None seen	Irregular thickness and character
Siltstone and iron oxides	Plants, mostly grasses	Erratic distribution. Possible sandy creek channels
Sandstone; wood fragments	None seen	Widespread. Uniform thickness and character

SOURCE: From D. W. Lane, *Bulletin of American Association of Petroleum Geologists,* vol. 47, 1963.

mentary environment. The overall sequence, however, can be explained very logically in terms of a gradual flooding of the land, an inward migration of the shore line, and an increasing depth of water at any one place. Apparently, during deposition of the Dakota sandstone in this area, the sea level was gradually rising relative to the land. This extension of the ocean at the expense of land area is called a marine *transgression,* and geologic history records many examples of the phenomenon. Once a logical explanation of a sequence such as the Dakota sandstone has been developed, it is very difficult to claim that the interpretation is completely in error. The geologist, of course, cannot answer the fundamental objection to his hypothesis that he was not there at the time the rocks were formed and thus does not have the most direct evidence as to their origin. As mentioned above, however, the object of geologic investigation is to determine the most plausible of a number of possible explanations.

CHAPTER 8

IGNEOUS AND

METAMORPHIC ROCKS

◄ Erupting volcano. (Courtesy of Instituto Salvadoreño de Turismo.)

$\mathbf{W}$e started our discussion of sedimentary rocks by classifying them into broad groups. The purpose of this classification was to provide a set of simple terms we could use to refer to a large number of rocks at the same time; similar problems are encountered in the study of igneous rocks. The classification of sediments was based first on composition, that is whether the material consisted of clastic silicates or chemical carbonates, and second on the size of the grains of the clastic rocks, which gave the subdivision between conglomerates, sandstones, and shales. In a wholly analogous fashion the classification of igneous rocks is based first on the size of grains and second on the mineralogical composition. Over 600 different names have been proposed for different types of igneous rocks. The average practicing geologist is familiar with some 15 to 25 of these names, and we shall refer to approximately 10 in this book.

IGNEOUS ACTIVITY

Description of igneous rocks

The classification scheme we shall use is shown in Fig. 8-1. The first part of this classification represents a subdivision between coarse-grained and fine-grained rocks. A coarse-grained rock is one in which the grain size is large enough for us to recognize individual minerals either with the naked eye or with the aid of a low-power magnifying lens. A fine-grained rock is one in which the grains are too small to be distinguished from each other and in which the "groundmass" appears homogeneous. Rock characteristics such as the sizes and shapes of grains and their arrangement are generally referred to in the broad category of *texture*.

It would be tempting to equate the term "coarse grained" with intrusive and "fine grained" with extrusive, and in many cases this relationship is undoubtedly correct. It is a mistake, however, to use terms in a classification scheme which imply anything concerning the origin of a rock. Thus if we use the term "intrusive" as a part of the classification scheme, we would have to be certain that the rock referred to had formed as an intrusion within the earth's crust. A more objective approach is to describe the rocks first and discuss the origin later.

Once we have subdivided the igneous rocks into coarse and fine grained, the next major breakdown is made on the basis of mineralogical composition. To describe coarse-grained rocks, we shall use the name *granite* for all rocks containing quartz; *diorite* for rocks without quartz but having a preponderance of feldspar (generally plagioclase); and *gabbro* for rocks in which dark minerals such as hornblende and augite predominate over other minerals. Actually the percentages of quartz, orthoclase or microcline, plagioclase, hornblende, augite, and olivine vary gradually from one rock to another, and the boundaries we have placed to delineate the various rock types are arbitrary but useful. In

155

Fig. 8-1 note the tendency of different minerals to vary concurrently. Thus, most rocks containing large amounts of quartz are also rich in potassium feldspar and comparatively impoverished in dark minerals such as hornblende and augite. Olivine occurs only in rocks comparatively rich in hornblende and augite, or in the special and rather rare rock *peridotite*. Olivine and quartz cannot occur together, because the two would react to form a pyroxene, a fact which may be verified by examining the formulas in the Appendix. This concomitant variation of mineral abundances is an extremely important clue which we shall use later to determine the mode of formation of different types of igneous rocks.

The fine-grained rocks have a range of chemical composition nearly identical to that of the coarse-grained rocks. The classification, however, is not based on chemical composition but on the presence of visible and readily identifiable minerals. Consequently, the rocks which are com-

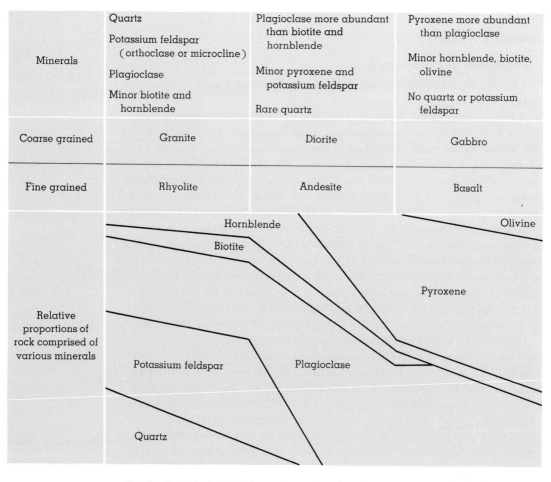

Minerals	Quartz Potassium feldspar (orthoclase or microcline) Plagioclase Minor biotite and hornblende	Plagioclase more abundant than biotite and hornblende Minor pyroxene and potassium feldspar Rare quartz	Pyroxene more abundant than plagioclase Minor hornblende, biotite, olivine No quartz or potassium feldspar
Coarse grained	Granite	Diorite	Gabbro
Fine grained	Rhyolite	Andesite	Basalt
Relative proportions of rock comprised of various minerals			

Fig. 8-1. Simplified classification of igneous rocks. The typical proportions of the various minerals in different rocks are shown in the diagram.

pletely fine grained are virtually unclassifiable except under very high-power magnification. Most fine-grained rocks, however, contain a small percentage of grains which are sufficiently coarse to be identified with the aid of a hand lens. These grains which are larger than their surrounding minerals are called *phenocrysts,* and a rock containing phenocrysts is said to have a *porphyritic* texture. The classification of fine-grained rocks, then, is based on the proportion of minerals which form phenocrysts in the hope that these phenocrysts reflect the general composition of the remainder of the rock. As we shall see later, this hope is only partially justified. The fine-grained portion of a porphyritic rock is generally referred to as the *groundmass* of the phenocrysts. The terms "porphyritic" and "phenocrysts" are not restricted to fine-grained rocks but may also apply to coarse-grained rocks which contain a few crystals distinctly larger than the remainder.

A few special rock names are not included in Fig. 8-1. The term *obsidian* refers to a glassy rock of rhyolitic composition. In general, fine-grained rocks consisting of small crystals cannot readily be distinguished from glassy rocks in which no crystalline material is present at all. The obsidians, however, are generally easily recognized by their black and highly glossy appearance. *Pumice* is a white porous glass of the same composition as obsidian. Apparently the difference between the modes of formation of obsidian and pumice is that in pumice the entrapped water vapors have been able to escape by a frothing process which leaves a network of interconnected pore spaces, thus giving the rock a highly porous and open appearance. Petrologists do not fully understand the reason for the escape of water from some lavas (as in pumice) and its retention by others (as in obsidian). One can readily make artificial pumice by heating obsidian at one atmosphere pressure.

Pegmatite is a rock which is texturally the exact opposite of obsidian. Pegmatites are generally formed as dikes associated with major bodies of granite. They are characterized by extremely large individual crystals; in some pegmatites crystals up to several tens of feet in length have been identified, but the average size is measured in inches. Most mineralogical museums contain a large number of spectacular crystals from pegmatites.

Peridotite is a rock consisting primarily of olivine, though some varieties contain pyroxene in addition. It occurs only as coarse-grained intrusives, and no extrusive rocks of equivalent chemical composition have ever been found.

Tuff is a rock which is igneous in one sense and sedimentary in another. A tuff is a rock formed from pyroclastic material which has been blown out of a volcano and accumulated on the ground as individual fragments called *ash.* The word "ash" refers to material erupted either as small drops of liquid or as small solid bits. Most pyroclastic activity results in the development of tuffs, and the word implies nothing about composition.

Two terms are useful to refer solely to the composition of igneous rocks regardless of their textures. The term *silicic* signifies an abundance of silica-rich and light-colored minerals, such as quartz, potassium feldspar, and sodic plagioclase. The term *basic* signifies an abundance of dark-colored minerals relatively low in silica and high in calcium, iron, and magnesium. Such minerals would include hornblende, augite, and calcic plagioclase. Some geologists refer to olivine-rich rocks as ultrabasic.

Volcanoes

The most direct evidence available to geologists concerning the origin of igneous rocks comes from the study of volcanoes (Fig. 8-2). We can investigate several different aspects of volcanic activity. First is the nature of the eruptive mechanism for individual volcanoes, that is, whether or not they erupt quietly or violently, intermittently or continuously. Second, we can investigate the composition of rocks erupted by individual volcanoes and, if possible, detect changes in composition throughout time. And third, we can discuss the distribution of volcanic activity around the modern earth and in the geologic past.

Some types of volcanoes, such as those of Hawaii, emit lavas rather quietly. The term "quiet" is somewhat of a misnomer, owing to the fact that the emitted lavas generally have a temperature of 1100 to 1200° C. and may shoot up in fountains several hundreds of feet into the air. In such volcanoes the lava simply overtops the lip of the vent, possibly by washing out one or more edges, and flows down the side of the volcano. The flow congeals somewhere on the side of the volcano or around the base, and throughout time a series of flows of this type builds up a smooth conical form which is characteristic of volcanoes (see Fig. 8-3). In Fig. 8-3 the vent has been drawn as a nearly vertical, smooth-walled column, though this may not be particularly accurate. Small subsidiary vents are common on the sides of large volcanoes, and in some areas a whole complex of orifices has been established. Volcanic *necks* represent rock congealed in a near-vertical vent and left behind by erosion of the surrounding extrusive material (Fig. 8-4).

Some volcanoes do not erupt as quietly as those of Hawaii. In many

Fig. 8-2. Wizard Island in Crater Lake, Oregon. The island is a small volcanic cone that has formed in the throat of the larger volcano, now occupied by Crater Lake. The lake has a diameter of about five miles. (Photo by T. H. Foss, National Aeronautics and Space Administration.)

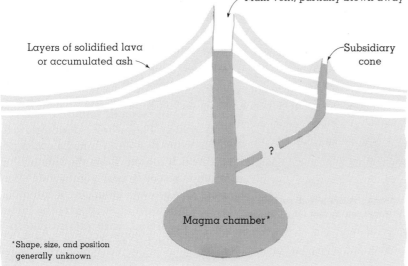

Main vent, partially blown away

Layers of solidified lava or accumulated ash

Subsidiary cone

?

Magma chamber*

*Shape, size, and position generally unknown

Fig. 8-3. Cross section of typical volcano. Steepness of sides increases with percentage of ash in erupted material.

volcanoes the outpouring of liquid lava is accompanied by an eruption of pyroclastic material. Much of the pyroclastic material is in the form of fine ash which spreads rather widely over the area, but some of the ejected material forms large blocks or volcanic *bombs* (Fig. 8-5) which may weigh on the order of several tens of pounds. Field investigation of such volcanoes is uncomfortable. Volcanoes that erupt in this fashion build broad conical structures in which layers of solidified lava are interspersed with layers of ash and other pyroclastic ejects. The profiles of such volcanoes naturally tend to be less smooth than those of volcanoes composed solely of solidified lava.

The most violent of volcanic eruptions has fortunately been observed in only a few instances. One of the best documented is the eruption of Mt. Pelee on the island of Martinique in 1902. The main eruption of Mt. Pelee was preceded by several weeks of ash fall and emission of gas from the volcanic top. All of this was noted with alarm by the inhabitants of the island, and several observers who were on ships offshore managed to survive the final catastrophe and have made very careful records of

Fig. 8-4. Remnant of congealed lava from throat of volcano. This small volcanic neck in Nevada has been exposed by erosion of surrounding volcanic flanks. The columnar appearance is caused by jointing formed when the lava cools. (Photo by R. B. Scott.)

Fig. 8-5. Volcanic bomb showing typical aerodynamically smooth shape. The bomb is about ten inches long. (Photo by J. J. W. Rogers.)

the entire eruption. On May 8, 1902, this preliminary phase of the eruption came to a violent end when a part of the volcano seemed to crack open and emit a large hot cloud. (Fig. 8-6.) This cloud was later found to have consisted of a mixture of superheated steam and volcanic ash at several hundred degrees centrigrade. The whole cloud glowed with a white heat and formed a coherent mass which moved down the side of the volcano at speeds near eighty miles per hour. This glowing cloud swept into portions of the town of St. Pierre, the main city on the island, with catastrophic results. The final stage of the eruption occurred considerably later when a spine of congealed, glassy material protruded in a virtually solid state out of the former neck of the volcano.

A similar eruption is presumed to be responsible for the complete dis-

Fig. 8-6. Glowing cloud erupted from Mt. Pelee in 1933. The cloud is several hundred feet high. (From F. A. Perret, "Volcanological Observations," *Carnegie Institution of Washington Publication No. 549,* 1950).

appearance of this island of Krakatoa in the Netherlands East Indies (now Indonesia) in 1883. The effects of this eruption were heard and seen from distances of several thousand miles.

Investigation of the composition of extruded rock leads to a general, although not very detailed, correlation between composition and intensity of volcanic eruption. In general, the quiet eruptions are characteristic of those volcanoes which emit basic or basaltic lavas, whereas the violent eruptions are characteristic of volcanoes emitting more silicic rocks. This distinction is apparently carried back into the geologic past. Most true volcanic rocks appear to be basaltic or andesitic in composition, whereas most tuffs are andesitic to rhyolitic. Laboratory experiments provide an explanation for the difference in behavior of the two types of materials. Basic melts tend to have a low viscosity and flow quite freely. Silicic melts, however, are highly viscous and presumably must be erupted from volcanoes largely by fragmentation to form pyroclastic debris.

In sequences of ancient volcanic rocks, it is possible to trace the variation in composition of the erupted material with time. Since a sequence of flows obviously becomes progressively younger upward in the section, it is simply necessary to take a group of samples from various places in the section and to plot a variation in composition against time of eruption. An example of one such study from the lavas of northern California is shown in Fig. 8-7. The results shown in this figure are similar to those obtained from the study of other volcanic sequences. In general, it appears that lavas become progressively more silicic as volcanic eruption continues, and this change in composition is known as *differentiation*. Apparently, the lava in the underground chamber from which the erupted material was derived changed composition progressively during the period of volcanic activity, and the lava erupted at any time reflects the composition of the liquid in the chamber at that time. In a later portion of this chapter, we shall discuss some of the problems involved in accounting for differentiation in igneous melts.

No very good figure is available as to the overall proportions of basalts, andesites, and rhyolites throughout the geologic record. Geologists have been impressed by the fact that a number of broad areas of the earth, such as eastern Oregon, have been the site of very thick accumulations of basalts, and it is generally assumed that basaltic lavas predominate over other types of volcanic rocks. We shall see that this predomin-

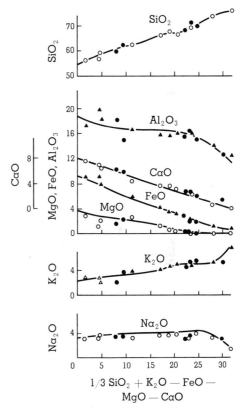

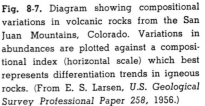

Fig. 8-7. Diagram showing compositional variations in volcanic rocks from the San Juan Mountains, Colorado. Variations in abundances are plotted against a compositional index (horizontal scale) which best represents differentiation trends in igneous rocks. (From E. S. Larsen, *U.S. Geological Survey Professional Paper 258*, 1956.)

ance of basic rocks is exactly contrary to the predominance of silicic rocks found among intrusives.

Volcanoes occur in a few highly localized areas around the earth. The major concentration of volcanic activity is in a circle around the Pacific Ocean. This circle has been termed the "ring of fire" and is also associated very closely with earthquake activity and other evidence of instability of the earth's crust. The interpretation of this instability will be discussed in a number of places in the following chapters. Other noted areas of volcanic activity are Italy, Iceland, the Caribbean Ocean, and a series of islands extending down the center of the Atlantic Ocean.

Not all volcanic rocks have necessarily emanated from true conical volcanoes. It is possible that the thick accumulations of basalts or of rhyolitic pyroclastics, which occur in parts of the western United States and other areas of the world, have simply been derived from broad fissures that never developed into topographic prominences. The Columbia River basaltic lava flows of northeastern Oregon and southeastern Washington, for example, extend over a roughly circular area with a diameter greater than 100 miles. It is difficult to conceive of a single volcanic vent which could have given rise to this tremendous volume of basalt. Thus, geologists have come to the conclusion that such accumulations have resulted by eruptions from elongate fissures.

Intrusive rocks

Although sedimentary rocks cover more than 75 percent of the earth's surface, igneous rocks constitute the major portion of the volume of the crust. Estimates vary somewhat as to the total percentage of the continental masses which consist of granite, but it is safe to say that approximately 80 percent of the crust underlying the continents is composed either of granite or closely related rock types. The reasons for this conclusion about the preponderance of granite are both geological and geophysical. The geological reason is that granites tend to occur in large masses and, where exposed in mountainous regions of high vertical relief, appear to have no floor; indeed, the contacts with wall rocks are either vertical or expand outward at depth. The geophysical evidence is based on both gravity and seismic measurements and has led to the conclusion that most of the earth's crust must consist of rocks of rather low density, such as granite.

As we shall discuss in Chapter 10, most continents have a core of exceptionally old rock. This rock also apparently underlies the sediments around the margins of the continent. This continental core consists primarily of igneous rock admixed with some metamorphic material. For the purpose of preparing geochemical balances such as we did in Chapter 6, it is generally assumed that the composition of the continental mass can be equated with a material of the approximate composition of granite.

In our discussion of extrusive rocks, we continually used the term "lava" to refer to a molten silicate extruded onto the earth's surface. An equivalent, and perhaps unnecessary, term for molten silicate that has crystallized within the earth's crust is the word *magma*. Strictly speaking, an igneous rock is one which has crystallized from a magma or a lava, although, as we mentioned in Chapter 6, the term "igneous" commonly refers to granites and granitic-appearing rocks regardless of their origin. Intrusive and extrusive rocks differ in a variety of ways, and it is instructive to start our discussion of intrusive igneous rocks with a list of the more important differences.

1. Intrusive rocks are coarser grained than extrusives. As noted earlier, this difference in grain size is presumably largely related to the fact that intrusive rocks cool more slowly than volcanic lavas erupted on the earth's surface. The relationship between the size of grains and the cooling rate of the melt is one which is easily studied in the laboratory on artificial systems. The basic explanation for the coarse grain size of slowly cooled melts is that in a melt which cools slowly the individually formed crystal nuclei have time to grow to appreciable size before new nuclei have formed. Where cooling is rapid, the growth rate is slow in comparison with the formation of new nuclei of individual minerals. The result is that the number of mineral grains, which is equal to the number of nuclei formed, is smaller in an intrusive rock than it is in an equal volume of an extrusive rock. With the exception of the margins of a few dikes and sills, glass is never found in intrusive bodies, though it is common in many types of volcanic rocks. The relationship between grain size and cooling rate is not exact, however, and may be influenced by a variety of factors. For example, a high proportion of water in a silicate melt tends to inhibit the formation of nuclei and thus promotes the development of a coarse-grained rock. The effect of the retention of water in melts accentuates the development of large crystals in intrusive rocks, because water is obviously more easily retained in an intruded magma than in an extruded lava.

2. Intrusive rocks show the effect of having been subjected to higher pressures than extrusive rocks. This statement is partly supported by the presence in many extrusive rocks of numerous small, slightly spherical, holes ranging in size from very tiny up to diameters of approximately 1 inch. These holes are referred to as *vesicles* and obviously represent bubbles of water vapor which have separated from the lava upon its release to the surface (Fig. 8-8). The exsolution of water from the lava and the development of these bubbles is caused by the release of pressure upon extrusion. (You may prove to yourself that the release of pressure permits gases to escape from liquids by simply removing the top from a carbonated soft-drink bottle.) With very rare exceptions, vesicles are simply not found in intrusive rocks, and the conclusion is that these rocks have developed under a high pressure. The effects of high pressures which are not uniform in all directions are also shown by the tendency of many igneous rocks to show a partial crushing and shearing of the component grains. This texture is not characteristic of all rocks but is by no means uncommon (Fig. 8-9).

3. The minerals of intrusive and extrusive rocks are somewhat different. As an example of structural reorientation in crystals, we men-

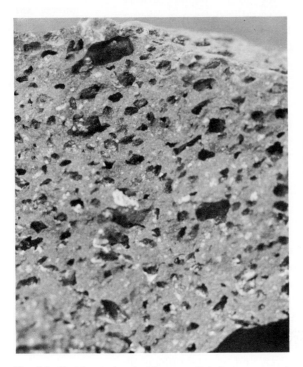

Fig. 8-8. Vesicles in basalt. These small holes are caused by escaping gas after eruption. (Photo by J. J. W. Rogers.)

tioned in Chapter 6 the tendency of perthite (the albite-potassium feldspar intergrowth) to form upon the slow cooling of orthoclase or microcline. A perthitic texture is common in most granites but is completely absent from the rapidly cooled potash feldspars of volcanic rocks (compare Figs. 8-10 and 8-11. Other mineralogical differences can also be found, such as the tendency of olivine to be somewhat more abundant in volcanic rock than in intrusive rocks of similar chemical composition. A discussion of all of the differences would involve a major excursion into mineralogical detail.

4. The proportions of rock types with different chemical compositions are quite different among intrusive than among extrusive rocks. As we mentioned earlier, most volcanic rocks have a composition of basalt or are at least reasonably basic. The typical intrusive rock, however, is a granite, and gabbros and even diorites are comparatively uncommon. This difference in the proportions of rock types has been explained by geologists in a variety of ways, none of which has gained any universal acceptance. One explanation is based on the fact that silicic lavas are more viscous than basic lavas, a fact which has been demonstrated both in the laboratory and by studying the nature of volcanic eruptions. The higher viscosity can be related to the higher degree of cross-linking among the more numerous silica tetrahedra. The theory is that highly viscous melts will not reach the surface as easily as less viscous ones, and therefore the granite magmas tend to crystallize as intrusive bodies, whereas the basic magmas are extruded to form basaltic lavas. An alternative theory, which we shall discuss in more detail later in this chapter, is that granitic and other intrusive rocks have not formed from melts at all but have originated by some type of metamorphic process.

Despite the various differences between intrusive and extrusive rocks, there are certain distinct similarities. As noted above, the range of composition of the two rock types is roughly the same, though the proportion of different compositions is different for the intrusive and extrusive materials. The concept of differentiation assumes that an original magma changes in composition sequentially, and that the rocks formed at various stages in the sequence will reflect the composition of the magma at that particular phase of its differentiation. Figure 8-7 showed trends in variation in composition of extruded material, and the nearly identical process has also been found for intrusive rocks. One major study of the

Fig. 8-9. Shearing of plagioclase in thin section of anorthosite. The bending and breaking of crystallographic and optical features of the plagioclase in this rock is quite apparent. Magnification approximately 100 times. (Photo by J. J. W. Rogers.)

Fig. 8-10. Perthite in thin section. The white streaks are sodic plagioclase presumably exsolved upon cooling from the surrounding potassium feldspar. Magnification approximately 100 times. (Photo by J. J. W. Rogers.)

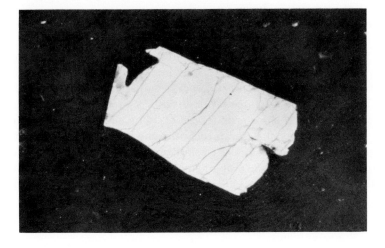

Fig. 8-11. Nonperthitic sodium-potassium feldspar in thin section of rhyolite. Note the absence of exsolution in this rapidly cooled crystal. Magnification approximately 100 times. (Photo by J. J. W. Rogers.)

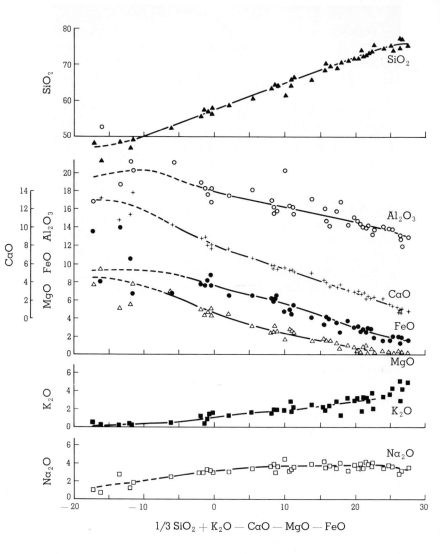

Fig. 8-12. Diagram showing compositional variations in intrusive igneous rocks from southern California. Compare with Fig. 8-7. (From Esper S. Larsen, *Geological Society of America Memoir 29*, 1948.)

igneous rocks of southern California, just south of Los Angeles, has led to a diagram as shown in Fig. 8-12 in which the change in composition with time of intrusion is shown quite clearly.

For extrusive rocks the relative sequence of formation was found simply by position in the layered section of horizontal lava flows. For intrusive rocks relative time of formation must be found by somewhat different types of evidence. In general, four lines of evidence may be used, most of which require that the two rocks compared be in contact with each other. Where a rock intrudes or invades a preexisting material, it has several effects on this material (Fig. 8-13). One effect is the incorporation of small fragments of the wall rock into the intrusive magma. These fragments are then caught in the crystallizing mass and form *inclusions* or *xenoliths,* and the presence of fragments of one rock in large bodies of another intrusive indicates the relative age quite clearly. A second line of evidence which is commonly used is the relationship also shown in Fig. 8-13 in which the later, or younger, intruding magma has sent small dikes and irregular cross-cutting stringers into the preexisting material. This cross-cutting of other rocks is another clear indication of relative age. A third type of evidence consists of finding places in which preexisting rocks have obviously been displaced or moved apart from each other by the intrusion of the younger magma. A fourth line of evidence is the chemical or mineralogical effect (e.g., baking) which a hot magma may have on a cold wall rock (Fig. 8-14). Once two rocks have been placed in a time sequence, then others may be related to either of the first two, and thus a whole history of events may be deciphered.

Large masses of intrusive igneous rocks such as granites are commonly called *batholiths*. Some batholiths have outcrop areas of several hundreds or thousands of square miles, whereas others are comparatively small. Most batholiths are characterized by a reasonable uniformity of rock composition and textural features. Some variations are present, but few, if any, batholiths would show compositional ranges from, say, granite to gabbro, or textural ranges from crystals of 1″ size to very fine grained. Some batholiths actually appear to be a complex sequence of intrusions, the borders between which are sharp in some places and somewhat fuzzy in others. Many large batholiths contain enormous masses of the country rock into which the magma has been intruded.

One of the important properties of batholiths is the nature of their contact relations with surrounding wall rocks or country rocks. Contacts

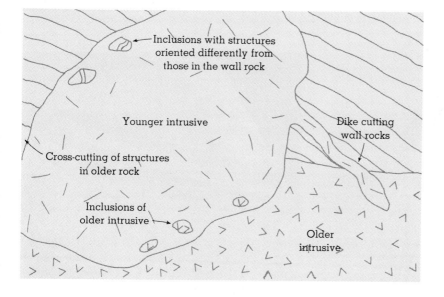

Fig. 8-13. Diagrammatic representation of criteria used to determine age of intrusions. Criteria include cross-cutting of former structures, dikes, and inclusions of older rocks.

Fig. 8-14. Baked zone (white) in sediments underlying dark basalt in Nova Scotia. (Photo by G. DeV. Klein.)

fall roughly into two categories which we might call *sharp* (Fig. 8-15) and *gradational* (Fig. 8-16). Granites showing sharp contact with wall rocks generally exhibit evidence of having cut through and perhaps shoved aside the surrounding rocks. For example, bedding planes in sedimentary country rocks may be sharply terminated at granite contacts. The bedding or other features may appear to have been distorted or crinkled, or, to use a term which we shall discuss later, "folded." Small

Fig. 8-15. Sharp contact between igneous rock (dark) and metamorphic rock. (Photo by R. E. Wilcox.)

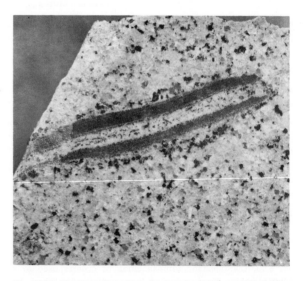

Fig. 8-16. Gradational contact between granite and inclusion of schist, Llano Co., Texas. The gradation is caused by reaction of the schist with the granite. (Photo by J. J. W. Rogers.)

dikes of granite, or perhaps pegmatite, are common around margins of such intrusions. The granite, in short, gives every evidence of having shoved its way into the position which it occupies and, in so doing, to have displaced the preexisting country rocks. Indeed, the word "intrusion" somewhat implies such a mode of emplacement. The general picture envisioned by many geologists for granite intrusion is one of a magma, whose density as a melt is less than that of the surrounding rocks, rising through the earth's crust and ultimately crystallizing in some place where it has managed to inject itself. As we shall discuss later, other pressures than a density difference may be wholly or partly responsible for such injection.

Granites which exhibit gradational contacts with surrounding wall rocks commonly do not show evidence of this type of injection. Such granites are generally characteristic of broad regions of intermingled igneous and metamorphic rocks. In many places in such areas, it may be difficult or impossible to determine an exact contact between intrusive rock and metamorphic wall rock. The origin of granites of this type is widely disputed. Some geologists attribute their formation to the injection of a magma and its complex intermingling with its surroundings. Other geologists believe that the granite simply represents a final stage in the process of metamorphism and that really no magma has been injected at all (see Fig. 6-9). The metamorphic process is called *granitization*.

Granitization has been invoked to explain a number of puzzling features of granites that we have already briefly touched upon. Two of the principal lines of evidence for a replacement origin of granites are the great excess of granites over gabbros, which is not explicable by fractional crystallization of a basalt, and broad gradations between granites and metamorphic wall rocks. In some places these contact zones may be several miles wide on the surface, and it seems unlikely that such a broad zone could be formed by reaction between magma and wall rock. Some granites have also been found to contain relic, or "ghost," variations in composition and texture which seem to parallel stratigraphic variations in adjacent sedimentary wall rocks, and some geologists claim to have traced sedimentary beds "into" granite bodies. Granitization also conveniently makes it unnecessary to displace rocks in order to form a granite, as is required by magmatic injection, and this problem becomes significant in explaining the origin of large batholiths. Most granites, however, do not show any of these features, and it is an open question whether they have formed by a magmatic or a replacement process.

It may seem paradoxical that contact metamorphism is less easily observed around large batholiths than around small bodies of magma. The reason, however, is not difficult to find. In an area in which a major batholith is intruded, the temperature of the surrounding wall rocks over a large region must be raised. The amount of heat associated with several hundred cubic miles of molten silicate is obviously enormous, and this heat presumably distributes itself over a broad enough area so that most of the rocks in the region are brought to a temperature approximately equal to that of the granite. Consequently, when the granite is intruded, it meets rocks which have already adjusted to the high temperatures. Small intrusions, such as dikes, however, may be injected directly into relatively cold wall rocks, and the resulting contact changes may be quite significant (Fig. 8-14).

Origin of igneous rocks

One of the major problems connected with the origin of igneous rocks centers around the necessity of providing an explanation for the compositional variations which these rocks show. We have shown by two examples that extrusive and intrusive sequences tend to differentiate in the same manner to yield silicic rocks from originally basic materials (Figs. 8-7 and 8-12). One major theory for the formation of igneous rock begins with the assumption that all original undifferentiated magmas have the composition of basalt. The idea is that the dense material in which the continents float is either a basalt or a material which can be easily melted, in whole or in part, to yield a basalt. The problem of explaining the generation of igneous rocks of non-basaltic composition, then, is simply one of explaining the differentiation of a basalt to yield progressively more silicic materials. The major explanation for this differentiation process is *fractional crystallization,* in which minerals separate from the originally basaltic melt in a distinct sequence. The early-separated minerals, being solids and thus generally more dense than the remaining melt, settle downward and leave behind a melt impoverished in the early-crystallized constituents.

The sequence of crystallization of minerals from a basalt may be investigated in two ways. In microscopic study of many igneous rocks it is apparent that certain minerals have crystallized before other minerals, either as shown by inclusion of small grains of previously-formed materials or by virtue of having the external shape of a grain partially controlled by the shape of some preexisting mineral. The general sequence of crystallization of the common minerals of igneous rocks can be worked out by such evidence (Fig. 8-17). The sequence of crystallization deduced from textural studies of actual rocks may be verified by laboratory experiments on the crystallization of basalt. The procedure is simply to melt a basalt completely (generally at about 1200° C.), then slowly cool the melt to various temperatures and determine which minerals are in equilibrium with the quenched, residual, uncrystallized melt at each temperature. The laboratory and observational evidence, fortunately, agree fairly closely in this particular case. In fact, in the laboratory it becomes apparent that the major minerals of igneous rocks may be arranged in a sequence in which, at least in some cases, early-forming minerals may react with the remaining melt to yield minerals of slightly different composition. Thus olivine, the first mineral to form as a basaltic melt begins to cool, may later react completely with the remaining melt at lower temperatures and be converted to a pyroxene. Similarly, calcic plagioclase is continually converted into more sodic plagioclase during progressive cooling and greater solidification of a basaltic melt. By placing all of the reactions and sequences of formation into one series, we can diagram the sequence of crystallization as shown in Fig. 8-18. This

Fig. 8-17. Sequential crystallization of minerals in an igneous rock. The well-formed sharply pointed crystals are plagioclase, which has crystallized first. The light-and-dark pattern is an intergrowth of quartz and potassium feldspar, which has grown around the earlier plagioclase. Photomicrograph of thin section is magnified approximately 100 times. (Photo by J. J. W. Rogers.)

series is referred to as the *Bowen reaction series* from the name of the man who originally suggested the possibility of such sequential reactions.

Crystallization according to the Bowen reaction series provides a mechanism for generating silicic magmas from more basic ones. The early-formed minerals, as shown in Fig. 8-18, are those which are comparatively rich in calcium, magnesium, and iron and relatively poor in silicon, aluminum, sodium, and potassium. If, for example, early-formed crystals of olivine settle out of the melt and accumulate in some conveniently out-of-the-way place, then the residual melt will be lower in magnesium content and higher in silicon content. By this process it is possible to generate granitic magmas, but the sequence of reactions is sufficiently complicated that an enormous amount of basalt must be differentiated in order to give rise to moderate amounts of granite. It is in part for this reason, and partly for other more detailed objections to the differentiation hypothesis, that some geologists feel that differentiation cannot account for the production of the large amounts of granitic rocks which are found in the continents. Differentiation by fractional crystallization, however, does provide a logical explanation for the associations of minerals in igneous rocks. Minerals which crystallize concurrently (such as olivine and highly calcic plagioclase, or quartz, potassium feldspar, and sodic plagioclase) tend to occur together in rocks. This fact may be verified by comparing Fig. 8-18 with Fig. 8-1.

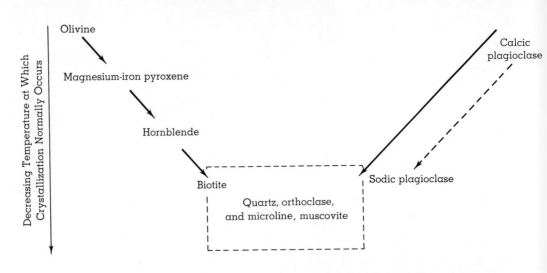

Fig. 8-18. Diagrammatic representation of the Bowen reaction series. Compare with Fig. 8-1 and note that minerals that crystallize together tend to occur in rocks together.

Another major proposal to account for compositional variations among igneous rocks is essentially the reverse of fractional crystallization. If a basaltic melt can differentiate to a granitic melt by sequential crystallization, then presumably a solidified basalt will melt in the reverse order so as to produce a granitic liquid first and leave behind a solid residue of basic material. It turns out that granite is commonly the first liquid formed when basalts and other silicate rocks are heated in the laboratory to moderate temperatures in the neighborhood of 600° to 800° C. The melting temperature can be shown to be greatly lowered by the presence of water. Many geologists, therefore, would explain the compositional variations in igneous rocks in general, and the production of large amounts of granitic magma specifically, by a simple fractional melting of whatever material happens to be available at the site of generation of heat.

The most logical place for such fractional melting is in the lower parts of sedimentary and volcanic sequences which are undergoing active downwarping and are involved in the formation of mountains. We shall discuss some of the problems of mountain building in Chapters 10 and 14. We can say here, however, that granites are generally closely related in time and space to the formation of mountains, and thus the possibility of formation of granitic magma by remelting of formerly sedimentary and volcanic materials must be strongly considered.

METAMORPHISM

As defined previously, metamorphism refers to the changes which take place in rocks when they are subjected to conditions differing from those which existed at the time of their formation. Thus a sediment deposited at the earth's surface under pressures of 1 atm and at temperatures of

20° to 25° C. undergoes profound mineralogical and textural changes when it is buried and subjected to temperatures of many thousands of atmospheres and temperatures ranging up to 600° to 700° C. The unquestioned increase of both temperature and pressure with depth requires that sedimentary rocks undergo metamorphic reactions simply as a result of burial under additional sediments. It is likely, however, that pressures and temperatures in excess of those caused by simple burial affect a large number, if not the majority, of all metamorphic rocks. One reason for this statement is that metamorphism commonly accompanies the process of mountain building, known as *orogeny*. We shall discuss this process in more detail in Chapter 10. It is sufficient here, however, to say that orogeny is generally accompanied by pressures in excess of the normal load pressure at any particular depth and is certainly accompanied by higher than normal temperatures. The excessive temperatures are indicated by the common occurrence of intrusive igneous rocks, such as granites, in areas which have undergone mountain formation.

Description of metamorphic rocks

A number of characteristics of metamorphic rocks themselves attest to the presence of high temperatures and pressures at the time of formation and also to the presence of directed pressures. By "directed pressure," or more accurately "directed stress," we mean a condition in which the stress in one direction is different from the stress in other directions. For example, if you crack an egg with the edge of a spoon, you apply a momentary directed stress perpendicular to the shell of the egg. Stresses associated with metamorphism are, of course, somewhat larger and of greater duration. Directed stress is indicated by the presence of planar and linear features in the typical metamorphic rock (e.g., see Fig. 6-9). In general, it is assumed that the major stress is oriented perpendicular to the layering in most metamorphic rocks. This assumption may not be entirely correct, but it is certainly safe to say that a rock which is not uniform in all directions must have formed under conditions in which the pressures in different directions were not equal.

High temperatures are indicated in metamorphic rocks by the nature of the minerals formed. Dolomite, for example, is uncommon in metamorphic rocks. As can be verified in the laboratory, dolomite tends to break down to calcite under high temperatures, and the resulting magnesium carbonate combines with other materials such as quartz to form magnesium silicates. Hydrated minerals such as clays are also comparatively scarce in metamorphic rocks, owing to the fact that the high temperature tends to drive off the included water and convert the minerals into anhydrous aluminum silicates (e.g., feldspar). High pressures during metamorphism are demonstrated by the greater density of metamorphic rocks than of the sediments from which they were derived.

The typical metamorphic rock consists of a small number of minerals having grain sizes on the order of 1 to 2 mm and showing a distinct layered structure. The small number of minerals reflects the fact that the rock has apparently come to an equilibrium with some set of temperature and pressure conditions. This conclusion is reinforced by the fact that the typical texture of metamorphic rocks, as is shown in Fig. 8-19, does not exhibit the sequence of formation of individual minerals that is shown by most igneous rocks (compare Fig. 8-20). Apparently, in a metamorphic rock all of the grains have formed at roughly the same time, have grown to approximately the same size, and have interfered with the growth of each other to prevent the development of crystal faces.

The directional structures in metamorphic rocks can be classified into two major types. One type of directional feature is a layering caused in part by the parallel orientation of platy minerals such as mica and in part by the tendency of thin bands of different types of minerals to form an alternating sequence of layers. These bands generally consist of light minerals, such as quartz and feldspar, in one layer and dark-colored minerals, such as biotite and hornblende, in the alternate layers. Regardless of the cause, a two-dimensional layered structure of metamorphic rocks is termed *foliation*. In addition to the two-dimensional feature, some metamorphic rocks show a one-dimensional structure called *linea-*

Fig. 8-19. Photomicrograph showing texture of a typical metamorphic rock. Note irregular shape of all grains, presumably indicating simultaneous growth. Magnification approximately 100 times. (Photo by D. C. Crane.)

Fig. 8-20. Photomicrograph of texture of a typical igneous rock. Note regular borders on some grains, which are presumably the early-formed members of the sequence. Magnification approximately 100 times. (Photo by J. J. W. Rogers.)

tion. This lineation may be caused by the alignment of elongate grains, such as hornblende, by streaks of minerals differing slightly in composition from their neighbor, or by a variety of other features. Naturally, the intersection of two layered features, such as an original bedding and foliation, causes a lineation.

The classification of metamorphic rocks is based partly on composition but largely on structures. The following are the major types of metamorphic rocks:

SLATE. Slate is a metamorphic rock characterized by such excellent foliation that it tends to split along foliation planes. Slates are so fine grained that individual minerals can rarely be distinguished, and the separation of different types of minerals into individual bands is not present.

SCHIST. Schist is a well-foliated rock in which the mineral grains are considerably coarser than in a slate. The foliation planes, in consequence of the coarse grain size, are not flat enough for splitting to occur along them. In a schist the individual light and dark minerals are not separated into bands.

GNEISS. Gneiss is a foliated rock characterized by the segregation of light and dark minerals into parallel bands. The foliation is generally less planar and less perfect than in schists, and the typical gneiss generally contains a higher percentage of feldspar than most schists.

The terms "schist" and "gneiss" are used regardless of mineralogical composition. If greater precision of classification is required, an adjective may be put before the rock name to specify the major mineral present.

Some metamorphic rocks are formed under conditions in which directed stress is absent. Such rocks generally do not show foliation or lineation, and the general term which may be applied to them, regardless of composition, is *hornfels*.

We must mention the names of three metamorphic rocks which are classified on the basis of composition. The term *quartzite* refers to a rock which consists almost entirely of quartz. Such rocks obviously have been formed by the metamorphism of quartz sandstones (known as *orthoquartzite*), and some geologists, in order to specify a metamorphic rock, use the term *metaquartzite*. A *marble* is simply a limestone which has been metamorphosed. The process is one of increasing the grain size of the calcium carbonate and forming, thereby, a rock which is highly lustrous and in which individual calcite crystals are easily recognized. *Eclogites* are rocks which are rarely found and are mentioned here only because it is possible that large portions of the area underneath the continents consist of such material. Eclogites have the composition of basalt but consist almost entirely of two minerals: one is a red garnet; the other is a bright-green pyroxene. Eclogites have a higher density than any other silicate rock, and this high density, together with their extreme scarcity on the earth's surface, has led geologists to the conclusion that they may represent the product of metamorphism at exceptional depths. Naturally the greater the depth of formation of a rock, the less likely it is that the rock will later be exposed on the surface. It has been proposed that the Mohorovicic discontinuity, discussed in Chapter 3, may represent nothing more than a transition from basalt to eclogite, and this is one of many hypotheses about the earth that will be tested by the Mohole Project's drilling to the Mohorovicic discontinuity.

Origin of metamorphic rocks

The composition, texture, and structure of metamorphic rocks are affected by a number of factors. One of the primary factors is, of course, the composition of the parent or original material before metamorphism. Thus a limestone cannot be converted into a quartzite, and a quartzite cannot be converted into an eclogite. Rocks of identical chemical composition, however, may be quite different after metamorphism depending upon the conditions of the metamorphic process itself. Metamorphic temperatures range over several hundreds of degrees, pressures range over several thousands of atmospheres, and directed stress may or may not be present. A fourth factor which may have considerable effect on the nature of the minerals formed is the presence or absence of large amounts of water vapor in pores between the minerals during metamorphism. This vapor, being highly mobile, may be present during metamorphism and then lost subsequently, possibly upon exposure of the rock to the earth's surface.

Most geologists feel that the major factor affecting the composition and mineralogy of a metamorphic rock is temperature. As a sediment such as shale is exposed to gradually increasing temperature, a whole series of reactions takes place. Clay minerals tend to form such minerals as muscovite and biotite, and upon increasing temperature the muscovite and biotite may react further with other materials to yield minerals such as feldspars, garnet, and perhaps amphibole or pyroxene. Rocks of similar chemical composition but different mineralogy are said to be metamorphosed to a different degree or to have a different *metamorphic rank*.

Another effect of the increase of temperature is the formation of larger mineral grains. In a fine-grained rock the surface area of all of the minerals together is larger than in a coarse-grained rock. This high surface area causes fine-grained rocks to be chemically less stable than coarser-grained equivalents. As a result, there is a tendency during metamorphism, or other geologic processes such as diagenesis, for the size of minerals to increase by a process of dissolving the fine-grained minerals and growing the coarser ones. In metamorphic reactions the sizes of minerals may also be controlled in part by the direction of major stress. Thus, sheet-like micas which are oriented perpendicular to the major directional stress may grow preferentially to micas which are oriented at some other angle to the stress. High pressures, whether directional or uniform, promote the formation of denser minerals for reasons analogous to the chemical law of mass action. Most common metamorphic minerals, however, show sufficiently small differences in density for pressure to be probably a less important controlling factor than temperature in determining the mineralogy of the metamorphic rock.

The effect of water vapor pressure on metamorphic reactions can be understood quite simply, if we consider a reaction such as the destruction of muscovite and formation of orthoclase upon increase of temperature.

$$\underbrace{KAl_2(AlSi_3)O_{10}(OH)_2}_{muscovite} \rightleftharpoons H_2O + \underbrace{KAlSi_3O_8}_{orthoclase} + \underbrace{Al_2O_3}_{reacts\ with\ other\ minerals}$$

The reaction obviously involves dehydration, and equally obviously a high water vapor pressure would tend to prevent such a reaction and would increase the stability of the hydrated muscovite. The effect of the water pressure in the above reaction is to stabilize the low-temperature mineral and prevent reaction from occurring. At first glance this may seem contradictory to the tendency of water or other fluid phases to facilitate reactions by providing a medium in which the reaction can occur. There is no discrepancy in the two facts, however. Fluid phases such as water do promote the establishment of chemical equilibrium, a fact which can easily be demonstrated in the laboratory (for example, a wet nail rusts faster than a dry one). The water simply speeds up the reaction in such cases but does not affect the final result (for example, both wet and dry nails turn to rust, but at different rates). Where water takes part in the reaction, however, as in the case of the dehydration of muscovite, then the pressure of water has an effect on the final product, i.e., on the equilibrium state.

Perhaps the major topic of discussion among metamorphic geologists today concerns the importance of variations in water vapor pressure. The discussion hinges largely upon the question of whether or not water pressure varies independently of temperature or whether it is largely controlled by temperature. If variations in water-vapor pressure are dependent largely upon temperature, and if total pressure is a minor factor in controlling the nature of mineralogical assemblages, then the metamorphic process can be explained in terms of only one major physical-chemical variable, namely temperature. It would then be possible to determine the variation in temperature throughout a metamorphic region from a simple study of the mineralogy of the metamorphic rocks formed, and rocks which showed greater degrees of metamorphism would be equated with higher-temperature metamorphic conditions. If, however, the vapor pressure of water is independent of temperature, then the mineralogy of a metamorphic rock would have to be explained in terms of at least two different variables, and a simple plot of temperature variations would be difficult if not impossible to construct. The argument is based largely on the details of metamorphic mineralogy, which we cannot discuss in an introductory course, but it shows no evidence of being settled readily.

The typical metamorphic sequence starts with an ordinary sediment and finishes with a rock of vastly different mineralogy, density, and texture. The first changes which affect a sediment after deposition are diagenetic processes, and these are not ordinarily considered a part of metamorphism. It is difficult, however, to draw an exact line between changes occurring on the sea floor, which we would call diagenesis, and changes caused by some elevation of temperature and pressure upon deeper burial, which we would call metamorphism. With increase in temperature and pressure, the ordinary shaly sediment is converted first into a slate, further into a schist, and finally into a gneiss. Clay minerals are destroyed at quite low temperatures in the sequence, certainly before the rock has become a well-foliated slate, and gradually the hydrated minerals are broken down in favor of anhydrous quartz, feldspars, and perhaps pyroxene and garnet. The segregation of minerals to form alternating bands of quartz and feldspar and of amphibole, mica, and pyroxene is a process which marks the transition from schist to gneiss; the segregation is apparently caused by increase in temperature for much the same reasons as grains tend to grow larger as the temperature increases. Depending upon composition of the source rocks, quartzite and marble may form and be interbedded with the other types of metamorphic rocks.

Let us, for example, assume that in some metamorphic area we find a trend from slates on the east to gneisses and other more highly metamorphosed rocks on the west; we would then say that metamorphic rank has increased from east to west. As indicated above, many geologists would correlate this increase in rank with an increase in temperature, though other factors may complicate the decision. The metamorphic process we have just described has led to the development of a series of foliated rocks in which the foliation surfaces are generally considered to be perpendicular to the major compressional stress. Metamorphism under these conditions is ordinarily termed *regional,* for such sequences of metamorphic rock are developed over very wide areas, in many cases measured in terms of thousands of square miles.

Another type of metamorphism has already been referred to briefly in Chapter 6 and may be called *contact metamorphism.* This represents a series of changes which take place in wall rocks surrounding intrusions. Where a magma is injected into much colder wall rocks, the rocks tend to change mineralogically in adjustment to the higher temperatures and develop a suite of minerals rather similar in most aspects to those developed during regional metamorphism. The major difference between contact and regionally metamorphosed rocks is the virtual absence of foliation or other directional features in contact rocks. The absence of directional features implies an absence of major directional stress, and at first sight, the absence of such stress seems to contradict the concept of a melt being thrust into a sequence of preexisting rocks. Apparently, however, most intrusions are formed in areas where the wall rocks may be shoved aside by the intruding rock with sufficient ease so that directional stresses are soon lost, and the metamorphism attendant upon increased temperature in the slowly heated wall rock takes place in a situation of almost uniform pressure.

The discussion of metamorphism thus far has assumed that rocks have been changed into new suites of minerals without significant change in bulk composition. (The loss of water upon higher temperature metamorphism is not considered to be a significant change.) In some areas, however, there is a rather clear relationship between the concentration of certain elements and the metamorphic rank. In such regions the common conclusion is that the elements whose abundances vary in this manner have been redistributed, or perhaps either introduced or removed, during the metamorphic process. This introduction and removal of chemical material is termed *metasomatism*. Of the various major rock-forming elements, only potassium and sodium seem to be commonly involved in metasomatic reactions. These two alkali elements are apparently rather readily dissolved in fluid (water) phases in the pores of metamorphic rocks, and alkali metasomatism is a common feature of a large number of metamorphic terrains.

Earlier in this chapter, we discussed the concept of granitization and defined it as the conversion of preexisting rock into a rock similar to a granite. Obviously, if the conversion takes place without chemical change, the preexisting rock must also have had the composition of a granite. Many geologists, however, conclude that rocks of virtually any composition can be transformed by the simple expedient of metasomatizing them with fluids containing the necessary chemical components. The most common reactions seem to be an addition of potassium and sodium, which correlates well with the mobility of these elements during metasomatic metamorphism, and possibly removal of basic material such as calcium and magnesium. Though metasomatism may affect rocks of any metamorphic rank, reactions leading to the production of granite appear to be associated with the highest possible degrees of metamorphism. This conclusion is, in part, related to the fact that granite generally is intermingled with high-rank metamorphic rocks and not with rocks which have been formed at lower temperatures.

Extreme metamorphism of a normal silicate rock may have several effects. One is the loss of directed stress, owing to a softening of the rock. (A liquid, for example, cannot maintain stress differences, as you may demonstrate by the fact that you cannot push a glass of water across a table by pushing against the top of the water surface. It is necessary to push against the glass.) This softening may, or may not, be a true melting with the formation of a liquid; if melting does occur, presumably the liquid formed will be granitic material (which melts at the lowest temperature), and thus it may be possible to produce a true granite magma. Whether the granites that are intermingled with metamorphic rocks have formed by partial melting and later crystallization or by simple metasomatism at the high temperatures of extreme metamorphism is uncertain.

Regardless of the detailed mode of formation of granite, there is an undoubted relationship between granite, metamorphic rocks, and the mountain-building process known as orogeny. A number of intricate, and probably erroneous, cause-and-effect sequences can be constructed to explain this relationship. It is possible, for example, that both metamorphism and mountain-building are caused by the intrusion of a granite magma derived from somewhere else, presumably at greater depths. The intrusion would cause a heating of the area to develop metamorphic sequences grading to lower-temperature rocks away from the center of granitic injection, and the intrusion might also cause a squeezing of the rocks laterally and vertically to produce the features we shall describe in Chapter 10 as characteristic of mountains. An alternative explanation is that mountain-building starts when originally cooled sediments are plunged to great depths in the earth by some mechanism of down-folding, and the resultant exposure to high temperatures causes expansion, partial melting, metamorphism, and decrease in density. The expansion and decrease in density would then cause an upward mountain-building, and the resultant granitic liquid would form complex inter-mingled structures with the remnant metamorphic rock. From the point of view of the petrologist, the problem is whether metamorphism causes the development of granite or vice versa. From the point of view of the structural geologist, the problem is whether mountain-building causes the development of igneous and metamorphic rocks or vice versa.

CHAPTER 9

PROCESSES AT
THE EARTH'S SURFACE

◄ Landsliding. (Photo by G. McClellan, Baylor Univ.)

In the past three chapters we have discussed the origin of various types of rocks. The discussion thus far has been partly abstract. A problem in presenting this material has arisen from the difficulty of finding some place to start describing the approximately cyclical nature of most geological processes. Thus, sediments are formed ultimately by material produced by the weathering of igneous rocks, and in consequence it is necessary to know something about igneous rocks before discussing sediments. Conversely, igneous rocks are related in their origin to the development of metamorphic rocks, and it is, of course, impossible to discuss metamorphism without knowing something about sedimentary rocks. Furthermore, all of these processes of the development of different types of rocks are related to other processes going on both on and within the earth. We have entered this cycle by discussing the origin of various types of rocks. Now we have arrived at the point where it is possible to discuss various processes on and near the earth's surface in regard to the rocks which they affect.

A SUMMARY OF PROCESSES

A rock at or near the earth's surface is in a complex chemical and physical environment. If the rock were an igneous or metamorphic rock which had formed originally under higher temperatures and pressures than those of the surface, it is exposed, perhaps for the first time, to the effect of low temperature, to the effect of liquid water, to the effect of low pressure, and perhaps to the effect of oxygen and organic activity. There is a tendency, therefore, for rocks to undergo chemical changes. These chemical changes form a part of the broad set of reactions known as *weathering*. One result of the weathering process is the development of soils, and a portion of this chapter will consider the types of soils formed in a wide variety of environments.

From a physical point of view, a rock at or near the earth's surface is in a dynamically unstable position. Whereas rocks which are deeply buried cannot be moved around easily without also moving out of the way a large mass of adjacent material, rocks at the surface can be pushed up or moved sideways without encountering any notable resistance. This instability of the earth's surface can be viewed in terms of changes of elevation or of lateral position. By warping (*folding*) or fracturing (*faulting*), a part of the earth's surface may be moved either upward, downward, or laterally in comparison with adjacent areas. The mechanics of such faulting and folding and the geologic results of it will be discussed in more detail in Chapter 10. In addition to simple movement, the elevation of some of the earth's surface can be decreased by erosion or increased by deposition.

In summary, we can consider that some hypothetical point on the earth's surface: (1) can be affected by chemical and physical breakdown processes; (2) can be moved upward, downward, or laterally; and (3) can undergo erosion or may be covered by deposition of sediment or volcanic rocks. This chapter and the three following chapters are devoted to a consideration of the geologic processes which bring about these various changes.

WEATHERING AND SOILS

As we mentioned in the first paragraph of this chapter, the chemical environment of the earth's surface is characterized by low temperature, low pressure, the presence of oxygen and liquid water, and the activity of plants and animals. In addition, there are fluctuations in temperature that may have a pronounced effect on both physical and chemical processes, and in some climatic zones there is the possibility of the alternate freezing and thawing of water and ice. An igneous or metamorphic rock placed in this environment is chemically unstable, though its various minerals differ in their reactions.

A simple way in which to study these reactions is to find an outcrop of igneous rock recently exposed on the earth's surface by erosion and to study, by means of drill cores or other suitable mechanisms, the variations in mineral and chemical composition of the rock from the surface down to what appears to be relatively unaltered original rock. Several studies of this type have been made, and the results of one of them are shown diagrammatically in Fig. 9-1. As shown there, materials such as aluminum and silicon are comparatively inert to removal during surficial weathering, whereas such elements as sodium and potassium are leached rather easily. Incidentally, this mobility of sodium and potassium correlates rather well with the fact that these two elements are the principal ones involved in metasomatism. Water, of course, is added to the rocks

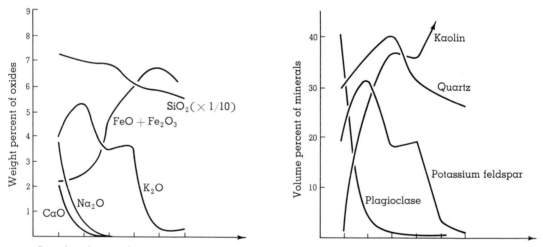

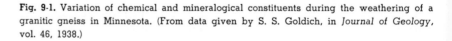

Fig. 9-1. Variation of chemical and mineralogical constituents during the weathering of a granitic gneiss in Minnesota. (From data given by S. S. Goldich, in *Journal of Geology,* vol. 46, 1938.)

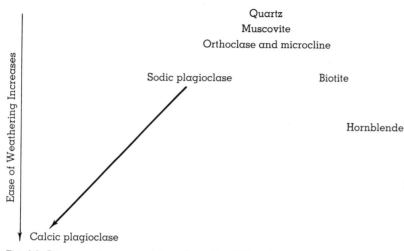

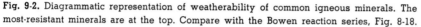

Quartz
Muscovite
Orthoclase and microcline

Sodic plagioclase   Biotite

Ease of Weathering Increases

                                     Hornblende

                                     Pyroxene

Calcic plagioclase   Olivine

Fig. 9-2. Diagrammatic representation of weatherability of common igneous minerals. The most-resistant minerals are at the top. Compare with the Bowen reaction series, Fig. 8-18.

during weathering, and the presence of oxygen in the earth's atmosphere causes a conversion of ferrous ion to ferric ion in these surficially exposed rocks. Although Fig. 9-1 refers to a study of only one locality, it has been the general observation that the ratio of ferric to ferrous ion is higher in sediments than it is in igneous and metamorphic rocks, presumably because of the effect of oxygen in the earth's atmosphere.

Not only do the chemical components of igneous rocks differ in their reaction to weathering processes, but also the individual minerals show markedly different resistance. Quartz, for example, is exceptionally stable, and this high stability undoubtedly accounts for the fact that quartz is the dominant mineral in sands. Conversely, minerals containing iron and magnesium are destroyed rather easily, and as we have already seen, such minerals are comparatively rare in sedimentary rocks. It is, in fact, possible to construct a sequence showing the relative stability relationships of the various normal igneous rock minerals in a weathering environment, and this relationship is shown in Fig. 9-2. We can compare Fig. 9-2 with the Bowen reaction series shown in Fig. 8-18 of Chapter 8, and the two sequences are obviously the exact reverse of each other. The reason for such a relationship is not hard to find. Minerals at the top of the Bowen reaction series are ones which have formed at the highest temperatures and pressures and, presumably, in the environments of the least water content. Thus, these minerals which contain ferrous ion, magnesium, and calcium are the ones which are most out of equilibrium with the environment of the earth's surface. Minerals at the base of the Bowen reaction series, such as quartz and muscovite, are almost completely stable at the earth's surface, and potassium feldspar is weathered only with considerable difficulty.

The chemical changes discussed thus far for rocks exposed at the earth's surface are not equivalent to the development of soils. Soil formation is a far more extreme chemical process and usually takes as its starting or *parent material* the type of weathered igneous rocks which might be found at the most weathered end of the series shown in Fig. 9-1. The type of soil formed in any area is controlled by a large number of factors. Different parent rocks, for example, yield slightly different types of soil. Furthermore, a good soil does not form instantly, a fact which conservationists have emphasized. Precise estimates of the time necessary for the formation of a good soil capable, for example, of growing a plant are difficult to make. Estimates are generally in the range of a few thousand years. It is obviously necessary, therefore, that soil be considered one of our most precious and irreplaceable resources.

We have mentioned parent rock and time as factors affecting the type of soil which is formed. Of far greater importance, however, is the factor of climate. From parent rocks of rather broad differences in composition, similar soils can be formed providing that the climate in which the different rocks are situated is identical. The term "climate," of course, includes such factors as the mean annual temperature, normal temperature fluctuations, and rainfall; also, since these factors may largely control the plant and animal life, the word "climate" implies a certain type of vegetation. We shall discuss the types of soils formed under four different climatic conditions. These conditions are: (1) forested areas in a temperate zone; (2) grasslands in a temperate zone; (3) deserts; and (4) tropical regions. Obviously, such a classification does not exhaust all of the various environments on the earth's surface, but it does provide us with a means of discussing the most important soils which are formed over the bulk of the earth's land area.

One of the most extensive types of soil in the world is the *podsol* formed in humid, temperate regions, generally with extensive forest cover and considerable rainfall. The soil thus formed shows a distinct *profile* or change in character with depth below the surface. Most soils can be characterized as consisting of three principal layers. The uppermost, or *A* horizon, is a zone in which acids released by the decay of dead plants tend to dissolve aluminum, iron, calcium, and other materials and move them downward by slow percolation through the soil. As shown in Fig. 9-3, therefore, the *A* horizon in a typical podsol consists of organic material intermingled with siliceous matter left behind by the downward-percolating waters. Below the *A* horizon is the zone in which the materials of the rock ultimately neutralize the organic acids filtering down from above. Thus, in this horizon the iron and aluminum which have been leached out of the *A* horizon are accumulated, and this zone of accumulation is termed the *B* horizon. In profile, as shown in Fig. 9-4, the *A* horizon looks leached and light in color despite its content of decaying organic material, and the *B* horizon is dark as a result of the accumulation primarily of iron oxides and hydroxides. The *C* horizon is a zone of weathered to fresh parent rock and presumably represents the material before major soil formation processes began.

The formation of such a soil profile obviously implies the ability of waters to percolate downward through the material and, hence, implies a certain permeability. Furthermore, it is necessary that waters which

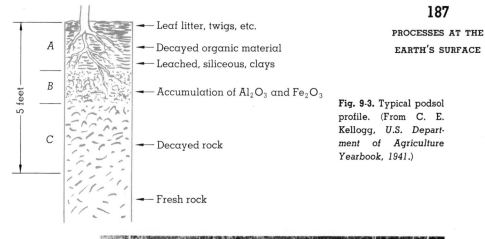

— Leaf litter, twigs, etc.

— Decayed organic material

— Leached, siliceous, clays

— Accumulation of Al_2O_3 and Fe_2O_3

— Decayed rock

— Fresh rock

A

B

C

5 feet

Fig. 9-3. Typical podsol profile. (From C. E. Kellogg, *U.S. Department of Agriculture Yearbook, 1941.*)

Fig. 9-4. Red-yellow podsolic soil formed from marine sediments in Louisiana. (Photo by R. W. Simonson, U.S. Dept. of Agriculture, Soil Conservation Service.)

have filtered downward and been neutralized in the *B* horizon have a place to which they can escape; otherwise, there is simply the formation of a layer of water which resists downward percolation from other rain waters, and the process of soil formation virtually comes to an end. The necessary drainage is best developed in areas of moderate relief, and excessively flat land may not show a very good development of soil. Podsols formed in this fashion are so widely developed in temperate forests that they have become known as "forest soils," though it is possible for them to develop in areas characterized by other types of vegetation. In the United States, podsols are characteristic of the heavily forested areas of the northeast and northern central portions of the country but are also found farther south.

A second type of soil is commonly found in plains areas, where the vegetation is largely grasses and the rainfall is commonly less than in areas in which podsols are developed. This second type of soil carries the name *chernozem* (Fig. 9-5), a Russian word applied to the black earth so characteristic of many of the steppe areas of Russia. Many of the processes characteristic of the formation of podsols are also found in the development of chernozems. The chernozem is characterized by an upper layer of dark, organic-rich, siliceous and aluminous material. The black color is caused by partially decayed plant material, and the leaching from the *A* horizon is not as extensive in chernozems as it is in podsols, because of the lower rainfall in chernozem areas. The *B* horizon is one of accumulation, but the material accumulated here is generally calcium carbonate rather than aluminum or iron. The less abundant rainfall characteristic of chernozem areas rather than of podsol areas permits only the moderately soluble calcium to be dissolved in carbonate-bearing waters. This calcium percolates downward, if the soil is sufficiently permeable, into the *B* horizon, and there calcium carbonate is deposited. The *C* horizon again refers to fresh or weathered parent material (Fig. 9-6). In the United States, chernozems or similar soils are extensively developed throughout the Middle West, although in many portions of the area the ideal chernozem development gives way to a less well-developed form of soil profile. In deserts, and generally in environments more arid than those of the Middle West, the calcium carbonate accumulation takes the form of small rounded structures called *nodules* or may occur as white powdery encrustations on the various soil grains. In some places the calcium carbonate permeates a rather thick layer and forms a hard, coherent mass which is quite resistant to agriculture. Calcium carbonate extensively developed in this fashion is designated *caliche*.

Fig. 9-5. Chernozem in northeast Texas. The black upper zone forms the black earth prairies of this area. (Photo by H. B. Stenzel.)

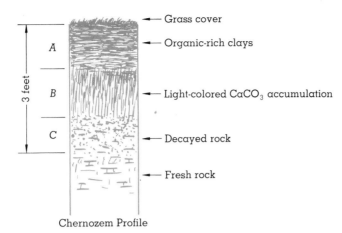

← Grass cover

A

← Organic-rich clays

3 feet

B

← Light-colored CaCO₃ accumulation

C

← Decayed rock

← Fresh rock

Chernozem Profile

Fig. 9-6. Typical cherno-zem profile. (From C. E. Kellogg, *U.S. Dept. of Agriculture Yearbook, 1941.*)

For obvious reasons, desert soils are either poorly developed or, in some areas, may be completely absent. The absence of rainfall and the concurrent absence of organic material reduces the chemical decay of the rock and prevents redistribution of materials which might be involved in chemical weathering processes. A slight downward movement of calcium may be expected in some areas, and some of the soils contain a small amount of organic matter in the upper layers. The dominant weathering process in the desert, however, is not a chemical decay but a mechanical breakdown of the rock (Fig. 9-7). We may, in fact, classify weathering into two processes: one is *decomposition*, which includes all those chemical reactions that convert minerals to other materials and cause movements of ions in solution from one part of the rock or soil to another part; the other type of weathering is *disintegration*, which implies merely a physical breaking apart of the various rock components. Whether disintegration can occur without some accompanying decom-

Fig. 9-7. Bouldery disintegration of granitic rocks in the southern California desert. (Photo by Mary Hill, California Division of Mines.)

position is a debatable point, but certainly in desert areas the dominant phenomenon is a mechanical breakdown. Chemical decay, of course, does produce incoherence of rocks and thus mechanical breakdown, but it may not be necessary for such purposes. One product of purely mechanical breakdown on steep slopes is a pile of angular blocks which accumulate in wedges at cliff bases. These piles are referred to as *talus* (Fig. 9-8).

Several methods have been proposed by which a rock may disintegrate without associated chemical decomposition. Only one need be mentioned here, and that is the effect of alternating high and low temperatures on a rock surface. In desert areas, temperature changes from day to night are quite extreme, particularly in contrast to the changes in more humid areas. In deserts an average daily temperature variation of 50° F. is quite normal. The alternate heating and cooling and consequent expansion and contraction of the rock surface presumably would contribute a certain amount of stress to borders between mineral grains and even within mineral grains. It is possible, therefore, that rocks break down under this alternation of temperatures. Alternate heating and cooling may be a satisfactory explanation for the disintegration of the outer layers of some rocks, but it is difficult to attribute extensive disintegration at depth to such a process. In a number of desert areas, however, granite and related rocks have been found so thoroughly broken up at depths of as much as several hundred feet that water wells can be profitably sunk into them. It is a common observation in deserts that coarse-

Fig. 9-8. Talus slopes in the San Juan Mountains, Colorado. (Photo by T. H. Foss.)

grained rocks, such as granites, disintegrate rather easily, whereas fine-grained rocks appear to withstand disintegration indefinitely. In view of the fact that rock at a depth of even one foot is certainly not affected by temperature variations, and at depths of several hundred feet temperature must be virtually constant, the disintegration process has not been satisfactorily explained.

Two extremely important types of soils are formed in tropical or subtropical areas and may be grouped under the general term *laterite*. In tropical regions, where temperatures are high and uniform and rainfall is intense, plants do not decay to the same organic products that they form in temperate areas. In tropical regions, the surface waters which cause leaching are, therefore, generally basic (pH of approximately 9). Basic solutions tend to dissolve silica but leave iron and aluminum oxides and hydroxides virtually untouched. If the soil is developed in an area where drainage is adequate, the silica-bearing, basic solutions migrate downward and are ultimately swept clear out of the soil profile. A small *B* horizon of minor accumulation is sometimes found in the form of clay minerals below the leached zone, but in many soils this zone is absent. The resultant product of the laterization process is, therefore, a poorly zoned accumulation of iron and aluminum oxides and hydroxides. The intensity of this laterization process ranges from slight to moderate in the southeastern part of the United States, and it is intense in certain areas of South America, Africa, and other truly tropical regions. Laterites and sub-laterites are easily recognized by their dark reddish color. The red color is not an infallible index to laterites, however, as shown by the fact that certain reddish soils in western Oklahoma and neighboring areas simply owe their color to the fact that they are developed on red sandstones as parent rocks, and the soil-forming process has not developed sufficiently to leach the red color from the upper layers.

The laterization process is obviously most extreme where it is developed on iron-rich parent rocks such as basalt. In fact, in some tropical areas, a poor grade of iron ore may be developed in this process. These are the true laterites, and most laterites occurring on other types of parent rocks should probably best be referred to as sublaterites. A similar process to that of laterization may occur on parent rocks which are relatively rich in aluminum minerals. One such rock is a type of igneous rock known as syenite, which is comparatively rich in feldspar and contains little or no quartz. Where laterization occurs on such rocks, the iron content is sufficiently low so that iron is not a major component of the resulting soil. The soil, therefore, consists primarily of aluminum oxides and hydroxides and is termed a *bauxite*. Bauxites are currently the major source of aluminum metal. The only large occurrence of bauxite in the United States is in Arkansas (Fig. 9-9), and most bauxites are distributed around tropical regions such as the eastern coast of South America and the western bulge of Africa.

The process of soil formation is, of course, not restricted to the present time. Ancient soils, however, are generally not preserved in the geologic record, because they are formed on land and consist of loose materials; therefore, they are removed very easily by erosional processes. Fossil soil profiles, commonly with characteristics similar to those of modern soils, have been found in a number of places in the geologic record. Such profiles have immense geologic value. If, for example, a soil profile can be recognized in rocks extending over a broad area and can be demonstrated to represent the same period of soil formation in all of these areas, then obviously the soil can be used to mark points in the geologic record which were at the earth's surface at exactly the same time. Such a recognition permits not only the reconstruction of the topography of that particular time but also allows a relative age relationship to be established for the rocks in the neighborhood of the soil profile. The establishment of such time-reference points is one of the most difficult but most important tasks of sedimentary petrologists and stratigraphers. This is a subject which is normally discussed in some detail in courses in historical geology.

MECHANICAL DEFORMATION

Let us turn now from the chemical processes which affect rocks at the earth's surface to the purely mechanical processes involving displacement, erosion, and deposition. The fact that large bodies of rock have been moved both vertically and laterally is undeniable. The few people who have stood on the top of Mt. Everest at a height of over 29,000 feet have stood upon typical marine sediments that were obviously formed below sea level, apparently about 400 million years ago. In the United States, marine sediments constitute a major part of the Rocky Mountains. Sediments of identical age to those of the Rocky Mountains, however, are buried at depths of many thousands of feet below sea level in some parts of the Middle West. The point is that different portions of the earth's crust move up and down both relative to each other and relative to sea level. This is not to say that the sea level itself remains constant. The amount of water in the ocean has undoubtedly changed, as will be discussed in more detail in Chapter 13, and the ice currently held above sea level in Arctic and Antarctic regions would, if melted, raise the level of the ocean by about 200 feet. The oceans, however, can hardly have lost 29,000 feet of depth since the time of formation of the rocks now forming the crest of Mount Everest, and the only possible conclusion is that blocks of land areas move vertically. In exactly analogous fashion

Fig. 9-9. Bauxite mine near Bauxite, Arkansas. (Photo by Phelps, Arkansas Publicity and Parks Commission.)

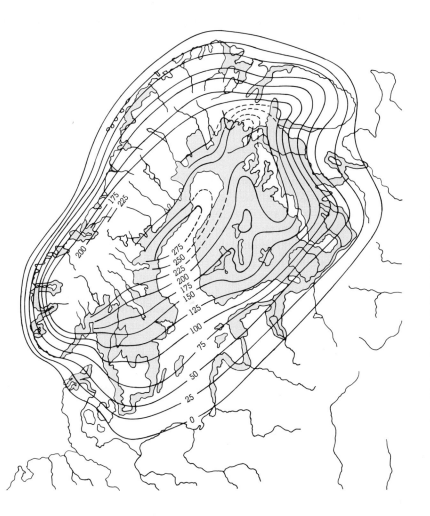

Fig. 9-10. Depression of Fennoscandia under the weight of the most recent ice cap. The contour lines indicate the amount of uplift after melting of the ice. The stippled area was covered by the sea after melting and before uplift was completed. (From W. B. Wright, *The Quaternary Ice Age*, Macmillan & Co. Ltd., London, 2nd ed., 1936, pp. 344–345; also from R. A. Daly, *The Changing World of the Ice Age*, Yale University Press, 1963.)

one may argue on the basis that rocks tens of millions of years old are now found at depths of ten to twenty or more thousand feet below sea level around the margins of the United States. One of the principal areas for accumulation of this sequence of sediments is around the coast of the Gulf of Mexico. Along this coastline, rocks apparently have been continually depressed for periods ranging over tens of millions of years, and we may, therefore, conclude that earth movement may be downward as well as upward.

Vertical movements have been observed within historical times. We shall discuss in Chapter 12 the fact that during the last million years the northern parts of Europe and North America have been repeatedly covered by extensive sheets of ice. These ice sheets, being heavy, tended to depress isostatically the land areas that they were overriding. After removal of the ice by melting, the land areas started to rise, and the rate at which this *rebounding* has occurred can be measured with a fair degree of accuracy. Some of the evidence for this post-glacial rebounding is shown in Fig. 9-10, which represents a study made in Scandinavia. The rate at which the land has been moving upward is more than one foot per century.

Land areas, however, move for reasons other than an isostatic compensation to unloading of ice. The fracture surfaces along which earthquake movements occur (i.e., faults) are zones of sudden movement (Fig. 9-11). One well-documented survey of a fault in central Nevada showed a total upward movement of one block relative to the other equal to 16 feet in one single earthquake pulse. The earthquake generated by this movement was, of course, enormous but by no means larger than others that have been observed.

The general instability around the Pacific Ocean, as shown by the intensity of earthquakes and the concentration of volcanic activity, has led to a number of accurate and continuing surveys, particularly in the United States. Land-level changes in portions of California have been extensively measured, and some areas seem to be rising or settling at rates of approximately one inch per year. Land may be caused to settle artificially in some areas by extensive underground mining or by excessive removal of water or petroleum. Subsidence of this type has occurred over an oil field near Long Beach, California, and movements here also are measured in terms of approximately one inch per year (Fig. 9-12).

In measurements made at the present time it is, of course, easy to determine which block of land is going upward with respect to sea level and which, if any, is going downward. Thus it is possible to determine absolute movements. In records of former movements, however, such as relative displacements of ancient rocks, it is rarely, if ever, possible to determine whether the block which is relatively up has indeed moved upward or whether, conversely, the block which is relatively down has moved downward. Movements that did not occur in recorded history are almost always referred to in terms of relative movement to some stated reference point.

Lateral displacements are generally not as dramatic and, therefore, not as easily recognized as the vertical displacements. Some lateral movement, however, has been verified by direct observation. For example, the

Fig. 9-11. Fault scarp developed during 1954 earthquake near Fairview Peak, Nevada. (Photo by H. Benioff.)

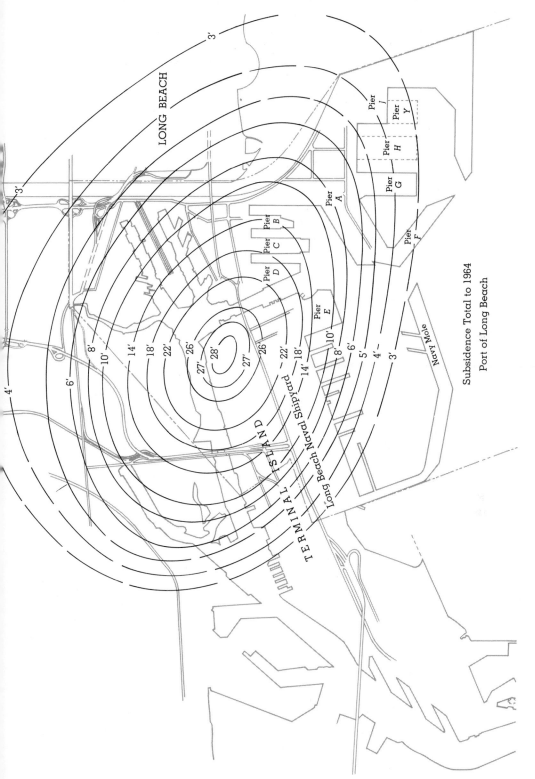

Fig. 9-12. Subsidence at Long Beach, California. Contours show total subsidence in feet during the period 1940–1964. Cause of subsidence is not completely known, but may be related to oil or water removal. (From Civil Engineering Division, The Port of Long Beach.)

San Francisco earthquake of 1906 was caused by sudden sharp displacement along the San Andreas fault. As discussed in Chapter 4, the San Andreas is a major fault which can be traced throughout most of California from the San Francisco area southward; it extends through northern Mexico into the Gulf of Baja California and northward from San Francisco out into the Pacific Ocean. Apparently, portions of this fault move at different times, and a whole series of earthquakes has been traced throughout southern California and attributed to movement on this particular fault. Movement that is noticed is almost invariably of a lateral nature.

A fault of this size, as we shall discuss in the next chapter, is not one simple plane but rather a broad zone, and hence any one displacement is not necessarily characteristic of the entire fault but may merely represent movement along one small portion of the zone. Maximum displacements of this type for the San Francisco earthquake are of the order of 20 to 25 feet, though in many places the displacement is considerably less. The time of movement of a fault in an earthquake is extremely short and, for practical purposes, may be considered instantaneous. Since the San Francisco earthquake, a number of very precise surveys have been continually in operation across the San Andreas fault zone. Movements are still continuing along this zone, and the rate of displacement, though variable from place to place, is generally measured in terms of a fraction of an inch per year.

A number of geologic questions have arisen as to the total amount of lateral movement (i.e., the sum of the individual earthquake movements) on the San Andreas fault during its entire period of existence. The evidence is far too detailed to be considered here, and much of it is disputed hotly. The minimum estimates for the total displacement are on the order of several tens of miles, and some estimates are as high as 350 to 400 miles.

In summary, portions of the earth's crust move up, down, and sideways at rates which vary from several feet in a fraction of a second to the more normal, much slower pace. Where active movement is taking place so that it may be detected at the present time, the rates in general are measured in terms of inches or fractions of inches per year. Many areas, however, exhibit no detectable movement at all, and thus the average rate at which points on the earth's surface are moved around must be much, much smaller than one inch per year. Though the rates of movement are small, the accumulated displacements through geologic time may be measured in terms of many miles. The rate of uplift averaged over geologic time must be essentially equal to the average rates of erosion and deposition, else the mountains would have been leveled long ago.

RATES OF EROSION AND DEPOSITION

As discussed in the introduction to this chapter, a point on the earth's surface may be mechanically unstable not only to the extent of being moved but also to the extent of undergoing erosion or being subjected to covering by other deposited materials. Throughout geologic time, deposition of sedimentary rocks has taken place primarily in the oceans. The same situation holds true today, and most of the land area of the earth is subjected to erosion, which takes place by a variety of processes we shall discuss in Chapters 11 and 12. The dominant method of taking up and removing material is by running water, and as we noted in Chapter 7, the Mississippi River alone delivers 500 million tons of sediment into the Gulf of Mexico each year. A rough estimate has been made of the total amount of sediment which is delivered by all rivers to the oceans around all continents during a year, and the figure is on the order of 10^{10} tons.

Erosion is particularly intense in mountainous regions where steep slopes offer ready access to running water or other erosional agents. The total rate at which any one particular area is being lowered is hard to calculate, but we can estimate a rough figure for the average yearly decrease in elevation of the land areas of the earth by taking the estimate of the total number of tons of sediments delivered to the ocean each year, dividing this by the total land surface, and calculating the thickness of sediment which this represents. This simple calculation yields approximately 1 foot per 10^4 years as an average rate of denudation.

In certain areas erosion is extremely rapid and violent. River banks cave in during floods, mountain sides collapse, vast land slides or rock falls occur, and wind storms may hollow out relatively deep holes in sandy deserts. The 1961 hurricane "Carla" which swept over the Texas Gulf Coast caused enormous changes in beach areas in a few hours; some of the damage is shown in Figs. 9-13 and 9-14.

It was once thought possible that the age of the earth could be determined by finding the number of years which would be necessary to bring the ocean water to its present sodium content. The theory was that if it were possible to determine the total amount of sodium added to the oceans by rivers each year, and then divide this number into the total amount of sodium in the oceans, the resulting number of years would equal the age of the earth (at least in terms of the period in which erosion had been taking place). The sodium chloride content of ocean water is reasonably constant at approximately 35 parts per thousand, and the amount of sodium delivered by all rivers in the world to the ocean can be tabulated to a fair degree of accuracy as approximately $1.58 \cdot 10^8$ tons per year. The resulting calculation is easily made and yields an estimate of $100 \cdot 10^6$ years for the age of the earth.

The more accurate dating by radioactive methods as described in Chapter 1 has yielded more precise ages of the earth on the order of 4 billion years. We may then ask ourselves the question of what is wrong with the calculation of age by determination of the sodium content of the sea. The answer to this question is based on two facts. First, sodium does not simply accumulate in the sea without ever being extracted from it. We have already noted the fact that halite forms beds in connection with deposits of other evaporite minerals, and thus we must conclude that there have been periods in which sodium chloride is removed from the sea. This fact alone would increase the age of the earth, but perhaps

Fig. 9-13. Section of Texas coast photographed before hurricane "Carla," 1961. (Photo by D. E. Feray.)

Fig. 9-14. Same portion of Texas coast shown in Fig. 9-13 photographed shortly after hurricane "Carla." Note destruction of buildings and erosion of coastline. (Photo by D. E. Feray.)

not appreciably in view of the fact that halite is a comparatively minor constituent of the sedimentary record. Much sodium is also recycled by spray-drying of sea water as the wind blows the tops off waves, evaporates the water, and blows the resultant particle of salt far inland where it can nucleate rain drops and return in streams to the sea.

The more important defect in the age calculation is the fact that erosion at the present time is undoubtedly more intense than it has been throughout most of geologic time. We have already noted in Chapter 7 that the normal condition of the earth's surface appears to be one in which the continents are flooded by at least some shallow oceanic waters which deposit the extensive marine sediments which cover most of the land areas of the earth. At the present time, however, these land areas are all exposed, and former marine sediments are well above sea level. In consequence of this comparatively high elevation of the land, the amount of erosion taking place now must be considerably larger than the amount that normally occurs. Precisely how exaggerated the present erosional rate is would be very difficult to say, but certainly it is sufficiently abnormal to discourage making age calculations based on data from the present day.

Figures for the rate of deposition of material are fairly easily obtained but are highly variable. For example, a rock fall which rapidly erodes the top of a mountain may deposit several hundred feet of rubble at the base in a minute or so. A site may be covered by several tens of feet of lava or volcanic ash in a period of a few hours or a few days. The volcano of Parícutin, in Mexico, which sprang virtually unannounced out of a corn field in an area south of Mexico City in 1943, built a cone 1400 feet high in the course of the first year of eruption (Figs. 9-15 and 9-16). The surrounding areas were covered by debris many feet thick in this same period of time. Residential areas around Los Angeles have occasionally been in the path of large bodies of mud-like water or water-like mud which have swept down out of the surrounding hills during the periods of infrequent rain fall. In some places these "mud flows" have deposited several feet of muddy sediment in a few hours. This phenomenon is rather common in arid areas throughout the western United States, but naturally it is not noticed as much in an ordinary desert canyon as it is in the living room of someone's house. Flood waters overtopping the banks of rivers in the Middle West have distributed clays and silts throughout broad regions and have, on occasion, deposited several inches of material in a period of a few days. Wind-blown sand in desert areas migrates rapidly, and it is not at all uncommon for several feet or perhaps tens of feet of sand to accumulate in a dune in a matter of a few hours or days during a major wind storm.

All of the numbers just given refer to deposition on the land. For general geologic purposes it is more interesting to determine the average rates of deposition in water, and particularly in the ocean. One well-studied example of deposition in bodies of water is in Lake Mead after the construction of Hoover Dam. Sediment that was being carried down the Colorado River was entrapped by the dam and began to settle in the lake. The rate of settling was, of course, a matter of major concern to the water-control engineers owing to the fact that if Lake Mead were to fill with sediment it would be a relatively unusable source of water power. Rates of accumulation vary somewhat from one part of the lake to another but are generally on the order of several inches per year. Similar accumulation of silt and fine sand is characteristic of harbor areas in many parts of the world. In fact, the operation of a major port generally involves the continual maintenance of dredges which clear out accumulating sediment and leave free passage-way for ships.

The rate of outbuilding of coastlines in areas of active deposition is

Fig. 9-15. Parícutin volcano, Mexico. (Photo courtesy of Mexican Government Tourism Department.)

determinable from sequences of maps made over a period of many years (e.g., Fig. 9-17, *A–C*). In the area of the coast of the Gulf of Mexico, maps can be obtained not only from surveys made by the United States but also from surveys made during periods of Spanish or French occupation. The rates of outbuilding in some coastal areas of particularly active sedimentation, such as deltas, are on the order of one foot per year. This obviously does not represent an accumulation of a one-foot thickness of sediment in the year. It may more normally be equivalent to the accumulation of some fraction of an inch. Furthermore, the outbuilding of a coast does not give precise data solely on the accumulation of sediment because the relative shoreline movement is controlled not only by fluctuations in sea level but also by local elevation or depression of the coastline and the land area behind it.

Some figures have been obtained for the rate of deposition of fine-grained sediments in the deep ocean. These figures must be calculated by obtaining dates on the sediment at various depths in borings made in the open ocean. The correlation of radiometric ages with depths indicates that the accumulation in these areas is, as expected, extremely slight. An average figure for this rate of accumulation would be several millimeters in 1000 years. Unfortunately, figures for accumulation of sediments in shallow water are quite variable and are not as easily obtained as in either land or open-ocean areas.

Now that we have broadly discussed the types of processes which may affect rocks at or near the earth's surface, we are in a position to investigate some of these processes in more detail. Chapter 10 considers the displacement of rocks, the conditions which control the fracturing or folding of rocks, and the general field of structural geology. Chapters 11

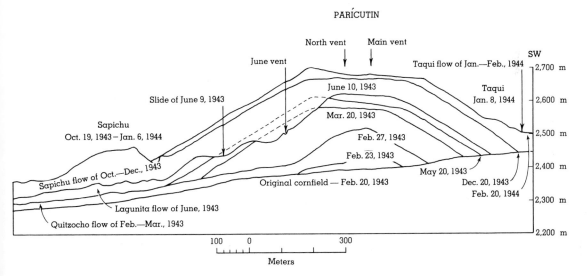

Fig. 9-16. Diagrammatic representation of growth of Parícutin volcano during one year. Original level was a farmer's cornfield. The main vent is Parícutin, with Sapichu and Taqui being subsidiary vents. (From W. F. Foshag and J. Gonzales, *U.S. Geological Survey Bulletin 965D*, 1956.)

A

B

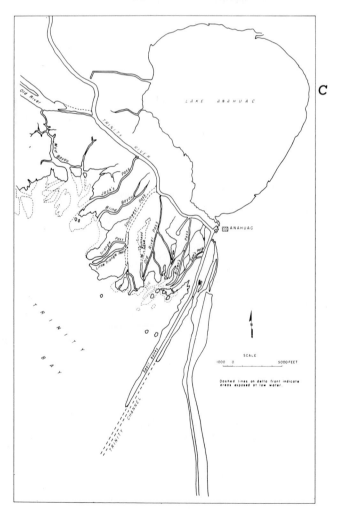

C

Fig. 9-17. *A–C.* Growth of delta of Trinity River, Texas, from 1851 to present. Note gradual encroachment across bay and present blockage of upper end to form a lake. (Courtesy of M. C. McEwen.)

and 12 deal with processes which currently cause erosion or deposition, and describes the effect of some of these processes on different types of sediment. The study of sedimentary rocks is not complete without a fairly detailed knowledge of some of these current processes, inasmuch as it is these processes which have eroded and transported the material that has then been deposited to form the sedimentary rocks of the past.

TOPOGRAPHIC MAPS

Since so much of the material covered in the present chapter deals with changes in elevations, it seems necessary to discuss the means by which geologists represent elevations on the earth's surface. The common method of such representation is a *topographic map*, which consists primarily of a series of lines known as *contours*. Each contour is a line drawn to represent one particular elevation on the earth's surface; thus a contour may be drawn for an elevation of 100 feet above sea level, or possibly 100 feet above some particular reference level other than sea level. Other contours are drawn at other intervals, and the resulting map has an appearance similar to that shown in Fig. 9-18. One method for learning to visualize contours is to realize that a contour line would represent the shoreline if the area were flooded by water up to the depth indicated by the contour.

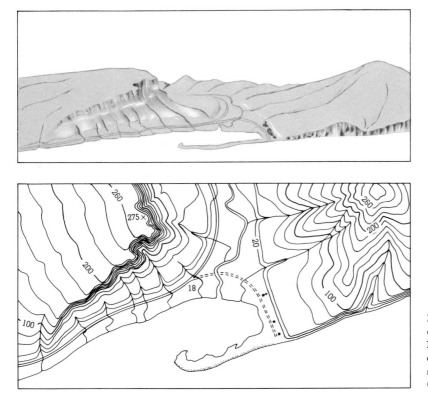

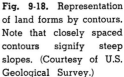

Fig. 9-18. Representation of land forms by contours. Note that closely spaced contours signify steep slopes. (Courtesy of U.S. Geological Survey.)

CHAPTER 10 STRUCTURAL GEOLOGY

◀ Folded sedimentary rocks. (Photo by B. C. Burchfiel.)

TYPES OF STRUCTURES

Since we have described the general condition of mechanical instability of the earth's surface in the preceding chapter, we are now in a position to discuss some of the specific results of this instability. Movement of bodies of rock relative to each other is generally given the term *deformation*. The results of such movement can commonly be described in terms of the development of either faults or folds, both of which terms have been mentioned briefly before. A *fault* (Fig. 10-1) is simply a surface, or zone of roughly parallel surfaces, along which relative movement has occurred. The fault is a fracture surface in the sense that the rocks on opposite sides have moved past each other, and previously coinciding points in the opposite blocks are no longer together. A *fold* is a bend in rocks (Fig. 10-2). In a fold, the orientation of features such as bedding planes changes from place to place. In a simple fold, surfaces parallel to folded material must slip past each other (as in bending a deck of cards), but the slippage between any two adjacent layers is extremely small, and no actual fracturing occurs.

Fig. 10-1. Fault offsetting sediments in eastern California. Note that the fault is a zone of weak, shattered rock which is easily eroded and forms a gully. (Photo by B. C. Burchfiel.)

Fig. 10-2. Folded limestones in Guatemala. (Photo by B. Burkart.)

Fig. 10-3. Strike and dip of inclined strata in New Mexico. (From *U.S. Geological Survey Professional Paper 505,* 1964.)

Before describing the various structures more accurately, it is first necessary for us to define the terms *strike* and *dip*. All planar features such as sedimentary beds have an orientation, or *attitude,* with respect to the earth's surface. Thus, when beds are parallel to the surface (indeed, they are generally deposited very near to that attitude), such beds are called "horizontal." Other beds may be inclined at some angle to the earth's surface. The orientation of a plane may be determined by the orientation of any two lines on it which are not parallel to each other. In geologic terminology, these two lines are termed the *strike* and the *dip*. The strike of a bed or other surface is the orientation of a line along the bed parallel to the earth's surface. The orientation of this horizontal line is generally given in terms of degrees to the east or west of north. Thus a bed may strike north 40° east, signifying that the orientation of a horizontal line upon it has a bearing 40° to the east of true north. The strike can be readily visualized as the line formed by the rock plane and the surface of an imaginary lake. The term "dip" refers to the angle with the horizontal surface made by a line in the bed perpendicular to the strike. This dip angle is obviously equal to the angle made by the bed or surface with the horizontal. The angle of dip of a surface is generally added to the notation for the strike. Thus a symbol N 40 E 30 W refers to a bed whose strike is 40 degrees to the east of north and which is dipping to the west at an angle of 30 degrees to the horizontal. The actual direction of dip, of course, is north 50° west. Figure 10-3 shows the determination of strike and dip diagrammatically.

We are now in a position to describe the various common types of faults and folds. Faults can be subdivided into three major categories, depending upon the direction of movement and its relation to the dip of the fault surface. These three types of faults are diagrammatically indicated in Fig. 10-4. A *normal* fault is one in which the downthrown block lies on top of the fault surface, and normal faulting thus results in an increase of the distance between two points on opposite sides of the fault plane. A *reverse* fault is simply the opposite of a normal fault and results in a shortening of the distance between two points. Reverse faults with extremely low angles of dip are commonly called *thrusts*. A *strike-slip* fault is one in which the movement is parallel to the horizontal, that is, parallel to the strike of the fault surface. Both normal and reverse faults may be grouped as *dip-slip* faults. For most faults the movement is neither purely strike-slip nor purely dip-slip, and the terms

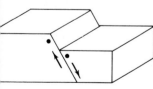
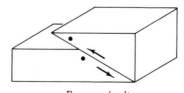
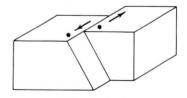

Normal fault

Reverse fault
(thrust if dip angle is very low)

Strike-slip fault

Fig. 10-4. Diagrammatic representation of the three types of faults.

applied to any particular fault simply refer to the dominant type of movement.

Fault surfaces are interesting features which bear close study where found, although actual exposure of the surfaces of most faults is comparatively rare. A number of features can be used to recognize fault surfaces and to determine something about the direction of displacement on the fault. The observable direction of offsetting of beds or other features is the principal type of evidence that can be used to reconstruct movement on a fault (e.g., Fig. 10-1). Such displacements are not always easily observed, however, particularly if the movement on the fault has been large and the blocks opposite each other are completely dissimilar. Geologists have used, with some hesitation, a feature called *slickensides* (Fig. 10-5) to determine the direction of movement. When two blocks of rock are moved past each other along a fracture surface, they rub against each other and tend to form a highly polished and commonly grooved surface. The grooves on the surface are caused by small, particularly resistant, projections from the sides of each block being dragged along the surface of the other block, and the grooves obviously are parallel to the direction of movement. The difficulty with the assignment of directions of movement from a study of slickensides is that they can give only an indication of the last direction of movement on a fault, and if movements

Fig. 10-5. Slickensides on rhyolite from west Texas. The specimen has a width of about one foot. (Photo by J. J. W. Rogers.)

have been repeated and complex, then the major direction of a movement may be quite different from the last one. Furthermore, slickensides on, for example, a fault striking north-south may indicate that the movement was lateral, but they do not indicate whether the eastern or western block moved to the north or south.

Another feature which may be used to indicate direction of movement on fault surfaces is the tendency of beds near the fault to be dragged along by the movement. This feature is appropriately termed *drag,* and the result of the dragging is that the beds are folded slightly in the direction of movement. Figure 10-6 shows a typical example of drag along a small fault. In addition to slickensides and drag, many faults are marked by the presence of a large amount of ground-up rock flour, commonly termed *gouge.* This material has been formed by the grinding action of the two blocks as they moved past each other, and the zones of gouge may be many feet wide on some faults.

Folds may be classified into two main groups, *anticlines* and *synclines.* An anticline is simply an upward arching of beds and a syncline is a

Fig. 10-6. Drag of beds along small fault. (Photo by T. H. Foss, National Aeronautics and Space Administration.)

downward arching. These two types of folds are shown in Fig. 10-7. Also shown in Fig. 10-7 is a fold which is not easily classifiable as either anticline or syncline and is referred to as a *monocline*. A line along the high point of an anticline or the low point of a syncline is referred to as the *axis* of the fold. Fold axes may be horizontal or they may dip, and a non-horizontal fold is said to *plunge*.

In addition to folds and faults, we must mention two other types of commonly developed structures. A *joint* (Fig. 10-8) is a fracture surface along which there has been little or no movement. Joints are common in all types of rocks. Many granites have extensive sets of joints, particularly near their margins where the intruded melt had crystallized before all movement had stopped. The resulting movement of the still-fluid components in the core of the granite batholith then caused stretching and deformation of the margin and the consequent development of large joint blocks. Joints are also present in both sedimentary and metamorphic rocks, where they are presumed to be incipient fracture surfaces caused by regionally developed forces. The term *cleavage*, when applied to rocks, has a meaning identical to that of cleavage in minerals; that is, rock cleavage signifies a tendency for the rock to split

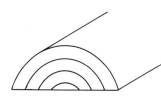
Anticline

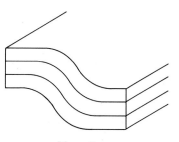
Syncline

Monocline

Fig. 10-7. Diagrammatic representation of three major types of folds.

Fig. 10-8. Intersecting sets of joints. (Photo by P. J. Pelton.)

along some set, or perhaps several sets, of parallel planes. In some rocks cleavage may simply be regarded as an exceptionally closely spaced jointing. In other rocks cleavage occurs because of some mineralogical orientation, as in slates, even though visible joint surfaces are not present.

GEOLOGIC MAPS

In order to describe completely the structures in any area of the earth's surface, it is necessary to prepare a geologic map. A geologic map is simply an ordinary topographic or other map on which the various formations have been located. The pattern formed by the various rock types is partly controlled by the relationship between the orientation of the rock bodies and topography and partly by the various structures. Thus, on a map, a plunging syncline which had been eroded down to a fairly level surface would have a pattern similar to that shown in Fig. 10-9. Figure 10-10 also shows the typical pattern made by a strike-slip fault and a similar pattern that might commonly be developed by a dip-slip fault. Note in Fig. 10-10 that the same surficial pattern can be obtained from both types of fault movements.

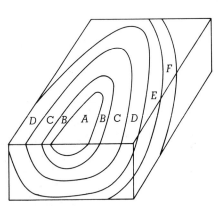

Fig. 10-9. Syncline plunging toward viewer.

Once the various patterns of structures and other features have been recognized on a map, it is possible to indicate these various features more clearly by symbols. For this purpose, a large number of dif-

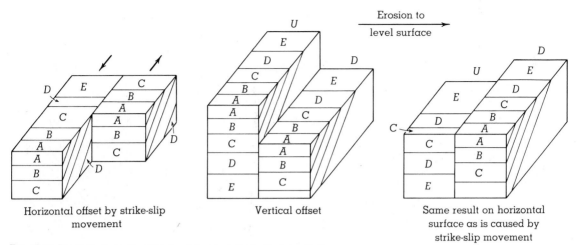

Horizontal offset by strike-slip movement

Vertical offset

Same result on horizontal surface as is caused by strike-slip movement

Fig. 10-10. Equivalent results of horizontal and vertical offsets on faults.

ferent structural symbols have been developed. The ones which are of interest to us in an introductory course are shown in Fig. 10-11. A complete geological map shows the outcrops of all of the different types of rocks plus symbols for each of the various structures. An example of a complete geologic map is shown in Fig. 10-12. This map should be studied with some care merely in order to note the details which must be put into the construction of a geologic map. The geology is superimposed on a contour map, and all of the various structural and other features are well displayed.

STRESS AND STRAIN

Structural geologists are not content with a simple description of the structures encountered on the earth's surface. The fundamental problem is to determine the manner in which these structures have formed.

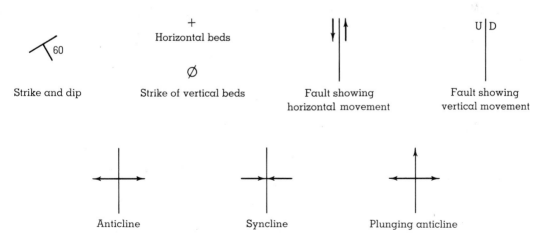

Strike and dip

Horizontal beds

Strike of vertical beds

Fault showing horizontal movement

Fault showing vertical movement

Anticline

Syncline

Plunging anticline

Fig. 10-11. Commonly used symbols for geologic structures.

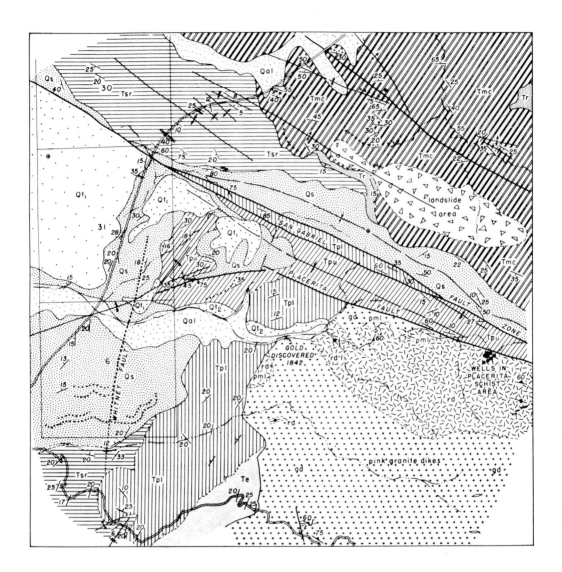

GEOLOGIC MAP OF PLACERITA AREA

1   0   1 Mile

Fig. 10-12. Geologic map of the Placerita area, California. Note the type of detail which is necessary for a complete geologic map. (Map by G. B. Oakeshott, map sheet 31, in *Geology of Southern California, California State Division of Mines Bulletin 170,* 1954.)

EXPLANATION

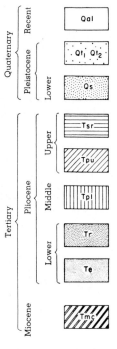

Quaternary	Recent	Qal	Alluvium
	Pleistocene	Qt₁ Qt₂	Terrace deposits (fanglomerate and stream gravels)
	Lower	Qs	Saugus formation (continental conglomerate and sandstone; often little consolidated)

Qal — Alluvium

Qt₁ Qt₂ — Terrace deposits
(fanglomerate and stream gravels)

Qs — Saugus formation
(continental conglomerate and sandstone; often little consolidated)

Tsr — Sunshine Ranch member
(continental greenish sandstone, mudstone, conglomerate, red beds, thin limestone beds)

Tpu — Upper Pico member
(marine coarse to fine sandstone, mudstone, conglomerate; fossiliferous)

Tpl — Lower Pico member
(marine conglomerate, sandstone, siltstone, fossiliferous calcareous sandstone)

Tr — Repetto siltstone member
(marine brown and gray siltstone and mudstone)

Te — Elsmere member
(marine fossiliferous, often petroliferous, sandstone and conglomerate, siltstone; becoming continental toward the north)

Tmc — Mint Canyon formation
(continental gray, buff sandstone and conglomerate; brown and greenish sandstone; greenish mudstone; thin red sandstone and claystone beds; tuff beds; lake beds)

Pico formation

Repetto formation

IGNEOUS AND METAMORPHIC ROCKS

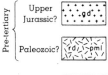

Pre-tertiary

Upper Jurassic? — gd — Granite, granodiorite, quartz monzonite

Paleozoic? — rd / pml — Rubio diorite gneiss (rd) Placerita crystalline limestone (pml)

———————— Contact

- - - - - - - - " , indefinite or gradational

———————— Fault

· · · · · · · · · · " , concealed

Axis of anticline

Axis of syncline

Dip and strike of beds

Horizontal beds

Foliation

Conglomerate bed

Tuff bed

Limestone bed

Basically, we can say that structures must result from movement in rocks and that this movement has been caused by the presence of nonuniform stress. We have used the term "stress" before, and although we are not in a position to give an exact definition of the word, we should discuss it more completely.

Stress is essentially a directional component of pressure. A marble at the bottom of a glass of water, for example, is under stress to the extent that the column of water is exerting pressure perpendicular to the borders of the marble. In this case the stress is uniform because the pressure exerted in all directions is equal. If, however, we take a pencil and push it down on top of the marble, the stress on the marble is nonuniform. That is, the pressure being applied in the vertical direction between the pencil and the bottom of the glass is greater than the stress which is being applied on the side of the marble by the water. These relationships are shown diagrammatically in Fig. 10-13. We have now applied a directed stress to the marble, and it is clear that such directed stress can occur only in solids and not in liquids. It is possible in all cases of nonuniform stress to analyze this stress into a number of components.

Marble at bottom of glass of water; stress identical in all directions

Marble at bottom of glass of water, with additional vertical stress caused by push of pencil;

$$\sigma_1 > \sigma_2$$

Fig. 10-13. Stresses on sphere. For explanation see text.

Three of these components represent pressures exerted along mutually perpendicular axes. The stresses in these three directions are referred to as the greatest, intermediate, and least stresses. We shall try to explain various structures in terms of their relationship to these different directions of stress and, hence, in terms of their relationship to the forces which have caused deformation.

The result of the application of stress to a body is the development of strain. *Strain* is merely the amount of deformation which a material undergoes. If, for example, you pull on the ends of a rubber band, you are applying stress to the band, and it is undergoing strain. The marble in the glass of water in Fig. 10-13 is being very slightly reduced in volume by the water pressure and slightly compressed at the top by the pencil. We can consider three basic types of strain, or deformation, in rocks. The first type of strain is a simple *elastic* deformation, in which the rock returns to its original state as soon as the stress is removed (Fig. 10-14). A

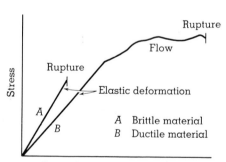

Fig. 10-14. Stress-strain relationships for brittle materials (which rupture before flowage) and ductile materials (which flow). Elastic deformation is the straight-line portion.

stretched rubber band will return to its original size when you stop pulling on it, and this type of deformation is then considered to be purely
elastic. When a body is strained past the limit of elastic deformation, however, one of two things may happen. The rubber band, if stretched too
far, will break, and fracturing is one of the adjustments of materials to
excessive strain caused by excessive stress. Other materials, however, will
simply flow rather than break. An example of such a material is butter,
or a spring which has been stretched so far that it
cannot return to its original position. Materials
which can undergo some elastic deformation before
flowing, and thus flow essentially as solids, are said
to be *plastic*.

A number of interesting observations on fracturing and flowage have been made in laboratory experiments. For example, assume that we take a cube
and apply three unequal stresses in mutually perpendicular directions as shown in Fig. 10-15. Assume also that the cube fractures before flowage
occurs. In general, fracture surfaces will be established much as is shown in Fig. 10-15; that is, the
various fracture planes will be oriented parallel to

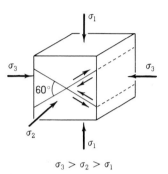

$\sigma_3 > \sigma_2 > \sigma_1$

Fig. 10-15. Fractures caused by stresses on
a reference cube. Note that fractures intersect at an angle of 60°, which is bisected
by the major stress, thus forming an angle
of 30° between the major stress and the
shear surfaces. Fractures are parallel to
the intermediate stress.

the intermediate axis of stress and will make a small
angle (generally about 30°) with the major direction
of stress. Though it is possible to form two planes
of fracturing with their acute angles toward the
major stress axis, in practice only one plane is commonly formed, and the other fracture direction is
represented by a group of very small and minor
breaks. The movement on a fracture surface is in a direction such that
the blocks move away from the major stress, as shown by arrows in
Fig. 10-15.

The stresses we have considered thus far are all ones in which the pressure is being applied in a direction toward the center of our experimental block. Fractures resulting from such compressive stresses are
termed *shear fractures*. It is possible,
however, to apply stress to a block by
pulling on the end in such a manner as
to pull it apart. Stresses of this type, as
shown in Fig. 10-16, are called *tensional
stresses,* and it is possible to apply both
compressional and tensional stresses to a
block in different directions at the same
time. Blocks under tension tend to fracture along a jagged plane perpendicular
to the main tensional stress. A block
which has undergone shear fracturing in
compression is still in many cases able to bear continued stress and may
fracture again. A block which has fractured in tension is obviously no
longer capable of bearing any type of tensional stress.

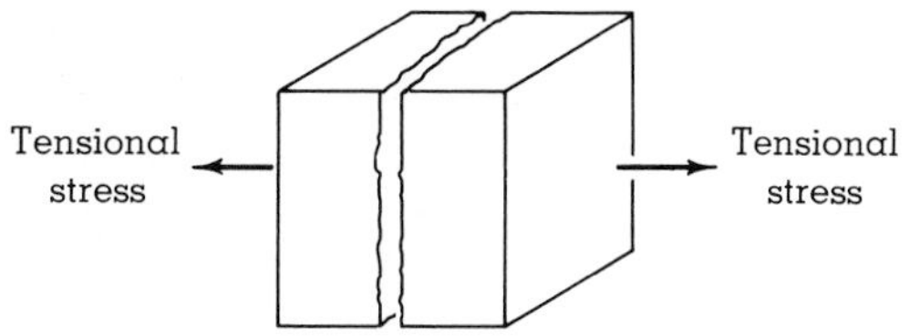

Tensional
stress

Tensional
stress

Fig. 10-16. Fracture caused by tension.

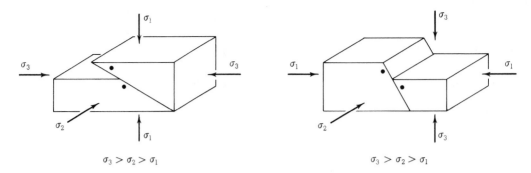

$$\sigma_3 > \sigma_2 > \sigma_1 \qquad\qquad\qquad \sigma_3 > \sigma_2 > \sigma_1$$

Fig. 10-17. Stress distributions responsible for normal and thrust faults.

With these various theoretical and experimental concepts in mind, let us now look at the types of stresses which must have existed in order to produce different types of faults. Consider, for example, a compression of the shallow part of the earth's crust in such a manner that the major compressive stress is oriented east-west; the intermediate stress is north-south; and the least stress, caused presumably by the shallow thickness of overlying rock, is vertical (Fig. 10-17). If fracturing occurs under these conditions, the faults formed should have a low angle of dip and should have a reverse or thrust type of motion. Indeed, most thrust faults do have a low angle of dip, and the possibility that thrusts have been formed by compression seems quite reasonable in view of the fact that thrusting inevitably shortens the distance between two points on opposite sides of the thrust plate. The stress orientation necessary to produce a normal fault must obviously be of the type also shown in Fig. 10-17. Here the major stress must be vertical in order to form an acute angle with the fault plane; the intermediate stress must be parallel to the fault; and the least compressive stress, or possibly even a tensional stress, must be nearly perpendicular to the fault plane.

An area in which a number of normal faults have been developed is obviously one in which there has been a stretching of the rocks along a line perpendicular to the strike of the faults. Such a stretching might be brought about geologically in a variety of ways, but one readily apparent mechanism is simply a slight upward arching of a region. The major area of development of normal faults in the continental United States is in the general area of western Utah, Nevada, and eastern California. This area not

Fig. 10-18. Thrust fault in Canadian Rockies. Note drag of strata above fault surface. (Photo by J. Teeter.)

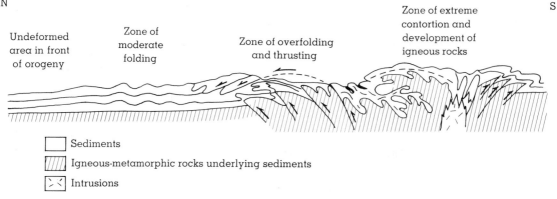

☐ Sediments

▨ Igneous-metamorphic rocks underlying sediments

☒ Intrusions

Fig. 10-19. Diagrammatic representation of major features of the Alps. The intensity of deformation decreases toward the north.

only contains a large number of normal faults but also is a region of generally high elevation, thus lending support to the concept of a gentle upward arching of the whole region.

The occurrence of thrust faults (Fig. 10-18) also fits fairly well into the structural scheme which we have indicated to explain their formation. Thrust faults are generally typical of mountain belts in which rocks have been intricately folded and possibly intruded by a great deal of igneous material. A cross section through the Alps, as in Fig. 10-19, shows obvious evidence of shortening of the area under the effects of extreme compression. The association of thrust faults with such mountain-building activity is thus quite logical.

The properties of faults which we have described thus far can be easily matched in simple laboratory experiments. All that is necessary is to construct a sand box containing one glass side for observational purposes and an end which can be pushed backward and forward (Figs. 10-20 and 10-21). Layers of sand, perhaps alternated with layers of chalk dust or other material for the purpose of easy visibility, can then be placed in the box and the end moved backward and forward. If the end of the box is shoved in-

Fig. 10-20. Formation of normal faults in a sand box. The fault develops where support is removed from one side. (From M. K. Hubbert, "Mechanical Basis for Certain Familiar Geologic Structures," *Geological Society of America Bulletin*, vol. 62, 1951, pp. 355–372.)

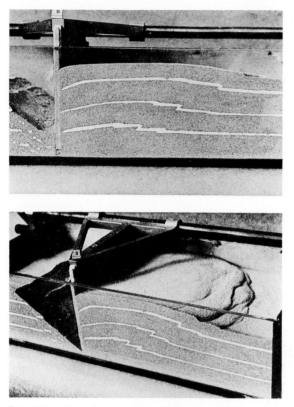

Fig. 10-21. Formation of thrust faults by compression in sand box. (From M. K. Hubbert, "Mechanical Basis for Certain Familiar Geologic Structures," *Geological Society of America Bulletin*, vol. 62, 1951, pp. 355–372.)

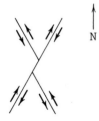

Fig. 10-22. Intersecting strike-slip faults as seen in map view. No simple stress pattern could account for this orientation.

ward as shown in Fig. 10-21, the major stress is directed into the sand, the least direction of stress is obviously vertical, and the result is the development of a thrust fault. If, conversely, a portion of the box is moved out, or perhaps simply removed, then the stress on the end of the pile of sand goes to zero, and the major stress is vertical and caused by the weight of the sand at any one point. The result, therefore, of removing support on the sand is to form a normal fault.

We have given some simple and probably correct explanations for a variety of faults. It would be a mistake, however, to imply that the major problems of structural geology in connection with faulting have been solved. Let us discuss two examples to show the types of problems which are still facing structural geologists. These two examples by no means exhaust the problems. Figure 10-22 is a map showing two intersecting strike-slip faults. The movement on these faults is indicated by arrows, and it is apparent that two opposite blocks are moving toward each other and two are moving away from each other. It appears therefore that the major direction of stress is oriented east-west and the least direction of stress is north-south, with an intermediate stress axis vertical. The problem with such an orientation of stresses, however, is that a major stress oriented east-west should form shear fractures with the acute angle between the fractures facing the direction of maximum pressure. It is clear that in this case the acute angle cannot face the direction of maximum compression, because the blocks within the acute angle would then be moving toward the major compressive stress. In short, no simple combination of stresses can explain the faults as shown in this figure. One suggestion has been made that in areas showing this type of faulting the original fracture planes formed the appropriate small angles with the major compressive stress and that these fracture planes were then rotated into their present positions. Such a major rotation of faults seems a bit unlikely, but other suggested explanations are equally unlikely.

A second, and far more important, problem confronting structural geologists is in regard to the development of thrust faults. As shown in Fig. 10-17, simple compression should develop simple thrust faults with low angles of dip. The dip of many thrusts, however, is far smaller than we might predict, and in some cases it is on the order of 0° to 5°. It appears as if some block of rock had simply been detached from the underlying materials and pushed over them on top of a horizontal thrust surface. Mechanically, the explanation of such a small angle of dip is difficult but not impossible. The real problem comes in understanding the ease of movement of the thrust. The overthrust block on many thrusts can be demonstrated to have been only a few hundreds or thousands of feet thick, though the total displacements can be proven to have been several tens of miles and, in some cases, may be even larger. It is difficult to understand how a sheet of rocks 2000 feet thick can have been moved 25 miles across a rough and irregular thrust surface without completely breaking apart the material in the upper block. Thrusts of this type, however, are common in the Rocky Mountains, and in many cases the beds in the overthrust block are as little disturbed as if they had been essentially unmoved. Some geologists, in attempting to account for the low angle of dip and the lack of disturbance of material in the overriding block, have proposed a mechanism generally termed *gravity*

Fig. 10-23. Sawed block of wax that has flowed under the influence of a large block of wax originally placed on one end of the block. The block of clear wax (on the left) has subsided and flowed out over the other wax, which originally was horizontally layered. (From Walter H. Bucher, *Geological Society of America Bulletin*, vol. 67, 1956.)

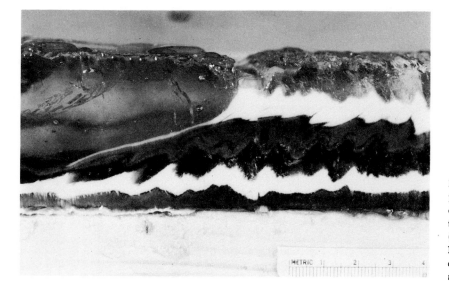

Fig. 10-24. Close-up of part of Fig. 10-23. Note deformation caused by this gravity flowage. (From Walter H. Bucher, *Geological Society of America Bulletin*, vol. 67, 1956.)

sliding. The basic idea is that the thrust is effectively a large landslide, in the sense that the material above the thrust surface is merely sliding slowly down hill. Such an explanation does not necessarily imply a later rotation of the fault surface in order to make movement look like upward thrusting rather than downward normal faulting. The block above the thrust surface may move uphill over a large portion of its length providing that some portion of the moving block occurs in a mountainous or high-standing land area. Experimental production of thrusts and over-riding blocks in models is shown in Figs. 10-23 and 10-24.

Thrusts in the United States are principally found in the Appalachian and Rocky Mountain areas. The Appalachian thrusts are generally associated with major folding and intrusion, as will be discussed toward the end of this chapter. The thrusts in the Rocky Mountains appear to be structures developed without accompaniment by other types of deformation. Another area of major thrusting is in southeastern Oklahoma and western Arkansas.

Major strike-slip faults are not common. The largest one in North America, and one of the largest in the world, is the San Andreas fault, which has already been described in Chapter 4 (Fig. 4-11). It has recently been proposed that a zone of strike-slip faulting parallels the entire Pacific Basin and is closely associated with the earthquake activity along the margin of the ocean (Fig. 10-25). Considerable additional work needs to be done in order to determine the direction of movement on

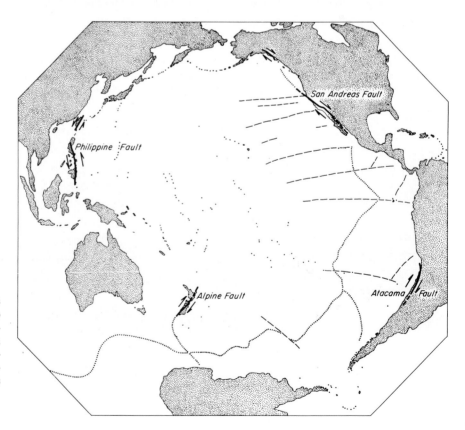

Fig. 10-25. Movements on major strike-slip faults around the Pacific Ocean. (From C. R. Allen, *Transactions of the Royal Society* (London), series A, 1965.)

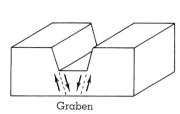

Graben

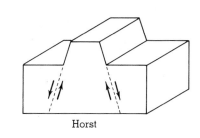

Horst

Fig. 10-26.
Diagrammatic representation
of graben and horst.

all of the various faults around the Pacific, but some geologists feel that there may be a general counterclockwise rotation of the Pacific Ocean basin. Such a rotation fits the direction of movement on the San Andreas but may not fit the faults in the Far East.

One characteristic feature formed by faulting is known as a *graben*. Grabens are simply blocks which have been dropped down between two normal faults and have the appearance shown in Fig. 10-26. Blocks that move upward in the opposite manner are referred to as *horsts*. Graben-formation by normal faulting is the explanation accepted by most geologists for the development of the deep lakes and valleys of east-central Africa extending from Lake Tanganyika up into the Red Sea and the Dead Sea (Fig. 10-27). The valleys and lakes formed in this manner are characterized by such features as great depth, parallel and steep sides, and elongate trends. The extent of downfaulting is shown, for example, by the fact that the surface of the Dead Sea is nearly 1300 feet below sea level. This set of valleys is commonly referred to as the African Rift Valley System, the term "rift" being derived from the presumed mode of formation as grabens.

FOLDING

In addition to fracturing, another response of rocks to compressive stresses is folding. The relationship between the major stress and the axis of folding may be demonstrated very easily by laying a sheet of paper flat on a table top and pushing on opposite ends. The fold axis thus formed is perpendicular to the major stress caused by the pushing. This simple relationship can be confirmed in certain natural combinations of folds and faults by noting the relationship of the fold axes to shear faults and, thus, to the stresses which cause the de-

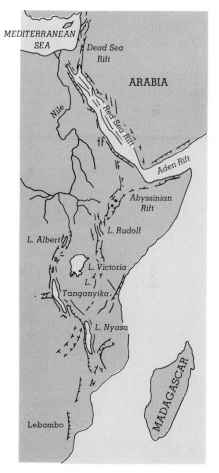

Fig. 10-27. East African rift zone. These linear depressions are commonly thought to be grabens. (From E. S. Hills, *Elements of Structural Geology*, John Wiley and Sons, New York, 1963.)

formation. Folds seldom occur singly but commonly form alternating series of anticlines and synclines (Fig. 10-28). The axes in these series are generally parallel, and presumably the major compressive stress is perpendicular to them.

Folding may or may not imply flowing. It is possible, for example, for beds to be deformed into a syncline or an anticline simply by moving slightly past each other much as a deck of cards might be moved if bent at the ends. Some types of beds, particularly comparatively soft material such as shale, may, however, actually undergo true flowage.

Structural geologists have long been concerned about the question of why rocks in one area will flow in response to compressive stress and in another area will fracture in response to stresses which appear to have been essentially the same. One principal explanation of this problem concerns the nature of the rocks undergoing the stress. A rock which is hard or brittle or resistant (the terms are somewhat synonymous) in its

Fig. 10-28. Folded rocks in Ellesmere Island, northern Canada. (Courtesy of Canadian Department of Mines and Technical Surveys.)

response to compressive stresses presumably will fracture before flowage occurs. Rocks, however, which are relatively soft or yielding probably will undergo flowage and may even become sufficiently like a fluid that fracturing cannot occur. In general, shales tend to flow, whereas sandstones, limestones, and igneous and metamorphic rocks commonly fracture.

The same material may undergo either flowage or fracturing depending upon the speed with which a directed stress is applied and on the temperature and pressure of the rock. A piece of butter taken directly from the ice box, for example, can be made to flow by squeezing the ends or pushing at virtually any spot. If you hold the cold butter by one end, however, and rap it sharply against a table, the bar will break. Also, when the butter warms up to room temperature, it will flow under its own weight and cannot be broken by any sudden stress. Flowage is promoted by high temperatures, high pressures, and slow rates of application of directed stress. A situation analogous to that of the butter is found at several hundreds of miles depth in the earth's interior. We have discussed in Chapter 4 the fact that earthquakes may originate at these depths and have demonstrated that earthquakes must be the result of fracturing processes. We know, however, from the mere existence of isostatic compensation (see Chapter 3) that rocks at depths of a few tens of miles are capable of flowing. In short, the earthquake presumably is the product of a short-term stress, and normal isostatic compensation represents flowage over a long period of time.

The mechanisms by which rocks flow are not wholly clear, and we cannot enter into an extended discussion of them here. One possibility is the formation of innumerable tiny fracture surfaces on which slippage may take place. The net result of this process would be, on a large scale, a movement of material from one place to another without the development of any particularly noticeable fault or fracture surface. Analogous to this physical possibility is a chemical process known as *recrystallization*. Recrystallization is a process in which grains are dissolved at one point and precipitated either at another part of the rock or at a different part of the grain in which solution is taking place. By this mechanism, material can be transferred, perhaps in pore solutions, from one part of the rock to another, and flowage may occur in this manner.

The maximum stress which a material can undergo before yielding to either faulting or folding is called the *strength* of the material (Fig. 10-14). Rocks vary greatly in their strength, with igneous rocks generally being considerably stronger than the average sedimentary rock. As an example, if we wish to break a small cube of typical granite by squeezing opposite ends in a vise and leaving the other sides open to the atmosphere, we will, in general, have to apply total stresses in the neighborhood of 25,000 pounds per square inch. Although a figure such as this seems quite high, it is really rather small in comparison with the stresses and masses of material in the earth. If, for example, we are able to take a cube of granite ten miles on a side and set this upon the earth's surface, the strength of the granite would not be sufficiently high at its base to withstand the weight of the overlying rock. This fact can easily

Fig. 10-29. Intricately deformed rocks in eastern California. (Photo by B. C. Burchfiel.)

be demonstrated by taking the strength mentioned above and knowing that the specific gravity of the average granite is 2.7.

EFFECTS OF DEFORMATION

Now that we have discussed the various possible mechanisms of deformation, we are in a position to describe the main effects of deformation as seen in the geologic record (Fig. 10-29). In general, a major deformation of the earth's crust results in the formation of mountains, and the process is commonly referred to as *orogeny*. We should mention here that some mountain ranges are formed by processes not associated with major deformation; an example is the Cascade Range of Oregon and Washington, which is constructed wholly by eruption of volcanic rocks. Most mountain ranges, however, are formed by the orogenic process discussed in this section.

The relationship between crustal compression and the development of mountains can be verified by a number of geologic observations. These observations are based largely on the fact that the rocks which currently occur in mountain ranges must at one time have been spread over a much broader area than they occupy today. The major structures formed during the orogeny are folds and thrust faults, and the shortening which accompanies thrusting and folding may be enormous. The total amount of shortening which takes place during the construction of a mountain range cannot, however, be determined simply by adding up the apparent shortening caused by the various individual thrusts and folds. One major difficulty with such a simple addition is the fact that a large part of the volume of rock which has been displaced by folding and faulting (so as to form a thicker vertical accumulation) is now occupied by granite. In fact, as we discussed in Chapter 8, in some areas the granites are thought to have been responsible for the shoving aside and consequent folding and thrusting of the surrounding rocks.

It is presumably the formation of granites and related igneous rocks which accounts for the formation of mountain roots. These roots were demonstrated by simple gravity measurements in Chapter 3. Thus, though areas of ancient orogenic deformation may be mountain ranges today, their elevation has not resulted simply because the rocks have been piled on top of each other and shoved upward. With apparently few exceptions, present mountain ranges owe their high elevation to the fact that they are floating isostatically on roots which were developed presumably during, but possibly shortly after, the major orogeny. We have here a typical example of the difficulties which geologists may encounter in trying to establish cause-and-effect relationships. Thus it is tempting at first glance to presume that a mountain range which is now well above the surrounding land surface has its high elevation as a result of having been thrust or folded upward. It is only after more careful geological and geophysical examination of the features of the mountain range as a whole, and of other mountain ranges in general, that it is possible to determine that the elevations are caused by floating on roots. Thus the folding and thrust faulting which characterize orogenic activity are merely associated with the development of high elevations in the form of mountains and are not the causative agents for the development of these elevations.

Episodes of ancient orogenic activity may be recognized in the geologic record if one can find an area in which there has been obvious folding, thrust-faulting, development of igneous rocks (primarily granite), and regional metamorphism. In North America features of this type are characteristic of an immense region in central Canada and neighboring parts of the United States. This is a region of very old rocks, as may be shown, for example, by radioactive age dating, and it may be considered a "core" of the continent. In this area the low elevation, exceptional flatness, and virtual absence of any unmetamorphosed sediments indicate an extreme depth of erosion. We are looking here, in fact, at what is presumed to be a large number of separate mountain chains eroded down to levels near or within their roots. This ancient, flat core is commonly referred to as a *shield*.

Orogenic rocks developed in the past 500 million years in North America are found in large portions of the Appalachian Mountains, in parts of the Rocky Mountains, in parts of the low mountainous regions of southern Oklahoma and western Arkansas, and in scattered areas to the west of the Rockies. The most recent deformation in the Rocky Mountain region apparently differs somewhat from the general pattern for mountain ranges, but we cannot go into the details here.

It is possible to find evidence of orogenic deformation even if the deformed rocks themselves are not exposed. The lack of exposure may be caused either by covering by later rocks or by virtually complete erosion of the deformed materials. Two types of evidence may be used for this purpose: (1) coarse-grained sediment; and (2) unconformities.

It is obvious that a mountain range or general area of high elevation must have a profound effect on the nature of sediments deposited around its margin. The intense erosion from mountainous areas must supply surrounding areas with a large quantity of debris, and the sediments thus supplied should have a coarser grain size than material which has been transported a long distance from some source area of relatively low elevation. The type of sedimentary material supplied by mountainous areas can be observed quite easily just by glancing at the debris carried by streams rushing out of the present Rocky Mountains. The pebbles, boulders, and coarse sand supplied to depositional areas in this fashion may differ markedly from the materials in underlying sediments. For

Fig. 10-30. Angular unconformity in southern Iran. (Photo by B. C. Burchfiel.)

Fig. 10-31. Angular unconformity between basalts and slightly metamorphosed sediments in eastern California. (Photo by B. C. Burchfiel.)

example, a bed of conglomerate lying directly above a sequence of sandstones and clay-bearing shales obviously causes a geologist to pause for thought. If the components of the conglomerate are largely igneous and metamorphic rocks, the possibility of an orogeny in neighboring areas is considerably strengthened.

Another type of evidence which may be used to recognize deformational activity is an interruption in the sedimentation process. Thus, in an oceanic area receiving a steady inflow of sediments, the process of deposition should be reasonably continuous at any one spot, though there must always be short periods of time in which deposition does not actually occur. Orogenies, however, may cause the uplift of broad areas and may, in fact, cause some minor folding

Fig. 10-32. Conglomerate at base of sedimentary formation at Stone City, Texas. (Photo by H. B. Stenzel.)

and tilting of beds in areas around the principal site of deformation. Uplifting, particularly above sea level, generally causes a cessation in sedimentation in any one particular area; then, when deposition is renewed after either lowering beneath sea level or, perhaps, a rise of sea level, there will be a break between the ages of the newly deposited sediments and the ones which underlie them. Not only may the uplift prevent deposition, but actual erosion may occur, though the erosion may be quite minor. Intervals of this type in the sedimentary record are termed *unconformities;* there seems to be no general agreement as to whether or not the word *unconformity* implies erosion during some interval or merely a period of nondeposition.

Unconformities may be recognized in a variety of ways. Where sedimentary strata are tilted and fresh sediment is deposited horizontally on top of them, the unconformity may have the appearance shown in Figs. 10-30 and 10-31. If the beds are not tilted, then it becomes more difficult to recognize a break in sedimentation. It may be possible, for example, to find evidence of erosion (Fig. 10-32) or weathering, possibly even the formation of a soil zone, at the top of the beds underlying the unconformity. Such evidence of erosion and weathering quite conclusively demonstrates an interval between the formation of beds below the unconformity and those above it.

Unconformities, of course, need not be restricted to contacts between sediments. In fact, wherever a sediment lies on a granite or metamorphic rock the contact between the sediments and underlying material must be some type of unconformity. The reason for this is that the granite and metamorphic rock could not have been brought to the earth's surface without erosion, and thus the surface at the base of the sedimentary record must be an unconformity (Fig. 10-33).

HISTORY OF OROGENIES

Having discussed some of the specific results of the orogenic process, we can now proceed to describe the normal history of orogeny. Most of the major mountain ranges of the earth have been studied geologically to a greater or lesser degree, and the detailed history of each one is, of course, different. Nevertheless, there are sufficient similarities in the history of development of typical folded and faulted mountain ranges that we can describe a general orogenic process.

One of the most fundamental observations in all of the geologic sciences was made by James Hall in 1859. Hall, working primarily in the Appalachian Mountain area, observed that sediments in mountain ranges were invariably thicker than sediments deposited during equal periods of geologic time in other regions (Fig. 10-34). Thus, for example, the sediments of particular geologic periods in the Appalachian Mountains are thicker than equivalent deposits in the Middle West. During a period of the earth's history known as the Paleozoic, which lasted approximately 300 million years (from 600 to 300 million years ago) the aggregate thickness of sedimentary rocks deposited in the middle-western part of the United States can be measured in terms of a few thousands of feet. This is an area which has not undergone orogenic activity during or since the deposition of the rocks. The thickness of sediments of Paleozoic time in the western part of the Appalachian Mountains is measured in terms of tens of thousands of feet. In the central and eastern part of the Appalachians, the thickness is probably much greater, though the intense metamorphism, structural deformation, and igneous intrusion in this area have made determination of original sedimentary features virtually impossible.

Hall's observation is generally true of orogenic belts anywhere on the earth. The conclusion to be drawn is that orogeny is preceded by the development of a deep basin of exceptionally thick accumulation of sedimentary material. The elongate nature of most mountain ranges, furthermore, implies that this basin was itself elongate. In the Ap-

Fig. 10-33. Sediments overlying ancient igneous rocks in Grand Canyon, Arizona. Lowermost bed is a conglomerate containing pebbles of the underlying rocks. (Photo by W. Schirra, National Aeronautics and Space Administration.)

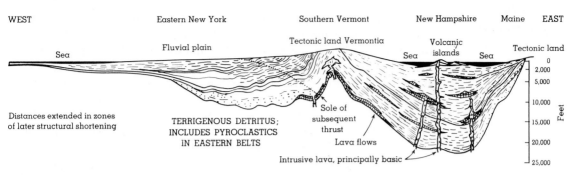

Fig. 10-34. Cross section through Appalachian geosyncline during early stages of its development. Note downwarping, an axis of high land, volcanic islands, shallow intrusions, and minor folding. (From Marshall Kay, *Geological Society of America Memoir 48,* 1952.)

palachian area, for example, the basin would have been approximately 1000 miles long extending in a roughly northeast-southwest direction. After the extensive deformation of the Appalachian orogeny, the original width of the basin in a northwest-southeast direction is essentially impossible to determine.

Large elongate basins, such as the Appalachian trough, which receive extensive accumulation of sediments are called *geosynclines.* In general, geosynclines appear to form around the margins of the igneous and metamorphic continental cores (shields) which we have already discussed briefly. In contrast to the rapid subsidence of the geosyncline, the shield is apparently stable, and shallow-water sediments of minor thickness are deposited on the margin of the shield adjacent to the geosyncline. This margin is termed a *shelf.* Thus the relationships of shield, geosyncline, and the transition between them are approximately as shown in Fig. 10-35. We should note here that the term "shelf" as used to designate the region of thin sedimentary rocks between the geosyncline and the shield is different from the term "shelf" as used to designate the shallow parts of modern oceans adjacent to continents. It is unfortunate that the same word has two different meanings.

An interesting confirmation of the general picture of sedimentation shown in Fig. 10-35 is provided by a detailed study of the rocks which are formed on the shelf and in the geosyncline. The sediments of the shelf generally consist of orthoquartzitic sands, shales, and limestones, with a little dolomite. The individual beds are thin, flat-lying, and continuous for many miles. The sediments of the geosyncline, however, contrast markedly with those of the shelf. Geosynclinal sands tend, in general, to be graywackes, with an extensive admixture of clay and fragments of volcanic and possibly metamorphic rock. Coarse sandy and silty shales are abundant in geosynclines, but limestones and dolomites are virtually absent. Another major component of the geosynclinal column is basalt or related volcanic rock (Fig. 10-34). The fact that the sediments of the shelf and the geosyncline are different demonstrates that the geosyncline is not merely an area which has subsided more rapidly than the shelf and thus accumulated a greater thickness of sediment. That is, the sedimentary environments of the geosynclines must have been different from those on their margins at the time the sediments were deposited.

If the sediments of the shelf and geosynclinal areas were similar, we might conceive of the possibility that, at any one time, the environment of deposition in shelf and geosyncline was the same. Thus the same type of sediments would accumulate in both places, presumably with the same depth of water and other environmental conditions, and the geosyncline would simply be an area in which the total amount of deposition was greater because of the greater accumulation of the typical shelf sediments. On the basis of the difference in types of sediments formed in the two environments, however, geologists presume that the depth of water in the geosyncline was somewhat greater at the time the sediments were formed than it was on the shelf. The depth of water in the geosyncline was at no time equal to the total thickness of sediments accumulated. That is, the geosyncline was never an empty basin which was gradually filled in. Sedimentationists and paleontologists estimate, without any high degree of confidence, that water depths in shelf areas were generally in the range of a few tens or possibly a few hundreds of feet. Depths of water in coinciding geosynclines were probably on the order of a few thousands of feet but certainly never reached the value of the thickness of the entire sedimentary column, which in some geosynclinal areas has been estimated in terms of several hundreds of thousands of feet. The geosyncline presumably was a place of continual subsidence and volcanic activity throughout its entire lifetime.

We must mention the fact that some geologists doubt the estimates of exceptional thickness which have been made for geosynclinal sediments. The picture envisioned by such people is different from the one we have presented, to the extent that they feel that successive layers of sediment are deposited sequentially outward from each other. This type of deposi-

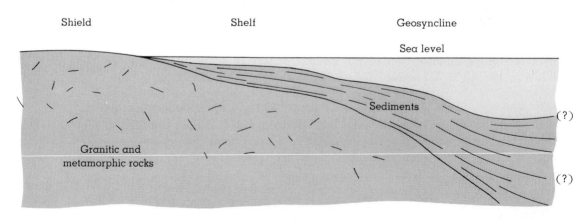

Fig. 10-35. Simplified relationships of shield, shelf, and geosyncline. Vertical distance greatly exaggerated. Question marks indicate uncertainty of relationships on outer edge of geosyncline.

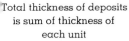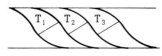

Total thickness of deposits
is sum of thickness of
each unit

Total thickness is less than
sum of thickness of
each unit

$T_1 + T_2 + T_3$

Fig. 10-36. Possible relationships of total thickness of sedimentary column to thicknesses of individual units.

tion is shown diagrammatically in Fig. 10-36, in which individual units of perhaps tens of thousands of feet thickness are offset from each other so that the entire thickness of the sedimentary section cannot be found by adding the thicknesses of individual beds or formations. Sediments deposited in this manner might have a total thickness of 50,000 feet resulting from the addition of the thicknesses of the individual units, whereas the actual thickness from top to bottom of the sediments at any one place might be only 10,000 feet. It would seem to be a simple matter of field observation to resolve the argument between these two points of view. The field evidence, however, is not yet conclusive. The difficulty stems partly from the tendency of geosynclinal sediments to be badly deformed during orogeny and partly from the general difficulty that geologists have in investigating only the surface of the earth when they are actually interested in three dimensions. The number of holes drilled for purely scientific purposes has greatly increased in recent years, and a few well-placed 25,000-foot holes would resolve this and many other problems.

The end of geosynclinal deposition is usually marked by the beginning of orogeny (Fig. 10-37), the mechanisms of which are discussed more completely in Chapter 14. There may, of course, be small periods of deformation during geosynclinal filling. The main orogeny causes geosynclinal sediments to be folded, faulted, and metamorphosed. Granites are intruded at this time, and at some period the development of a large granitic mountain root probably coincides with the formation of a mountain chain. In the Appalachian and many other major orogenies, thrusting invariably takes place toward the shield from the geosyncline, and folds may also be bent toward the shield. Exactly why this particular direction of thrusting is preferred over thrusting in the opposite direction, away from the shield, has not been satisfactorily explained. In this manner, rocks of the geosyncline are thrust over correlative rocks formed in environments on or close to the shelf.

The major compressive phase of the orogeny may give way to a later relaxation of stress, possible upwarp of a broad area of mountainous topography, and the development of land-laid sediment. The relaxation of stress may, in part, cause the formation of normal faults over the previously formed metamorphic and granitic rocks. In the relatively

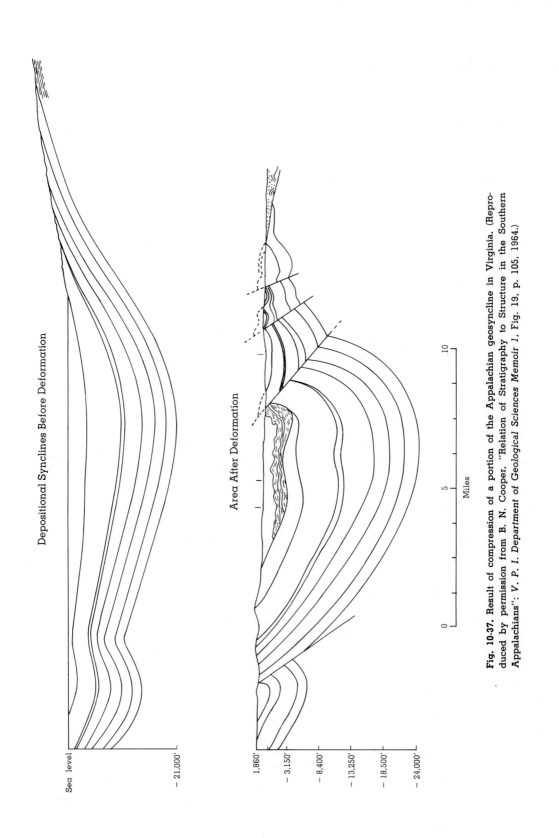

Depositional Synclines Before Deformation

Sea level

− 21,000'

Area After Deformation

1,860'

− 3,150'

− 8,400'

− 13,250'

− 18,500'

− 24,000'

0　　　5　　　10

Miles

Fig. 10-37. Result of compression of a portion of the Appalachian geosyncline in Virginia. (Reproduced by permission from B. N. Cooper, "Relation of Stratigraphy to Structure in the Southern Appalachians": *V. P. I. Department of Geological Sciences Memoir 1*, Fig. 19, p. 105, 1964.)

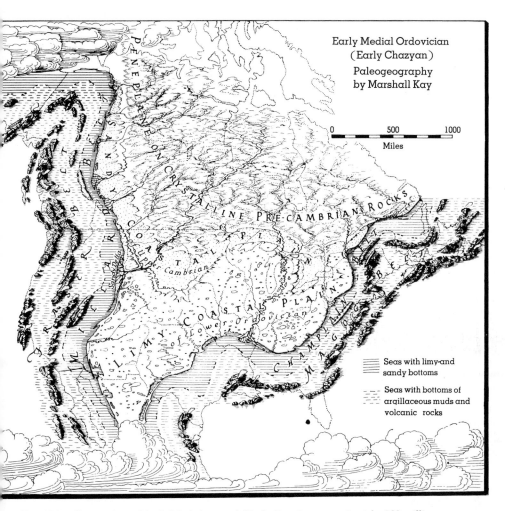

Fig. 10-38. Geosynclines (shaded belts) around North America approximately 500 million years ago. (From Marshall Kay, *Geological Society of America Memoir 48*, 1952.)

well-studied Appalachian Mountains, for example, such normal faults, in many places grabens, are seen to cut through rocks and structures formed during the orogeny. The grabens thus formed may be the site of accumulation of sediments and, in places, additional basaltic rock. The cross-cutting relationship of the graben and associated features with the orogenic structures clearly dates the normal faulting as later than the major orogeny.

We have already noted that the continental shield appeared to consist of the remnants of a large number of mountain belts which had been eroded to considerable depth. We have also noted the fact that later geosynclinal development was generally on the margins of the shield area (Fig. 10-38). These facts have led some geologists to suppose that continents are formed by a process of *out-building*, starting from a small nucleus and developing by the process of forming geosynclines adjacent

235

to the stable area. Orogenies, then, develop granitic and metamorphic rocks similar to those already existing in the shield and simply add the geosynclinal areas to the shield. This is, in effect, a process of welding which enlarges the shield by the width of the mountain belt. Some evidence for this point of view has been found by studies of the ages of mountain belts, particularly granites, in the shield area of central Canada. The ages of formation of a variety of different rocks and minerals in this area are shown in Fig. 10-39. It will be noticed that the ages become generally younger as one goes away from the central part of the shield. From this point of view, the last major additions to the shield are those of the Appalachian and Rocky Mountain regions.

The evidence of continental out-building has been challenged in a variety of ways, including presumed inaccuracies in measurement of dates and inadequate representation of all of the rock ages in the North

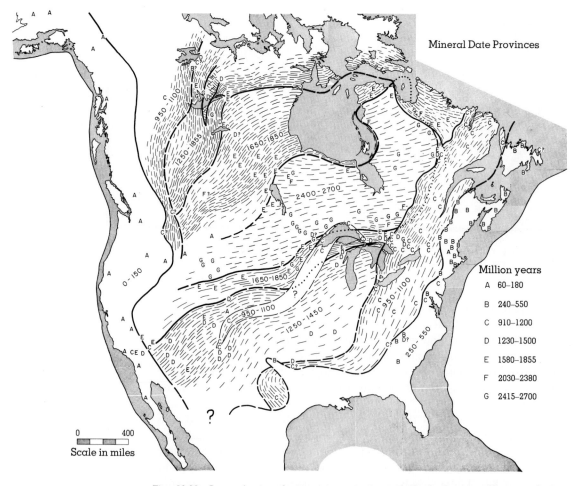

Fig. 10-39. Ages of minerals in various portions of North America. Many geologists interpret this evidence as indicative of a growth of the continent outward. (From G. Gastil, prepared by San Diego State College Audio-Visual Services.)

American continent. There is also the disturbing fact that most continents do not show the nice symmetrical relationship North America shows. Thus in Africa or South America a proposal of this type is far more difficult to substantiate than it is in North America. At the present time geologists must consider out-building as an interesting, though not fully verified, theory.

Thus far we have said nothing about the basic causes of orogeny. In some manner compressive stresses are generated in the earth's crust. Furthermore, there is either a source of igneous melts or a source of heat which produces igneous melts and attendant metamorphism. The mechanisms for generating both the stresses and the heat may be related to processes occurring in the mantle. We shall discuss these problems and a variety of related ones in Chapter 14.

CHAPTER 11 RIVERS

◄ Meandering river. (Photo by W. Krawiec.)

Running water is a geologic agent of tremendous importance. A major portion of the earth's landscape owes its present form to the action of water. Most of the material now contained in sedimentary rocks was at one time moved by running water, and today (as noted in Chapter 9) rivers annually bring to the sea 10^{10} tons of sediment. In this chapter, we shall discuss the geology of rivers and the landscapes formed by them.

Before entering into detailed discussions of the movement of sediments or the sculpturing of landscapes, we must stop to recognize a geologic observation that is as fundamental as that of the recognition of geosynclines by Hall. In 1802, John Playfair formalized the principle which, simply stated, says that where two rivers join each other they do so at a common level. That is, at the junction of two rivers the upper level of water in one river is exactly the same as the upper level of water in the other river (Fig. 11-1). At first glance, this statement seems trivial and unnecessary. Consider, however, the problem of determining a cause-and-effect relationship between rivers and the valleys in which they flow. It is possible, for example, that valleys exist independently of rivers and that rivers simply flow in them because the valleys are topographically low spots. Thus the valley is the agent which determines the position of the river and is in no way dependent upon the river. This possibility is completely disproved by Playfair's simple observation. If the valleys were

Fig. 11-1. Two streams joining at grade in the Philmont Ranch country of New Mexico. (From *U.S. Geological Survey Professional Paper 505*, 1964.)

not the effect of rivers which flow in them, then presumably the valleys might intersect each other at any relative level. That is, a tributary might enter the wall of another valley several hundred feet up on the valley wall. Under these circumstances, virtually all rivers would join each other in waterfalls. Thus Playfair's principle leads to the unquestionable conclusion that valleys have been cut by the rivers which flow in them and that the river is the causative agent of the formation of the valley.

Playfair's observation immediately carries with it several important implications. If a river can cut a valley, the river must obviously be able to pick up and carry debris from the floor and sides of the valley. Consequently, a river is able to erode rocks and to transport sediment derived by this erosional process. Furthermore, if a river can pick up and move sediments, it can presumably deposit them. Therefore, we expect to find, both at the present time and in the geologic sedimentary record, rocks which have been formed by deposition from rivers.

STREAM TRANSPORTATION

Let us turn now to a more complete discussion of the transportation of sediments by running water. The sediment moved by a stream is called the *load,* and the load may be subdivided into two portions. One portion is chemically dissolved material which simply travels downstream with the water; the other portion of the load consists of solid particles moved by the force of the running water.

One part of this solid load is the *bed load,* which consists of that material which is rolled, pushed or swept along the bed of the stream (Fig. 11-2). The surface of this material is continually being affected by the action of the running water, but sediments slightly below the surface may remain in a fixed position for a considerable period of time. Most of the solid material which a stream transports, however, is carried almost permanently within the body of water itself. This sediment is referred to as the *suspended load,* and the various grains are held in the water by small whirls and eddies which occur in virtually all running water and are referred to as *turbulence.* These small eddies are really

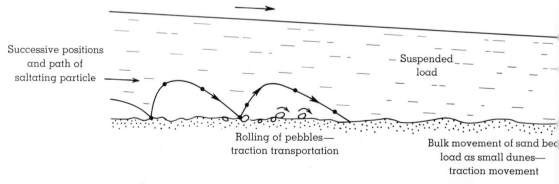

Successive positions and path of saltating particle

Suspended load

Rolling of pebbles— traction transportation

Bulk movement of sand bed load as small dunes— traction movement

Fig. 11-2. Diagrammatic representation of mechanisms of transportation in streams.

whirlpools with diameters measured in millimeters instead of feet. The effect of eddying is to cause portions of the water in any stream to be moving in an upward or downward direction rather than simply horizontally in the direction of general flow. A stream in which individual particles of water may be moving in these different directions is said to be undergoing *turbulent flow*. Turbulence tends to keep material in suspension by providing upward-directed forces which catch grains as they are settling through the water and direct them upward and back into the main body of the stream.

It is possible for water to flow in a nonturbulent or *laminar* fashion if two conditions are satisfied. First, the rate of flow must be very slow. Second, the water must be flowing over a very smooth surface without any projections that cause turbulence to start. These conditions are rarely met in geology, and for practical purposes the flow of all water in streams must be considered turbulent.

It is immediately obvious that the bed load of a stream will consist of large particles, such as pebbles and sand, whereas the suspended load will consist of the finer silt and clay. Some particles, of course, may be too large to be moved at all. The term *competence* is used to refer to the maximum size of particles a stream may move.

The mechanism of movement of particles of different grain sizes can be quantified by experimental work. It is easily possible to measure in the laboratory the velocity with which spheres of different size settle through water, though no one equation adequately describes the settling velocities of particles of all sizes. As examples of settling velocities, however, spherical grains with a diameter of 1/16 mm settle at a rate of 4 mm/sec in absolutely quiet water, and grains with a diameter of 0.008 millimeter settle at a rate of 0.15 mm/sec. It should be obvious that a stream in which all flow is laminar cannot carry a suspended load.

The sedimentary material carried by a stream is not adequately specified by the competence alone. Streams vary in their ability to pick up material depending on the velocity. In general, a swiftly moving stream can carry far more suspended load than a stream which is moving quite slowly. The amount of solid material which a stream is capable of moving is termed the *capacity*.

The actual mechanism of movement of sedimentary particles can be classified into three different categories (Fig. 11-2). The first category, *suspension,* depends upon the turbulence of the stream to keep fine-grained materials from settling to the bottom. A second mechanism of movement is *traction,* which refers to the pushing, rolling, or pulling of grains on the bed of the stream. A grain undergoing traction transportation is likely to be relatively large, at least sand sized, and roughly spherical. The amount of sediment moved slowly by traction is difficult to determine in the average stream, but it is probably not large. The effectiveness of traction movement is, in part, hindered by the distribution of velocities in the average stream. Running water is affected by the sides and bottom of the stream just as any other moving material is. The result is that water velocities are much lower near the bed of a stream than they are in the middle or the top and consequently are not effective

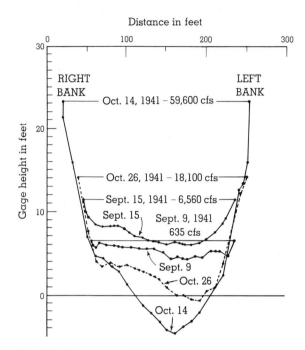

Fig. 11-3. Cross section of channel of San Juan River, Utah, during progress of flood in 1941. Note deepening of floor as flood progresses. (From L. B. Leopold and T. Maddock, Jr., *U.S. Geological Survey Professional Paper 252,* 1953.)

in moving sediment. A third mechanism of sedimentary movement is termed *salta-tion.* Saltation refers to the tendency of some grains to bounce along the bottom in long jumps. Grains which are plucked out of the bottom by exceptionally tur-bulent eddies or other means may be caught up in the stream and moved downstream for some distance before they settle out. When they settle out, they strike the bottom and may either bounce back into the stream again or may send another grain up into the water. Saltating grains tend to be of sand size, and saltation is of less im-portance in water than it is in wind transportation, where it is the major mechanism by which sediment is moved.

We have seen that, in general, sedi-ments are more readily carried by streams moving at higher velocities than by those moving comparatively slowly. High ve-locities not only cause a more rapid transportation of individual sedimentary particles, but they are also capable of bringing more sedimentary particles into suspension or into some form of traction

Fig. 11-4. Floor of the Mississippi River near Vicksburg, Mississippi, exposed by water diversion. The floor consists of loose sand sculptured into dune-like shapes by the water flow. (Photo courtesy of Esso Production Research.)

movement. In fact, it seems likely that in most rivers the major amount of transportation caused by the river is accomplished during flood stages. This statement can be verified by observation made on the base of a stream. During normal river flow, the bottom of a stream occupies a relatively constant position. Minor deposition and erosion takes place, but there is no major shifting of sediments. During flood stages, however, the bottom levels of some streams have been seen to drop by several tens of feet. The process is diagrammatically shown in Fig. 11-3, where it is seen that during flood the materials which customarily occupy a rather fixed position at the base of the stream are picked up by the greater water velocities and greater turbulence and moved in suspension. Small streams which are running across bare rock outcrops cannot, of course, deepen themselves in this fashion. The average river, however, has a considerable thickness of sediments on the bottom, and this material almost certainly is moved only by suspension transportation during flood (Fig. 11-4).

DEPOSITION

Rivers deposit sediments by a process exactly opposite to that which causes running water to pick them up. In general, material is deposited by a decrease in turbulence, however that decrease is brought about. A slowing of river velocities may, of course, cause the decrease, but it is also possible that sediments are deposited merely where the river crosses a bottom area which is smooth enough so that turbulence is not well developed. We mentioned above that rivers move large quantities of sediment under flood stages. Also during these stages large amounts of material may be deposited, especially if a river overtops its bank and spreads widely over the surrounding area. A river spreading over its floodplain will generally carry a large amount of silt and clay in suspension. This material settles out to form floodplain deposits and build up the valley floor around the river (Fig. 11-5).

Rivers must deposit their sedimentary load when they enter standing bodies of water in which currents are far less strong than in the river. A river entering the ocean commonly deposits much of its coarser sediment, or bed load, very close to the river mouth. Thus, a wedge of rather coarse sediments, commonly referred to as a *delta* (Chapter 7), is built

Fig. 11-5. Looking down into the floodplain of the Uncompahgre River, Colorado. The river is just reaching flood stage and is beginning to overflow its banks, as can be seen by water along roads and other low places. (Photo by T. H. Foss.)

up around the mouths of many rivers. This coarse-grained material may obviously be distributed away from the mouth of the river by various marine processes. The very fine materials are generally carried further away from the river mouth, though if river currents are very sluggish and marine currents nearly absent, even clays may be deposited close to shore. The deposition of clays, in fact, may be accelerated by the effect of salt water. Many clay particles in rivers are kept in suspension partly by the fact that they have a small surface charge which tends to repel other particles. Upon entering salt water, however, the higher dielectric constant of the water reduces the effect of the surface charge and permits clays to coagulate to form larger grains which may settle comparatively rapidly. Lakes and other standing bodies of water are, of course, sites of deposition for much the same reasons that oceans are.

As a result of the fact that most sedimentary grains are deposited from water, it is interesting to note that grains which occur together in sediments tend to have settling velocities which are roughly equal. For example, many sediments contain a small proportion of minerals, such as hornblende, which are denser than the normal quartz and feldspar. Invariably the dense or heavy minerals have a smaller grain size than the quartz and feldspar, and the reason is that high-density minerals settle more rapidly than low-density minerals of equal size. Thus a small heavy mineral will be associated with grains of a larger light mineral.

HYDRAULICS AND STREAM PROFILES

In order to describe more quantitatively the manner in which a river flows and carries sediments, we will want to know about the interrelationships of a number of hydraulic factors. For example, the amount of water which passes a certain point in a stream in any given interval of time is dependent upon the velocity of the stream and its cross-sectional area. Velocity, however, is certainly not independent of either width or depth, and we may expect relationships between all three of these variables. Without making any effort to explain these various relationships, it is possible to make simple measurements of width, depth, and velocity in a large number of streams and derive a set of empirical equations relating these variables. The relationships for these three factors in one stream are shown graphically in Fig. 11-6, and the equations are as follows:

Let Q = quantity of water flowing past a point (discharge)

$\quad$ w = width of water surface

$\quad$ d = mean depth of water

$\quad$ v = mean velocity of water

Then, from the geometrically linear relationships shown in Fig. 11-6.

$$w = aQ^b$$
$$d = cQ^f$$
$$v = kQ^m$$

where a, c, and k are proportionality constants, and b, f, and m are slopes measured in Fig. 11-6.

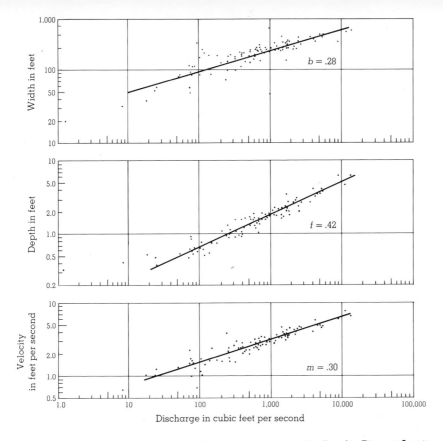

Fig. 11-6. Width, depth, and velocity plotted against discharge in the Powder River at Locate, Montana. The symbols b, f, and m refer to parameters in the equations in the text. (From L. B. Leopold and T. Maddock, Jr., *U.S. Geological Survey Professional Paper 252*, 1953.)

Furthermore

$$Q = wdv$$
$$= aQ^b \cdot cQ^f \cdot kQ^m$$
$$= ackQ^{b+f+m}$$

Therefore,

$$b + f + m = 1$$

and

$$a \cdot c \cdot k = 1$$

The simplicity of these equations for any one point in the stream is quite surprising.

We may also investigate the typical changes in these different variables from the headwaters to the mouth of a stream. Here the surprising and unexpected relationship is that the velocity of a stream, instead of growing less as it approaches the mouth, actually increases. We normally think of mountain torrents as being quite rapid and of large rivers as flowing rather slowly, but this is a typical case in which our senses are fooled by the surroundings. Actually the Mississippi River is flowing faster than most Rocky Mountain streams.

The amount of sediment carried by a stream is related to both the volume of water and its velocity. The relationship between suspended load and stream discharge (quantity of flow) is shown graphically in Fig.

11-7. Some of the scatter of points shown in Fig. 11-7 is undoubtedly related to other factors, such as the irregularity (roughness) of the floor of the channel. As mentioned previously, a rough floor tends to cause considerable turbulence and thus promotes the transportation of suspended material.

In a preceding section we mentioned the variation in properties of a stream along its length. One of the most important properties is the elevation, and a chart in which the elevation of a stream is plotted against distance from headwater to mouth is called the *longitudinal profile* of the stream. Most streams have longitudinal profiles roughly similar to those shown in Fig. 11-8. The profile is quite steep near the headwaters and gradually becomes more horizontal as the mouth is approached.

The ultimate result of stream activity is to reduce the elevation of the land surface over which it flows. For any stream, the theoretical lowest level which can be reached in this manner is the elevation of the stream mouth. This elevation is referred to as the *base level* of a stream. The base level for a stream is generally a body of standing water. Thus the ultimate base level for all streams is sea level, except for those few streams which drain into basins below sea level, such as Death Valley. A stream which flows into a lake, however, has a temporary base level equal to that of the elevation of the lake. The base level established by a lake is called temporary because, presumably, the lake will be destroyed by general lowering of its outlet at some later time in the erosional process of the stream; stream waters will then continue to erode toward some even lower base level.

The inclination of a stream at a point is called the *gradient* and is simply the slope of the tangent to the curve representing the longitudinal profile.

Although the ultimate result of stream activity is erosion and lowering of the land surface, this does not mean that all streams are causing erosion in all portions of their length at all times. Consider, for example, a stream which washes out of a high mountain range and enters a flat plain, similar to that which is shown in Fig. 11-9. The sharp decrease in gradient at the exit from the mountainous area causes a reduction in the velocity of the stream and reduces the stream's capacity—that is, its ability to carry sedimentary debris. Thus there is a tendency for the coarser-grained materials which have been picked up by the stream in the

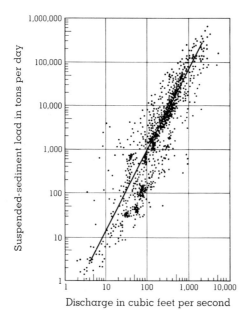

Fig. 11-7. Suspended load plotted against discharge in the Powder River at Arvada, Wyoming. (From L. B. Leopold and T. Maddock, Jr., *U.S. Geological Survey Professional Paper 252*, 1953.)

mountains to be deposited where the stream enters the plains. In this manner, the stream builds up the land surface at the juncture between the plains and mountains, even though it is eroding at higher elevations. This combined deposition and erosion tends to form a smoother stream profile than existed previously. In general, the erosional and depositional activities of streams act to reduce the irregularities in their profiles.

We can now summarize the activities of a stream under three different conditions:

1. Where the sediment load of a stream is less than its capacity, and the gradient is reasonably high, the stream tends to erode.

2. Where the sediment load of a stream is greater than capacity, possibly as a result of some sharp decline in gradient, the stream tends to deposit.

3. It is conceivable that large stretches of a stream might be in a system of equilibrium in which the load and capacity are equal. Thus there would be no tendency for the stream either to erode or to deposit material, and the material carried by the stream would simply be

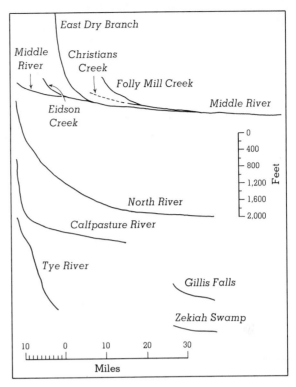

Fig. 11-8. Longitudinal profiles of a number of streams in Virginia and Maryland. (From J. T. Hack, *U.S. Geological Survey Professional Paper 294B*, 1957.)

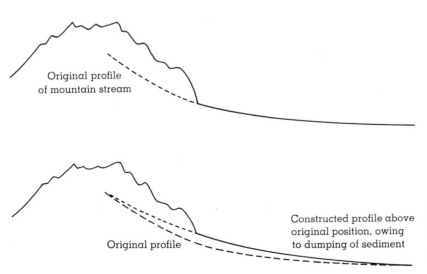

Fig. 11-9. Construction of stream profile by dumping of sediment where gradient is sharply reduced downstream.

swept past this particular stretch without any appreciable effect. A stream in this equilibrium condition is said to be *graded*. It is obvious, of course, that no stream may remain graded for long periods of time without the help of other geologic processes. In order for a graded condition to exist, there must be a source of sediment which the stream may carry through its graded stretch. Since, in the absence of other geologic phenomena such as mountain-building, sources of sediment are not infinite, it is apparent that streams which are graded must ultimately reach a condition in which they begin to erode again.

It is interesting to note that the longitudinal profiles of many streams follow a curve which can be represented by a rather simple mathematical equation. This equation can be derived by assuming that the tendency of a stream to erode at any particular point along its profile is directly proportional to the height of a stream above base level. Thus let

$$H = \text{elevation above base level}$$
$$x = \text{distance downstream from source}$$
$$a \text{ and } b = \text{positive constants}$$

If the tendency of a stream to erode (dH/dx) is proportional to its elevation above base level, then,

$$\frac{dH}{dx} = -bH \qquad \text{or} \qquad \frac{dH}{H} = -b\,dx$$

thus
$$\ln H = -bx + a \qquad \text{and} \qquad H = ae^{-bx}$$

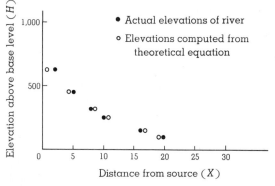

Fig. 11-10. Comparison of theoretical and actual longitudinal profile of a river. Theoretical points are calculated by best fit of actual data to the equation derived in the text. (Actual data are from J. T. Hack, *U.S. Geological Survey Professional Paper 294B,* 1957.)

This equation leads to a set of curves, one of which is shown graphically in Fig. 11-10. It is apparent that the mathematical curve is a very good approximation to the actual measured stream profile. It may be presumed that streams which have profiles of this type are graded.

We have now reached an extremely difficult problem in all types of geologic research. That is, does the correspondence between the theoretical and the actual mean that the assumptions involved in deriving the theoretical are correct? In this case, does the correspondence of theoretical and actual stream profiles mean that we are correct in assuming that a stream erodes at any point with an intensity proportional to the elevation of that point above the base level? For example, it is possible that the equation of the profile of a stream could have been derived on the basis of other assumptions than the one which we chose to make. Furthermore, although our chosen assumption may be correct, it may have nothing to do with the evolution of a stream profile. The point is that it is impossible to exhaust the various types of explanations or models which may be advanced to account for an observed fact In this case the fact is the profile of the stream. The explanation we have given here is based on one very simplified assumption. It seems likely, therefore, that the mathematical equation from which we started the derivation is at least approximately correct. The mathematical equation, however, could have been derived on the basis of a virtually infinite number of other geological assumptions. Thus, the presumed correctness of the mathematics does not demonstrate the accuracy of the assumption. The geological assumption which we have used has been chosen solely on the basis that it is geologically plausible. As we mentioned in our discussion of the determination of the environments of formation of sedimentary rocks, one of the major tasks of the geologist is to determine that explanation which seems most likely among the many possible explanations for a geologic phenomenon.

LAND SCULPTURING

Let us consider now the activities of streams whose gradients are either greater than, or less than, the gradients of streams which are in a graded condition. Streams with high gradient, that is with elevations above grade, tend to reach grade by erosion. Such streams commonly erode very rapidly; the valleys they cut are sharp, and the amount of deposition is minimal (Figs. 11-11 and 11-12). The steepness of the valley walls attests to the fact that downcutting of the valley bottom greatly predominates over lateral cutting of the walls.

Stream gradients may be reduced by methods other than downcutting.

Fig. 11-11. V-shaped, youthful valley in San Juan Mountains, Colorado. (Photo by T. H. Foss.)

Fig. 11-12. Gullying initiated by a small furrow cut in farm land to improve drainage. Sarpy County, Nebraska. (Photo by R. C. Kubic, Soil Conservation Service, U.S. Department of Agriculture.)

One such method is the lengthening of the stream profile, within any given range of elevation, by a process known as *meandering*. Meanders are simply a series of broad curves in a river (Fig. 11-13); by following this curving pattern, the stream requires a greater length of flow to drop a certain height than if the path between the two elevation points were straight. A stream, being inanimate, obviously does not consciously lengthen its profile by means of meandering. Laboratory studies, however, have been conducted of water flowing in channels cut through sands and silt. Invariably, if experiments are carried on for a long enough period of time, the sediments in the bank of the stream become unstable at some point and cave into the stream. The caved-in sediments present an obstacle to stream flow and deflect the water toward the opposite bank. This deflected water impinges on the opposite bank and causes greater erosion there than had previously been the case. The opposite bank then tends to wear away into a shallow curve. When this curve is formed, the water coming out of it is deflected back toward the bank from which the original cave-in had come. Additional erosion and further curving is initiated, then, at the point where the water impinges on this bank, and by this sequential process a series of irregular curves is formed in the course of the stream. The meanders formed in this process tend to lengthen themselves, and ultimately a broad and complex meander pattern is formed, such as is shown in Fig. 11-14, *A–D*.

Meanders are essentially self-perpetuating—that is, the stream water is deflected in such a manner around the various curves that erosion is continually taking place on the outside of a meander curve, and the rela-

Fig. 11-13. Typical meandering river, Bayou Chene, in southern Louisiana. (Photo by W. Krawiec.)

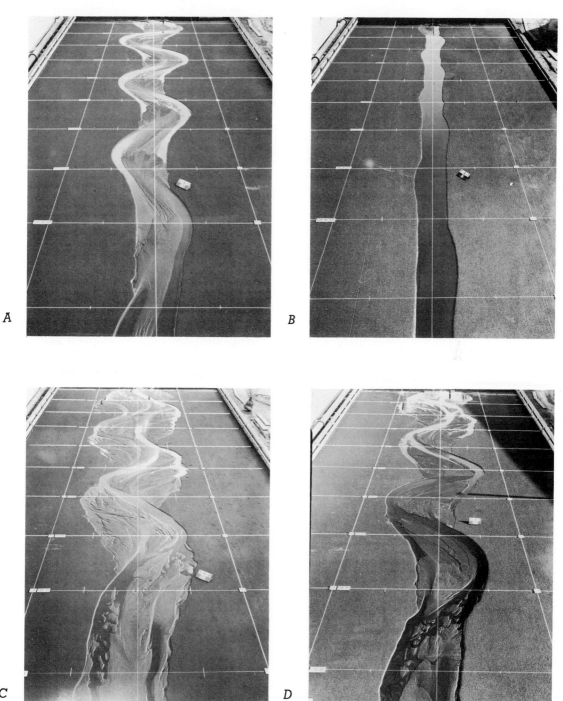

Fig. 11-14. Sequence of photographs which show progressively from *A* to *D* the evolution of meanders in a stream. As described in the text, meandering generally starts as a result of a cave-in along one bank as water is poured along the original artificial channel cut in the loose sandy material of the flume bed. The meanders extend themselves, and deposits are formed in the meander belt. In order to maintain resemblance to natural conditions, sand is added to the water at the source. (U.S. Army Photographs by U.S. Army Engineers Waterways Experiment Station, Vicksburg, Miss.)

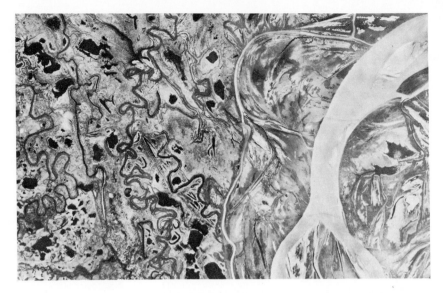

Fig. 11-15. Extreme meanders developed in the flat floodplain of the Kuskokwim River, Alaska. (Photo by Fairchild Aerial Surveys, courtesy of Esso Production Research.)

tively slow-moving water on the inside of the curve becomes a site of deposition of sediment. Thus by continued erosion of the outer bank and deposition along the inner bank, meanders tend to lengthen themselves until they form exceptionally intricate loops. The extreme stage of this process is shown in Fig. 11-15. Ultimately the meanders become sufficiently intricate and the necks between adjacent points sufficiently thin that the stream is able to wash past some meander-bend by eroding through the thin neck. When this happens, the meander area is essentially cut off, for the stream water will naturally follow the steepest gradient—that is, the shortest path between two points in a downstream direction. Thus all of the water is diverted through the cut-off channel in the former meander neck, and the meander tends to dry up or be filled with sediment. Cut-off meander bends developed in this fashion may become lakes partially filled in or enclosed at either end, and the resultant pattern is sufficiently unique that it has been given the special term of *oxbow lake* (Fig. 11-16). Practically all streams meander to a greater or lesser degree except in those portions where erosion is exceptionally rapid. The ubiquitous occurrence of meandering merely serves to indicate that stream flow, in general, is a relatively unstable process.

We have indicated in the special and rather minor case of meander cut-offs that streams may change their course from time to time. In some case changes may be quite significant. Some of the

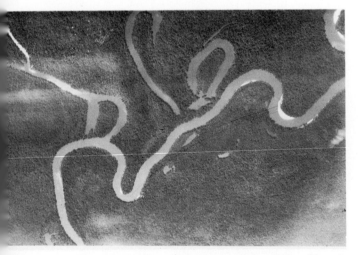

Fig. 11-16. Oxbow lakes developed by Sabine River in southern Louisiana. (Photo by G. M. Griffin.)

causes for changing courses of streams might be meander cut-off, blockage of the former stream path by landslides or volcanic filling, faulting, warping or other structural activity, and in some cases the activities of man in building dams, levees, and similar river-control devices. The continual shifting of a stream from one position to another means that the entire valley which it hollows out is wider than the meander belt at any one particular time. Thus a stream flowing in a general north-south direction may impinge at one time on the eastern side of the valley, pushing the walls farther to the east, and at a later time may impinge on the western side of the valley and cause the western valley slopes to retreat. The portion of the valley which the stream is not occupying at any particular time tends to be filled in with sediments from the valley walls or, more commonly, with sediments deposited from the stream during flood-stages; during floods the bank is overtopped, and the waters spread throughout the entire valley. Thus the generally flat floor of a typical stream valley is entitled a *floodplain,* and it is this plain which is filled by major flooding. A typical valley floodplain with a stream occupying one portion of it is shown in Fig. 11-5. Broad valleys and floodplains are formed only when a stream has eroded its valley down sufficiently so that it is no longer expending all of its energy in cutting vertically. That is, if the stream is deriving a capacity load from previously untouched rock at the floor of the valley, there will be no opportunity for the stream to pick up very much material from the walls and thus cause the walls to move backward and broaden out the valley. When the gradient has been reduced, however, to the point where the stream is no longer cutting downward quite so actively, then erosion of the walls starts, the valley is

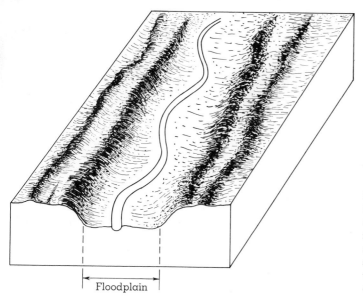

Floodplain

Fig. 11-17. Relationship of river and floodplain to valley walls. The walls are steepest where the river directly impinges on them. This is a late stage in the erosional cycle, as shown by the fact that the valley is wider than the area which can be cut by the river in any one position.

Fig. 11-18. The Red River, Oklahoma and Texas, is a braided stream along part of its course. (Courtesy of U.S. Department of Agriculture.)

broadened, floodplain deposits may form, and the continual sweeping of the river from one side of the valley to the other causes the ultimate development of the typical valley-floodplain complex that is shown in Fig. 11-17. The floodplains of the Nile and many other rivers are particularly fertile, as each flood renews many of the essential nutrients in the soil.

Streams whose gradients are more gentle than that of a graded condition can reach grade by the simple expedient of depositing material and thus building up their elevations. Such a condition, obviously, cannot occur throughout the entire length of the stream but may be characteristic of portions of its length. Our previous example of a mountain stream spreading out onto a flat plain is a typical case of a stream in which a portion of the gradient is below grade. One phenomenon which occurs in streams of this type is called *braiding* and results from a rapid dumping of material at some point in the stream where capacity is no longer sufficiently large to handle the sedimentary debris being developed upstream. The term *braided* refers to the tendency of the deposited sedimentary material to choke the stream and cause the waters to separate into a number of smaller interconnecting channels. A typical example of such a stream is shown in Fig. 11-18.

One feature common to many streams is the terrace, which can be formed in both an erosional and a depositional fashion. *Terraces* are broad, relatively flat areas on the sides of valleys above the level of the stream. Generally, they dip slightly downstream. One major method of terrace formation is the cutting action of streams on the valley sides (Fig. 11-19). Thus where a stream impinges against the rock of the valley wall, it may cut laterally and plane off a smooth, relatively horizontal area bordered by the valley wall at one side. Terraces on opposite sides of the valley are obviously caused by the switching of the stream back and forth from one side to the other. A series of terraces may be formed within a broad valley as a stream continues to erode lower. Naturally, many upper terraces are destroyed by erosion as the stream reaches lower levels, but in some cases a considerable sequence may be formed. The terraces at the top of the valley are obviously older than those at the bottom, thus reversing the normal age sequence found in stratified rocks. Terraces on opposite sides of the valley may be at identical levels or may be offset to somewhat different levels. The relative level between terraces on opposite sides of the valley depends upon the rate at which the stream switches from side to side in its erosional downcutting. Erosional terraces are commonly rather narrow but in places can become very wide, flat plains.

Fig. 11-19. Multiple terraces on both sides of the Uncompahgre River, Colorado. (Photo by T. H. Foss.)

Terraces may also consist of the remnants of stream and floodplain deposits left behind as the stream erodes progressively lower in the valley. In order for such terraces to form, it is necessary that the erosion take place in a series of steps. Between each period of downcutting there is a period in which stream deposits were formed and in which floodplain deposits filled in and leveled off the remainder of the valley. Later downcutting, perhaps caused by general uplifting of the area, would cause the stream to erode away many of the former deposits. In some valleys, however, these depositional terraces are left as small remnants along the upper portions of the sides.

HUMID LANDSCAPES

Now that we have mentioned a number of the features developed along rivers themselves, it is possible to turn our attention to the evolution of various types of landscapes. We shall first discuss the typical sequence of development of features characteristic of a humid landscape and then a similar sequence of features found in more arid areas. As a starting point for our discussion of the evolution of a typical humid landscape, consider a relatively flat surface extending over many hundreds of miles. This surface may have formed, for example, by the uplift of a series of sediments which remained fairly horizontal, or it may have formed in a variety of other ways. The establishment of drainage (stream) patterns on such a surface is difficult, water tends to collect in various low spots, and the few rivers which do develop are generally rather small. One typical feature of such a landscape is lakes. If this area now undergoes significant uplift, the development of major streams takes place at a rapid pace both by downward erosion and by *headward erosion,* that is, lengthening the stream valley by erosion in an up-slope direction at the head of the valley. The valleys of both major streams and tributaries are cut deeply, and the barriers which contributed to the former development of lakes are rapidly cut away, and the lakes disappear. In this early stage of erosion, floodplains are not formed, and the base of the valley therefore tends to be only as wide as the stream. Such valleys which widen only slightly upward are said to be "V-shaped" (Fig. 11-11). Landscapes of this type are said to be *youthful.*

At a later period of stream evolution, as streams erode down toward their base level, valley-widening begins as the result of two processes. One process, a comparatively minor one, is the actual effect of the stream on the wall of the valley, causing the caving-in of banks and removal of material. A more significant method of valley-widening is the carrying of surface debris to the streams by water running over the valley sides. Rain water, as it falls upon normal rock or soil, tends to form small rivulets or gullies (Fig. 11-20) or in some cases flows as a thin sheet toward the valley bottom. These rivulets and sheets, which are hardly of significant size and cannot be called streams, are capable of bringing a large amount of material from valley walls down to the stream itself. In this way a major amount of material is delivered directly to the stream, and it is unnecessary for the stream to do any more than to transport the

Fig. 11-20. Initial stages of gullying, near Santa Maria, California. (Photo by L. Leifer, Soil Conservation Service, U.S. Department of Agriculture.)

debris. Another method by which material is delivered to the stream is presumably of great importance, although it is difficult to evaluate. This method is the steady downhill movement of rocks and soil, much in the manner of an extremely slow landslide. Landslide and other mass movements of this type are discussed more thoroughly in Chapter 12, but we may mention here the large amount of material which can be poured directly into the stream by such processes. By a combination of various methods, then, a stream valley becomes widened and generally becomes more gently sloping as the stream begins to reach its base level. The typical landscape of this stage of erosion consists of gently rolling hills with intervening shallow stream valleys and a well-defined system of drainage which has prevented the formation of lakes or other features of a flat landscape. Such a landscape is called *mature*.

If there is no additional uplift of the area or other reason for the stream to begin eroding more strenuously (Fig. 11-21), this stage of roll-

Fig. 11-21. Goosenecks of the San Juan River, Utah. These extreme meanders formed on a level surface when the river was in an advanced stage of the erosional cycle. At this time the area was uplifted (rejuvenated) and the meander pattern was cut into the underlying rocks. (Photo by J. J. W. Rogers.)

1 Youth

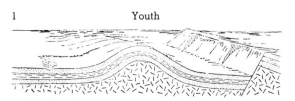

Simple, block-like undissected masses; a few streams.

2 Maturity

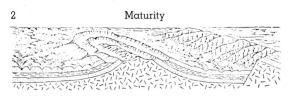

Completely dissected, no original surface preserved.

3 Old Age

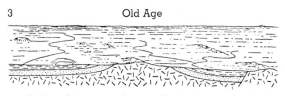

Reduced to a peneplane; with a few monadnocks.

4 Rejuvenation

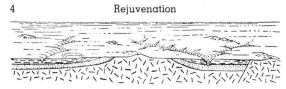

Peneplane raised; a few streams incised below the surface.

Fig. 11-22. Geomorphic cycle of a humid region. (From *Geomorphology, An Introduction to the Study of Landscapes*, by A. K. Lobeck. Copyright © 1939 McGraw-Book Company. Used by permission of McGraw-Hill Book Company.)

ing landscapes and valley widening passes gradually into the final stage of stream development (*old age*). In this final stage, the mass movements and stream erosion have planed off the landscape to a virtually flat surface, possibly leaving behind small remnant knobs of reasonably resistant rock, but generally forming a featureless plain. On such a plain, instead of having a well-defined drainage pattern, the streams probably meander rather sluggishly in various directions. The surface formed in this fashion is called a *peneplain,* which signifies a broad, flat, and laterally very extensive area developed solely by erosion. Not all flat surfaces have been formed by erosion. Many represent the result of a depositional in-filling of previous irregularities in the surface, possibly with a final capping of some horizontally deposited and laterally extensive sediment, or possibly somewhat leveled over by volcanic activity. Plains of this type are not referred to as peneplains, and no special term is applied to them. Although the definitions of peneplain and depositional plain are quite clear, in some cases it may be difficult geologically to distinguish one from the other. The entire sequence of landscape evolution is shown diagrammatically in Fig. 11-22.

ARID LANDSCAPES

Arid landscapes differ significantly from those formed in humid regions for a number of reasons. One of these factors is the increased activity of wind in arid regions, where its effectiveness is not reduced by plant cover or by the binding action of moisture in the loose rock and soil on the surface. Another factor is probably the absence of moisture in surficial materials, which thus prevents the extensive downhill movement which is characteristic of humid areas. The wet soils of humid regions move downhill fairly readily, thus rounding the hills and giving a subdued aspect to the landscape. In arid regions, however, the development of soil is minimal, and the hard rocks which occur on the surface are not capable of such down-slope movement. Thus, in an arid region the widening of valleys presumably is the result solely of direct stream erosion. In arid regions, therefore, the typical stream valley has walls which are quite steep regardless of the stage of development of the stream itself. When the stream reaches a stage in which it is capable of widening its valley, the walls are simply pushed backward but not downward. The valley-widening is aided in part by rock falls and small landslides from the valley sides, but these processes are intermittent as compared to the continual down-slope movement in humid regions. The sequence of evolution of arid landscapes is shown in Fig. 11-23.

One feature characteristic of many arid landscapes is a basin of interior drainage. Such a basin is wholly enclosed by higher land on all sides so that drainage is not connected ultimately to the sea, and streams merely flow into the basin. The formation of closed basins is, of course, promoted by a general absence of water, which prevents the development of through-going drainage patterns and the opening of channels from the ocean back into all parts of the land area. Absence of water, however, is not by itself capable of causing a basin of interior drainage to form. In most cases basins of interior drainage represent structural low spots, perhaps grabens developed recently by faults extending to the surface. Some low spots, such as Bad Water in Death Valley (279 feet below sea level) or the Dead Sea (nearly 1300 feet below sea level), were obviously formed by structural down-drop. It is clear that in the absence of the establishment of some low base level by structural means it is impossible for stream activity to cause erosion below sea level.

As an example of the features which may be formed in a basin of interior drainage, we may look at Death Valley, California (Figs. 11-24 and 11-25). Here the valley is bordered by mountains extending many thousands of feet above the basin floor. The break between mountain and valley floor is sharp in most places, and the intermittent streams have deposited large amounts of material at the base of the mountain slopes. Naturally, stream activity in an area such as this is highly irregular. Deserts vary

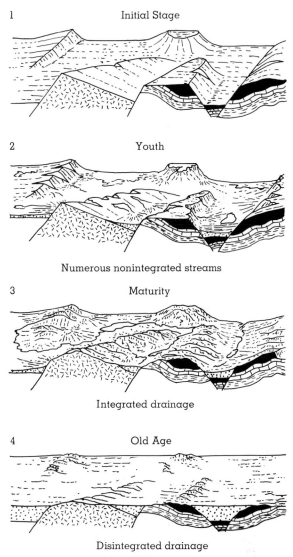

Fig. 11-23. Geomorphic cycle of an arid region. (From *Geomorphology, An Introduction to the Study of Landscapes,* by A. K. Lobeck. Copyright © 1939 McGraw-Hill Book Company. Used by permission of McGraw-Hill Book Company.)

Fig. 11-24. Death Valley, California. (National Park Service Photograph by Norman A. Bishop.)

in the amount of rainfall which they receive, but in many areas streams contain water only once, or perhaps twice, a year. The remainder of the year, the bed is dry and filled with sand left over from the last flooding. The large amounts of material deposited by the streams at the base of the mountains in Death Valley have the shapes shown in Fig. 11-26. In aerial view the sediments appear to fan out from the stream valley onto the

Fig. 11-25. Death Valley, California. (National Park Service Photograph by Norman A. Bishop.)

Fig. 11-26. Alluvial fans in Death Valley, California. (National Park Service Photograph by Norman A. Bishop.)

valley floor, and the overall shape is much like that of a fan. Deposits of this type, therefore, are called *alluvial fans,* the term "fan" coming from the general shape, and the term "alluvial" referring to deposited material. Geologists commonly use the word *alluvium* to refer to valley-fill deposits of all types. Also in Death Valley are several other features we should take note of. The loose debris that forms by disintegration of rocks in and around the valley is, of course, subject to wind activity, and sand dunes are found in some portions of the valley. (The process of the formation and movement of sand dunes is discussed in more detail in Chapter 12.) The infrequent rains dissolve a small amount of the more soluble portions of the rock, and upon washing into the valley, they commonly deposit this material by evaporation. Thus, salt forms a white encrustation upon many of the stream channels within the floor of Death Valley (Fig. 11-24).

A feature typical of many arid landscapes is a *pediment,* which is a rock surface cut back into a mountain from the adjoining valley (Fig. 11-27). In contrast to the cutting of terraces by streams in humid areas by the impinging of a stream against the wall of the valley, pediments are formed by the abrasional action of streams issuing out of the mountain and flowing downward toward the valley floor. These streams tend to scour the rock into a flat surface with a roughly triangular shape and an

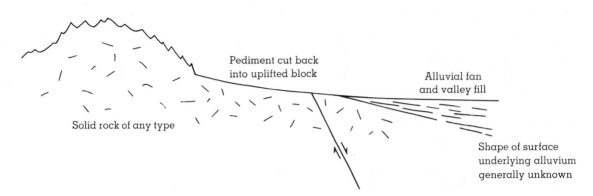

Fig. 11-27. Relationships among pediment, fan, and mountain range in arid regions.

apex at the point where the stream issues from the mountains. Thus a pediment, at first glance, looks very much like an alluvial fan, and in fact the tendency of many pediments to be covered by a shallow layer of stream-deposited alluvium a few feet thick makes the similarity even more striking. One of the difficulties confronting a geologist working in deserts is that of distinguishing between fans and pediments. In some mountain ranges, the pediment represents a zone of erosion between the fan and the valley wall (Fig. 11-27).

Some enclosed basins are sufficiently broad and flat for the central portions of their floor to receive very little material from the valley side. In such cases, the sediment that is blown or washed into these areas tends to be relatively fine-grained silt or clay. The silt and clay gradually accumulate to form thin, remarkably flat layers which may extend over several square miles. These broad flat deposits of fine-grained sediments in the central part of the valley are termed *playas* (Fig. 11-28).

Fig. 11-28. Playa covered by thin sheet of water. (Photo by T. W. Donnelly.)

In areas where rainfall is sufficient to form either streams or underground circulating waters which are capable of reaching the central portion of a valley, the dissolved salt carried by these waters may precipitate in the valley floor. In this way it is possible to build up considerable thicknesses of salt and related evaporite minerals. Sometimes enough water accumulates to form an actual saline lake, such as Great Salt Lake, Utah. In other places the only indication of such precipitation is a thick layer of horizontally laminated salt deposits. These dry lakes can be of considerable economic importance. Most of the lithium produced in this country, for example, is obtained from underground brines pumped from beneath the salt crust of Searles Dry Lake, California.

Features such as pediments and fans are, of course, not restricted to areas of interior drainage. In fact, the general process of arid-area erosion by retreat of the valley walls is independent of whether the drainage is open to the ocean or closed.

One of the major current arguments in the field of geomorphology concerns the relative effectiveness of valley-widening by a general reduction of slopes, as we discussed for humid areas, or by a pushing back of steep slopes, as we discussed for arid areas. Some geomorphologists, for example, feel that the widening of valleys by the retreat of steep slopes is as effective a mechanism in humid regions as it is in arid regions. The brief explanations which we have given here for the origin of various types of landscapes are somewhat idealized.

Before leaving the subject of deserts, we should mention the fact that most deserts do not contain much sand. This statement is true of the deserts in the southwestern part of the United States and northern Mexico, of the Sahara Desert, of the deserts in the Arabian Peninsula, indeed of virtually any desert in the world. The romantic picture of

Fig. 11-29. Desert topography in sand sea in the Empty Quarter of southern Saudi Arabia. (Photo courtesy of Arabian American Oil Co.)

Fig. 11-30. Sand sea in Arabia. (Photo courtesy of Arabian American Oil Company.)

deserts as a vast sea of sand across which the stately and virtuous camel may plod is simply not a correct one.

In the Sahara Desert, for example, over three-fourths of the desert surface consists of nothing but bare rock, and this proportion is probably also accurate for deserts in most other parts of the world. There are, however, a few large areas extending for tens or hundreds of miles which contain nothing but sand. Many of these areas are in the western portion of the Sahara Desert and occupy a major portion of Algeria. A similar sand desert in the southern part of the Arabian Peninsula is known as the Rub Al Khali, or Empty Quarter (Figs. 11-29 and 11-30). The name is derived from the fact that in these broad sand areas not even desert nomads are capable of living, except perhaps in scattered oases.

EFFECT OF ROCKS ON STREAM PATTERNS

One of the interesting aspects of the study of geomorphology is the opportunity it affords to determine the geology of an area by the pattern which rivers have on its surface. The map pattern of the rivers is commonly referred to as a *drainage pattern* and is a product of interaction between river erosion and the underlying rocks. The pattern is also partly dependent on the stage of development of the landscape, but in most areas the nature of the underlying rocks is reflected in virtually every stage of landscape evolution. In this section we shall discuss the mechanism of stream erosion and its interaction with underlying rock structures.

The resistance of rocks to erosion is not solely a function of the type of rock, because the amount and type of sediment carried by a stream is a major factor in determining the rate at which materials will be eroded. We may easily verify in the laboratory the fact that water carrying sediments is a far more potent erosional agent than clear water. In fact, clear water has virtually no effect on hard rocks. Suspended or saltating sedimentary grains, however, may be driven with considerable force by stream activity against rocks. The result of the innumerable impacts of this type is to round off sedimentary materials and to form a smooth, or possibly even polished, surface.

The process described above is known as *abrasion* and refers to the general tendency of rock materials to be reduced in size during transportational processes. In the average stream, for example, the mean size of sediment in suspension decreases downstream. This decrease is not, however, necessarily a result of abrasional processes. We have already noted the fact that finer grains tend to settle less rapidly than coarse grains, and thus there is a natural tendency for streams to carry finer grains more rapidly and more effectively downstream than their coarser equivalents. The downstream decrease in grain size, therefore, may simply be the result of the separation of coarse and fine materials, sometimes referred to as *sorting,* and not a result of abrasion. This is a question which has stimulated considerable research by sedimentary petrologists, but no definitive answer has yet been obtained.

Abrasional action of particles carried by a stream, or dragged along the bottom, is shown by the nature of the floor of many streams. Where a stream flows across bare rock and the stream bottom is not simply an accumulation of sand, the floor is generally extremely irregular. The irregularity is caused by abrasional or grinding action of pebbles and other materials as they are swirled around the bottom by the turbulence of the stream. In places this grinding action may form deep, smooth, and almost circular holes or may leave an irregularly pitted, highly rough surface.

A typical and simple example of the effect of underlying rocks on the nature of streams is the development of a waterfall. Waterfalls form primarily where layers of rock which are highly resistant to stream erosion overlie considerable thicknesses of much softer rock. Where the resistant rock is broken through, the erosion of the underlying material tends to take place quite rapidly, and the stream quickly becomes oversteepened. A typical example of the development of a waterfall in this

Fig. 11-31. Horseshoe Falls, one of the three portions of Niagara Falls. (Photo by Power Authority of the State of New York, courtesy of Niagara Falls Chamber of Commerce.)

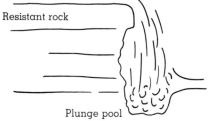

Fig. 11-32. Cross section of typical waterfall.

fashion is Niagara Falls (Fig. 11-31). Here a resistant dolomite composes the lip of the falls and holds up the waters of the Niagara River. At the lip of the falls the water plunges abruptly past softer underlying rocks and drops about 170 feet. A cross section downstream through Niagara Falls is typical of many other waterfalls and appears as in Fig. 11-32. The force of the cascading water is sufficiently large to cut a plunge pool at the base of the falls. This pool is below the surface of the river further downstream, where erosion is not as violent. Waterfalls gradually retreat upstream as pieces of the lip are eroded and fall off into the plunge pool and are carried further downstream.

A feature similar to waterfalls is a river form known as *rapids,* which are really simply a series of small waterfalls. Rapids form where resistant rock prevents the development of a smooth stream profile and permits the formation of short stretches of very high gradient.

We have noted the fact that different types of rock have a pronounced effect on the development of a stream and the landscape patterns formed by stream erosion. In humid areas, resistant rocks are generally sandstones and various granites and metamorphic rocks. Limestones tend to dissolve, and shales consist of material which is quite easily eroded. Except in the case of shales, these resistances are virtually reversed in arid areas. Here the absence of water prevents the solution of limestones and causes them to be a resistant rock type. Conversely, the tendency of coarse-grained igneous and metamorphic rocks to undergo granular disintegration in desert areas generally renders these rocks fairly soft and permits them to be eroded quite readily. Regardless of climate, resistant rocks tend to form cliffs, steep slopes, and projections above the surrounding landscape. Nonresistant rocks are easily eroded to low slopes, and where a series of resistant and nonresistant sedimentary layers is exposed, the different rock types can be recognized by alternation of steep and gentle slopes.

Since we have discussed the interrelationships of rock resistance and stream abrasion, let us now return to a consideration of the patterns formed by streams. As a first example, consider the pattern that might form on a granite or flat-lying sediment. Without any directional control by underlying rocks, the streams should have virtually no pattern at all and might be expected to wander erratically, as shown in Fig. 11-33*A*. In contrast to this aimless pattern, the drainage pattern which might be formed on a series of inclined sedimentary rocks is quite different. On such rocks, the soft shales and other materials would be eroded far more rapidly than the relatively hard sandstones and, in a desert area, the limestones. Streams, therefore, will preferentially elongate themselves along the shale beds, and there would be pronounced linearity to the stream pattern. Naturally, some streams would cross the rock structures, but the major pattern would parallel the sedimentary strike (Fig. 11-33*B*). Another type of pattern may be developed around small high areas which are formed by some structural process. These high areas might, for example, be developed by the shallow intrusion of a magma or might be the surface expression of an underlying salt dome. (Salt domes will be discussed in Chapter 15, but we may say here that they simply represent a rise through the sedimentary section of a plug of salt, much in the shape of an intruded igneous rock which does not erupt onto the ground surface.) Water, naturally, will tend to run off such high areas, and a pattern of radially outward drainage may be developed similar to that shown in Fig. 11-33*C*. Such high areas may also simply cause the deflection of streams, and unnatural bends in streams in petroleum-producing areas are currently being examined for the purpose of determining whether or not they may have been caused by some sort of structural high spot. We shall see in Chapter 15 that oil commonly accumulates in areas which are structurally above the surrounding rocks, and thus the detection of such areas by geomorphologic or other methods is of considerable economic importance.

Not all stream patterns are controlled solely by sedimentary features or structural uplifts. Jointing, for example, has a pronounced effect on the development of streams. Joints, whether open or not, are zones along which surface waters may penetrate, and weathering and subsequent

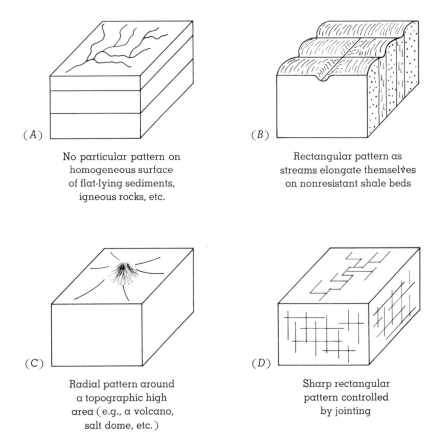

(A) No particular pattern on homogeneous surface of flat-lying sediments, igneous rocks, etc.

(B) Rectangular pattern as streams elongate themselves on nonresistant shale beds

(C) Radial pattern around a topographic high area (e.g., a volcano, salt dome, etc.)

(D) Sharp rectangular pattern controlled by jointing

Fig. 11-33. Various types of stream patterns. These are idealized patterns which would be developed on the types of rocks shown in each diagram.

erosion may be intense. Thus, in many areas, joint surfaces represent planes of relatively decayed rock. Figure 11-33D shows the type of stream pattern which might be formed in an area containing two intersecting sets of joints. The effect of joint or fault surfaces on streams is sufficiently pronounced so that geologists commonly attempt to recognize faults in areas of poor exposure by an investigation of stream patterns. Thus a stream which wanders erratically over the earth's surface through most of its course but follows an absolutely straight path for a few miles is suspected of having encountered a fault or some other linear feature. In desert areas, in particular, faults are commonly marked by elongate topographic depressions brought about by the ready removal of disintegrated rock.

We have by no means provided here an exhaustive treatment of the types of stream patterns and their modes of formation. The object of the preceding discussion has simply been to indicate that features such as streams are closely controlled by the underlying rock types. We have seen examples of the interrelation of the different aspects of geology in many places in the book thus far and will see more in the remaining chapters. These examples serve to indicate the fact that geologists simply cannot operate without a broad knowledge of the subject.

CHAPTER 12 — SECONDARY SCULPTURING AGENTS AND PROCESSES

◀Desert sand. (Courtesy of Arabian American Oil Company.)

Running water is the most important single agent causing the sculpturing of the earth's surface and the transportation of sediment. In this chapter, however, we shall discuss other agents which are responsible for the formation of certain landscape features and also for the movement of significant amounts of material. The term *mass movement* applies to the down-slope movement of large volumes of rock and soil. The movements may be rapid, as in landslides and rock falls, or they may be comparatively slow and continuous. Wind activity is a major feature of many deserts and has been responsible in some parts of the earth for transportation of large quantities of sand, silt, and dust. The movement of ice in glaciers has been responsible not only for the configuration of a large number of mountain ranges but has also been a major cause of the development of the present topography of much of northern North America. These various processes naturally operate together in many situations, and the earth has been sculptured by the complex interaction of these and many other influences.

MASS MOVEMENTS

Landslides

Landslides are the most dramatic forms of mass movements (Fig. 12-1). They occur when a mass of rock on a cliff or mountain face becomes unstable, either because the cliff has been oversteepened by some erosional process or because heavy rains have softened the rock and permitted it to move. In some cases landslides may be triggered by earth movements, such as earthquakes, or they may occur without an obvious outside triggering action. In populated areas landslides may, of course, be catastrophic.

The most catastrophic landslide ever recorded occurred on October 9, 1963, on the side of Mt. Toc, in northern Italy. On that day, over 250 million cubic yards of rock suddenly collapsed into the reservoir behind the Vaiont Dam, which had been constructed in a valley leading into the major Piave River Valley. The collapse of this mass within a period of less than one minute filled the reservoir for a length of over one mile and caused the stored water to pour over the dam and into the Piave Valley one mile downstream. The wall of water, which was over 200 feet high as it entered the main valley, swept downstream and destroyed everything in its path. Over 2600 people were killed, and a number of towns were totally eliminated. The sliding was caused by a number of factors, and among the most important of these were:

1. The valley walls were exceptionally steep, and indeed, this area had long been known for landsliding.
2. Sedimentary rocks on both sides of the valley dip toward the valley, which is thus a syncline, and many of the rocks are soft shales without much resistance to shear.

3. Heavy rains for two weeks prior to the sliding had saturated the ground, thus further reducing the strength of the rocks.
4. Construction of the dam had caused formation of the large reservoir, which provided a hydraulic pressure at the base of the rocks on the former valley floor and also caused seepage of water into the banks.

Any one of these factors by itself might not have caused sliding, but their combination was disastrous. The landslide occurred when the water-saturated, weak, dipping rocks simply could no longer support their own weight.

As an example of landsliding caused by earthquakes, we may consider the Hebgen earthquake of August 17, 1959, in southwestern Montana. This earthquake occurred in areas infrequently affected by such shocks, and in consequence a fair amount of unstable material had accumulated on the mountain sides throughout the region. The result was that shortly after the earthquake a large slide occurred on a spur of the Madison Range, and several million cubic feet of rock and dirt hurtled into the valley of the Madison River. The slide and its results are shown in Figs. 12-2 and 12-3. As a result of in-filling of the valley and deposition of a large volume of rock across the course of the river, a lake was formed. The area, fortunately, is not densely populated, and damage was minimal. These two examples serve to introduce us to the several problems of the mechanism of landslides and other mass movements, the topographic results of such movements, and the evidence that may be ob-

Fig. 12-1. Landslide along coast at Santa Monica, California, 1958. (Photo by Pacific Air Industries, Inc.)

Fig. 12-2. Madison
landslide caused by
Hebgen Lake earth-
quake. (U.S. Forest
Service photo by W. E.
Steuerwald.)

served in the geologic record to indicate the presence of former mass
movements.

Detailed studies of landslides indicate that many of them have a cross-
sectional form roughly as shown in Fig. 12-4. The critical features shown
in this picture are a surface of slippage, which is concave upward, and
the protruding mass at the outer end of the slide, which is commonly
referred to as a *toe*. The mechanism of movement of rapid landslides
apparently involves primarily the development of a curved surface of
shear. Sliding then occurs when the weight of the rock exceeds the weight
which may be supported. In other words, when the shear stress generated
by the rock overburden is greater than the shear stress which may be
supported at any point, the rock slides along a shear surface developed

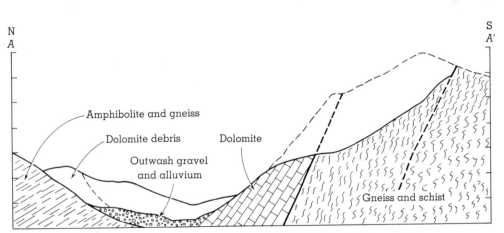

N   S
A   A'

Amphibolite and gneiss

Dolomite debris   Dolomite

Outwash gravel
and alluvium

Gneiss and schist

Fig. 12-3. Cross section of Madison slide shown in Fig. 12-2. Dashed line indicates original
topography before slide. (From J. B. Hadley, *U.S. Geological Survey Professional Paper
435,* 1964.)

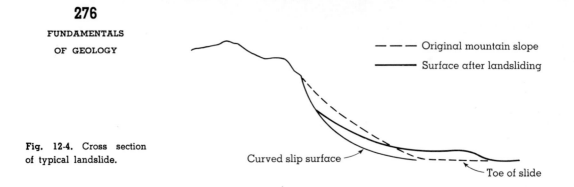

Fig. 12-4. Cross section of typical landslide.

much as a fault surface is developed in response to directed stress. The shearing stress must, of course, be largest at the base of the mass before sliding commences, and it is presumably here that the initial slip surface develops. As the slide begins, the slip surface is apparently rapidly extended back into the mountain and upward. The fact that the overburden at higher levels is not capable of developing independent slip surfaces may prevent the slip surface from being extended as a straight plane. In this manner it is possible to account, rather weakly, for the curvature of the landslide surface.

The total duration of most landslides is measured in terms of a few minutes. The material which slides down the mountain, therefore, gains considerable momentum by its high speed and tends to flow out over the valley floor. In some cases, broad valleys may be covered by such a flowage. The resistance to flow, of course, becomes quite large as the slide material moves across a flat surface, and it is this resistance which causes the material in the front of the slide to be piled up in a large protruding mass, the toe.

An immediate question concerning landslides is why the shear strength of the rock on the mountainside is suddenly exceeded. In answer to this question, three processes can probably be considered the major immediate causes of most landsliding. One mechanism to produce stresses exceeding the shear strength is to reduce the strength by soaking the rock or soil in water. A saturated rock, in which the component grains are lubricated by water in the pores and on the grain borders, simply does not have the strength of a dry rock of comparable composition and structure. It is for this reason that landsliding commonly accompanies heavy rains or floods. Naturally, relatively impervious rocks such as granite are less affected by this soaking in water than soils or loose sediments. Another mechanism for causing landsliding is the increase of shear stress and the reduction of strength of rocks by loading the inclined surface of the rock on the mountain or cliff side. Such loading may occur naturally, but it is commonly the result of injudicious construction of buildings or other man-made features. The loading causes a compression of the rock and, in particular, tends to flatten out clays and other minerals of similar shape. This slight deformation within the rock body tends to promote the formation of surfaces of easy slippage. That is, the rock forms surfaces on which resistance to shear is reduced below the normal value for the material, and in these cases if a sufficient weight of overlying rock is present, landsliding will occur. A third method for the creation of landslides is oversteepening of cliff faces. This may be done naturally by, for example, river erosion on the outside of a meander bend, or it may be done artificially by quarrying, or road or house construction (Fig. 12-5). The removal of material at the base of the cliff removes support for the overlying rock. Oversteepening can also be caused by faulting or other tectonic movements.

The slip surface formed by landslides is actually a small fault plane. The only particular feature which distinguishes landslide slip surfaces from true fault planes is the fact that the slip surface is of limited extent and obviously does not extend into rocks underlying the landslide mass. Geologists, however, are frequently confronted with the difficult problem of determining whether some surficially mappable slip surface represents merely a landslide surface or whether it is the surface expression of a fault which extends to considerable depth. This is a question that must be answered by examination of the surrounding rocks and not by an investigation of the slip surface itself. If the surface occurs on the side of a mountain and is bounded on the valley side by a chaotic jumble of landslide material, then of course, there is little problem. Furthermore, if the surface can be traced along strike for considerable distances and particularly into flat areas or areas in which landsliding obviously could not have occurred, then again there is no problem in recognizing the fault.

Consider, now, the type of problem posed by mass movement such as is shown in Figs. 12-6 and 12-7. The geologist sees only the surface trace of the slip plane and the downward offsetting of strata towards the valley. The preservation of geologic features such as stratifica-

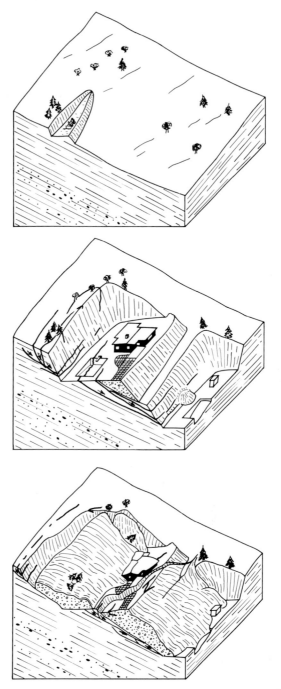

Fig. 12-5. Stages in the development of a hillside. The hill slope is parallel to bedding of loose shales. When the slope is graded by bulldozers and water seeps into the ground, the shales begin sliding. Note that surface cracks, particularly where they cut a swimming pool, permit additional water to enter the ground. (From Dr. Richard H. Jahns, *Engineering and Science*, December 1958, published at the California Institute of Technology.)

Fig. 12-6. Destruction of property by minor sliding in the Palos Verdes Hills, southern California. (Photo courtesy of California State Division of Mines and Geology.)

tion and the normal sedimentary sequence obviously indicates that the landsliding movement was not a rapid and chaotic event. Apparently a very slight instability on the mountainside has permitted the formation of a landslide slip surface on which movement is relatively slow. Movement of this type is commonly referred to as *slumping,* and the results are the downslope shifting of blocks without concurrent destruction of the features within the mass. The geologist who is able to examine only the surface features in cases of this type may find it virtually impossible to determine whether or not movement was essentially a landslide movement or whether a true and vertically extensive fault has been developed.

The distinction between slumping and landsliding is merely the rate at which the movement takes place. In slumping, the movement is either slow enough or of a limited enough extent so that the structures of the moved block are not disturbed. Slumping occurs on both small and large scales. Figure 12-7, for example, shows a number of small slumps along the oversteepened edge of a river bank. In some of the desert mountain ranges in the southwestern part of the United States, geologists have recognized slump blocks many miles long. As can be predicted from the curved nature of their slip surfaces, many slump blocks undergo a slight rotation as a result of their movement. On a large scale this rotation of beds may pose serious problems for a geologist interested in determining structures.

Fig. 12-7. Slumping along a river bank cut in soft sediments in North Dakota. (Photo by D. R. Crandell, *U.S. Geological Survey Professional Paper 307,* 1958.)

Creep

In addition to landsliding and slumping, there is another and even more important mechanism of mass movement which is termed *creep*. Creep is simply the steady, but exceptionally slow, down-slope movement of loose rock and soil. The rate and amount of creep is increased by the presence of water, and evidence for creep is most commonly found in humid parts of the country. The evidence that creep has occurred on some particular hillside takes a variety of forms (Fig. 12-8). For example, it is not uncommon to find trees which have been bent in the manner shown in Fig. 12-8. Since trees always tend to grow vertically upward, the curvature shown by the tree trunks in this picture signifies a steady rotation during growth as the soil layers moved down hill. Inanimate objects such as fence posts and telephone poles are, in general, simply tilted in a down-hill direction. Creep may have a profound effect on the orientation of sedimentary beds. The more weathered portions of beds closest to the ground surface may be involved in down-slope movement with the resulting change in attitude similar to that shown in Fig. 12-8. This figure illustrates another of the difficulties in geologic mapping, namely that of determining whether or not the surficial outcrop one is investigating is actually representative of the true orientation of the underlying rock.

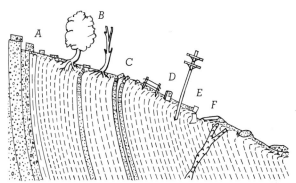

Fig. 12-8. Common evidences of creep. *A*—moved joint blocks. *B*—curved tree trunks. *C*—downslope bending of strata. *D*—displaced posts and fences. *E*—broken walls. *F*—displaced roads. (From C. F. S. Sharpe, *Landslides and Related Phenomena*, Columbia University Press, New York, 1938; Fig. 2, p. 23.)

Rates of creep are highly variable, depending upon rock type and climate. Measurements can be made by observations of tilted features such as shown in Fig. 12-8, and in general the rate of creep is measured in terms of fractions of an inch per year.

The mechanism of creeping is obviously somewhat different from the mechanism of landsliding or slumping. In creep no particular slip surface can be recognized, and the rate of movement simply decreases from the land surface until it reaches zero at some point several feet below the surface. In short, creeping is essentially a form of rock flowage. We encounter here the same difficulties in explaining the mechanism of flow as we did in Chapter 10 in our discussion of the response of rocks to directed stress. In loose, well-watered soil, rock grains apparently can slip past each other, and this is probably the major mechanism for slow down-slope movements.

Although creep is slow, its importance is enormous. Much of the material that streams transport has been delivered to them by such mass movements which make easily erodable material available on the stream banks. The gently rolling, rounded landscapes typical of humid areas are probably developed largely as a result of creeping movements. One line of reasoning that may be used to verify this last statement is based on the typically concave upward profile of a stream. Streams with this type of profile obviously would sculpture hills into a form in which the slopes increased in steepness toward the hilltop. Ideally, streams establishing their typical profiles by running radially down all sides of the hill would leave a sharp point at the top of the hill, and all of the slopes would be concave upward. Features approximating this type of topography may be found in desert regions but are not common in more humid areas. Even in humid regions, the lower slopes of hills generally are concave upward, but the upper stretches are invariably rounded off into a profile which is convex upward. It is logical to propose that mass movements, such as creep, are primarily responsible for this rounding process.

Ancient mass movements

It is difficult to find ancient rocks which have been transported into their present position by landsliding or other mass movements. The major reason, of course, is that mass movements occur in land areas with considerable elevation, and deposits in these areas are more subject to erosion than they are to covering and preservation by later sedimentation. Typical recent landslide deposits are characterized by a wild jumble of materials of all different sizes and all different rock types. Obviously, as material is tumbling down the side of a hill, rocks from all levels and all sources are picked up and mixed together. Furthermore, there is a tremendous amount of crushing during landsliding, and the result is the formation of a large quantity of debris and fine-grained rock flour which is packed together with the coarser, unbroken fragments. A rock with these properties should not be too difficult to recognize geologically, although there are certain problems of confusion with other types of deposits. For example, the debris deposited by glaciers may, at least in part, be similar in both composition and structure. Alluvial fan deposits and other coarse materials formed by a short interval of transportation also have properties similar to those of landslide debris.

As an example of an ancient landslide we can consider the Tin Mountain landslide just northwest of Death Valley, California. In the valley below Tin Mountain is a large mass of chaotically jumbled (brecciated) material several hundred feet thick which may be recognized as a landslide by the following features:

1. The mass consists of angular pieces of rock typical of the sediments outcropping on the cliff face of Tin Mountain. These angular fragments, which range from silt up to blocks with a diameter of eight feet, rest on sediments in the valley floor which are totally different from any rock type in the overlying mass.

2. Several large landslide scars occur on Tin Mountain.

3. The surface of the mass in the valley floor has the hummocky appearance characteristic of the topography developed on modern landslides.

The amount of material involved in the slide may be estimated from the sizes of the scars on the adjoining mountain face. The total volume is approximately 2350 million cubic yards, which is ten times as much as that involved in the Vaiont Dam slide.

Other types of mass movements

We have not discussed in this section certain types of mass movement which are relatively restricted in their occurrence. In Arctic regions, for example, spring thaws commonly leave hillsides with a thick mantle of water-saturated soil, moss, and bits of rock. This material commonly flows down even very gentle slopes. The process of alternate freezing and thawing in more temperate regions has been considered by some geologists to be a major mechanism for breaking up rock and moving it downslope. In some mountainous regions, vast accumulations of boulders fill valley floors and may undergo some movement which might be characterized as a type of rock flowage. The exact mechanism by which these rock flows move is uncertain, but there is no doubt that the total mass occupying the valley floor is actually moving downhill as a whole. A very dramatic form of movement intermediate between mass movement and stream flow is the *mud flow* (Fig. 12-9). After heavy rains in desert areas, mud-laden water or water-soaked mud with specific gravities in the range of 1.5 to 2.0 may move down dry canyons at speeds up to a few tens of miles per hour.

WIND

As an agent of transportation, wind is far less effective than water in moving large amounts of sedimentary material. The activities of wind are, of course, primarily observed in deserts, where the absence of plant life, coherent soil, and moisture to bind grains together permits wind to pick up surface material far more readily than in a humid area. In this section, we shall study the mechanisms by which wind transports sedimentary particles, the types of deposits which are formed by wind activity, and the evidence for wind erosion.

Mechanisms of transportation

Just as streams transport particles of different sizes in different ways, so wind is also capable of moving material by different processes. Suspension in air is far more difficult than suspension in water simply as a

Fig. 12-9. Mud flow in dry canyon in New Mexico. The height of the flow is approximately one foot. (Photo by R. C. Murray.)

Fig. 12-10. Dust storms in eastern Colorado in 1935. This is typical of the dust storms resulting from wind erosion of dry crop lands in the "Dust Bowl" of the early 1930s. (Photo by Soil Conservation Service, U.S. Department of Agriculture.)

result of the difference in densities of the two media. Nevertheless, it is possible for wind to pick up dust and other extremely fine material and transport it for long distances in a suspended state. Large dust clouds, for example, are characteristic of storm activity in desert areas, and the quantity of material transported in such storms may be enormous. Figure 12-10, for example, shows a dust cloud in Colorado in 1935. In broad, flat stretches of the Sahara Desert dust-laden winds with speeds up to 40 or 50 miles per hour have been reported to require several hours to pass some particular point; such storms are a major hazard to travel. In the early 1930s in the United States the "Dust Bowl" of western Oklahoma, Kansas, and neighboring regions was buffeted by dust-carrying winds for several days at a time. In the Dust Bowl area, dust was picked up from crop-lands which, owing to drought and overplowing, could no longer support crops which would prevent erosion by prevailing winds. The effectiveness of such wind erosion is shown in Fig. 12-11. Exactly similar undesired effects were produced in the 1960s by the "Virgin Lands" programs in the U.S.S.R. The ability of dust to be transported by winds, particularly in the upper atmosphere, is also

Fig. 12-11. Bushes whose root systems help prevent wind erosion. Soil around the bushes has been blown away. (Photo by Soil Conservation Service, U.S. Department of Agriculture.)

attested to by the fact that volcanic ash from highly explosive eruptions is sometimes carried completely around the earth. The ash, for example, from the eruption of Mt. Katmai in southern Alaska in June, 1912, caused a darkening of the sky observed over much of the northern hemisphere.

Sand-sized and coarser material obviously cannot be transported in suspension by wind, except by the most violent winds. The dominant method for the movement of sand appears to be saltation, a process which we discussed more completely in our study of stream transportation in Chapter 11. Saltation, or the jumping of grains along the ground from point to point, is far more effective as a mechanism of wind transportation than in the case of water transportation, for the simple reason that the grain, upon bouncing up from the surface, does not meet as much resistance in its path in air as it does in water. Depending upon the velocity of the wind, the grains may bounce to considerable height, possibly as much as ten feet. The major concentration of saltating material is, however, near the ground, and a man standing in a small windstorm in the desert may find his legs buffeted by sand while the upper part of his body is in perfectly clear air. Grains larger than sand size are virtually immovable by wind, although some tipping or rolling may take place in the most violent storms. Saltating grains impart a slight forward motion to loose grains on the surface when they bounce, and thus sand grains confined within the surface deposit may also move slowly down-wind.

Abrasion and erosion

Although wind is less effective than water as an agent for transporting sediments, it is far more effective as an agent of abrasion. This greater effectiveness apparently comes from the lack of cushioning between two grains as they strike together in air. In water, two grains that hit each other have been slowed down a bit by the viscosity of the water, and there may be a small cushion of water preserved at the point of impact. Despite the greater efficiency of abrasion by wind than by water, so much more sediment is transported by water than by wind that water probably accounts for much more abrasion on the earth than does wind.

The effects of wind abrasion can be seen in a variety of ways. A dramatic example is the sand-blasting action of windstorms on artificial objects. For example, cars which have been trapped in desert sandstorms have suffered almost complete removal of paint and the frosting or pitting of windows so as to render them nearly opaque. This abrasional action is seen somewhat less spectacularly at the bases of many desert cliffs. Here, small pits or holes of diameter up to several feet can be formed where wind activity is particularly intense. Apparently these pits are formed simply by the sand-blasting effect of saltating grains as they are hurled against the cliff. Some geologists feel that this mechanism operating on one or both sides of a narrow neck of rock may account for the formation of natural arches, such as is seen in Fig. 12-12. The reason for the preservation of the arch at the top is simply the fact that wind activity is not effective at that height. Other geologists have ques-

Fig. 12-12. Arch at Arches National Monument. (Photo by J. C. Hafter.)

tioned the ability of wind to effect as much erosion as is needed for the production of large natural arches and have proposed a large number of other possible explanations involving etching by ground or surface waters.

In addition to the major pitting and erosional effects, another piece of evidence which demonstrates the intensity of wind abrasion is the common occurrence of polished pebbles and boulders in desert areas. In our discussion of stream transportation in Chapter 11, we mentioned that continued abrasion of small particles on coarser materials tended to wear off the corners of the coarse materials and convert them into smoother, more spherical shapes. This abrasional process apparently takes place far more readily in areas of wind-blown sand, and highly polished rocks are fairly common in deserts. The sand grains which accumulate in dunes are also more spherical and more highly polished than those which occur in the ordinary river and ocean deposits. It seems likely that this greater rounding has taken place as a result of the greater effect of wind abrasion.

Another result of wind erosion is the formation of a blow-out or depression which has been scoured by the wind and from which the debris has been removed by wind transportation. On a small scale the result may be the development of a pit a few yards across, at the end of which is an accumulation of sand that was too coarse for the wind to carry more than just barely over the lip of the pit. It has also been proposed that some types of large enclosed basins which do not seem to have been formed by any structural process may be developed by wind erosion.

Deposits

Deposits of wind-blown material are referred to by a variety of names. Single, isolated accumulations of sand, virtually regardless of their size, are commonly called *dunes*. Some desert areas also contain broad accumulations of sand in which individual dunes are essentially unrecognizable. Since dunes and other types of wind-blown sand accumulations are a characteristic feature of most deserts, we shall want to discuss their mode of formation and properties in somewhat greater detail.

Migrating sand grains naturally tend to be deposited where the velocity of the wind decreases. Consider, therefore, a situation in which wind is blowing over a source of sand, perhaps weathered granite or some other material. The sand grains picked up in the source area will be transported out over the desert floor and may, if no impediment is in the way, be carried for many miles. Where the speed of the wind decreases, however, or the surface becomes sufficiently rough to prevent the saltation process, the sand grains may begin to accumulate. Once a small pile of sand is formed, the wind begins to shape it into the aerodynamically most suitable form. The form commonly adopted is shown in Figs. 12-13 and 12-14 in both plan view and cross section. Note that the gently sloping side of the dune is toward the wind, and the steep face is away. Thus, wind blowing steadily in one direction will encounter minimum resistance as it hits the dune,

Fig. 12-13. Transverse dune complex composed of slightly overlapping barchans. (Photo courtesy of Arabian American Oil Company.)

will be swept up across the top of the dune, and move onward. In consequence of this steady flowing motion, the area directly behind the crest of the dune, in the lee side, will be an area of essentially dead air. Thus, sand grains saltating or being dragged on the surface across the crest of the dune will tend to fall down and accumulate on the leeward side.

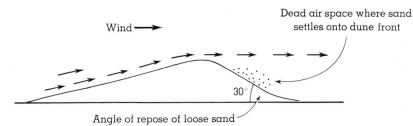

Wind ⟶

Dead air space where sand
settles onto dune front

30°

Angle of repose of loose sand

Fig. 12-14. Cross section of barchan showing movement of sand over the top.

The slope of this side is, in consequence, comparatively steep, for it simply is the slope of a mass of loose material standing without support. The angle of inclination of such a slope is called the *angle of repose,* because it is the inclination taken by unsupported stationary materials. The speed of the wind is greater around the margins of the dune than it is over the top, where resistance is somewhat larger. In consequence of this greater speed, the ends of the dune are swept forward to give the typical horn shape shown in Fig. 12-13. A dune of this type is called a *barchan,* and the shape is characteristic of isolated dunes on rock floors in deserts over the entire world.

The barchan, once formed, is a stable and self-propagating structure. Sand blown from the windward side of the dune over the crest accumulates on the leeward side, and by a repetition of this process the dune moves forward in the direction in which the wind is blowing. The horns, of course, precede the main part, and the result is simply a steady migration of the dune without change of shape across the desert floor. Barchans, naturally, cannot develop or move where the resistance to sand motion is large or where the floor is rough enough for the shape of the dune to be broken up. Barchans range in size from a few tens to a few hundreds of feet between the tips of the horns.

Another type of dune structure may be formed in areas where the supply of sand is too great to permit the establishment of individual isolated bodies such as barchans. Figure 12-15, for example, shows a series of sand ridges consisting essentially of coalesced barchans. The direction of the wind is easily determined by the fact that the windward sides of the ridges are gently sloping and the leeward sides are at the angle of repose (about 30°). Ridges of this type may extend parallel to each other for many tens of miles in some deserts, and such features are commonly

Fig. 12-15. Barchan complex coalesced to form fairly extensive transverse dunes. (Photo courtesy of Arabian American Oil Company.)

called *transverse dunes* because they are elongated in a direction perpendicular to the major wind direction. Naturally, changes in wind
direction from time to time have an effect on the shape of the ridges
and, indeed, on the shape of any type of sand dunes. Large ridges, however, which may be a hundred or more feet high, are not easily affected
by small changes in wind direction, and generally the prevailing wind
direction forms a ridge which is sufficiently stable to resist alteration.

Another type of dune has for many years successfully resisted the
efforts of geologists to determine its mode of formation. These are the
longitudinal dunes, in which sand ridges run parallel to each other, in
some places for many tens of miles, but in which the elongation is
parallel or at a small angle to the direction of prevailing wind. In a
genetic sense, the transverse dunes may be considered to be somewhat like
large barchans and to have formed in a similar fashion. Longitudinal
dunes, however, are obviously quite different. There is, of course, no distinction of windward and leeward side in such dunes owing to the fact
that the prevailing winds are parallel to
the crest. The intervening valleys are
generally bare rock floors, and the chan-
nelling of the wind caused by the
parallel dune ridges causes these floors
to be swept quite clean of sand. It has
been suggested that sand swept out of
the rock floors accumulates on the down-
wind ends of the longitudinal ridges and
thus causes the ridges to grow in a down-
wind direction. This, however, is only a
possibility and certainly has not been
demonstrated to be the answer to the
question of the origin of these dunes.
Figure 12-16 shows a series of small dunes
and sand ridges which have coalesced
into long bands extending parallel to
prevailing wind directions.

Fig. 12-16. Longitudinal dune ridges in the Empty Quarter
of Saudi Arabia. (Photo courtesy of Arabian American
Oil Company.)

In large sand accumulations where the
supply of sand is virtually limitless, it is
very difficult, if not impossible, to recognize individual dunes. The general
landscape is simply one of alternating elevations and depressions, all of
which are filled with sand and in which no general directional trends can
be observed (see Figs. 12-29 and 12-30). Once a feature of this type is
established, the surface wind directions are, of course, affected by the
irregularity of the topography, and the resulting irregular wind directions
tend to maintain the irregularity.

Although dunes are most commonly found in deserts, they are not
restricted to them. Most beaches have prevailing on-shore winds, and
the result of these winds is to pick up sand from the beach and transport
it back to the slightly more rugged topography behind the beach proper.
In consequence of this process, a series of dunes is commonly formed at

Fig. 12-17. Dunes at back of beach in Alabama. Grass helps stabilize the dunes. The area behind the dunes (to the left) is a shallow lagoon. (Photo by J. J. W. Rogers.)

the back of most beaches (Fig. 12-17). Along some coastlines marked by cliffs, the force of on-shore winds is sufficiently high that they may pick up sand and drive it some distance up the cliff. The on-shore winds are deflected upward along the cliff face and, as a result, may bring dune sands with them up to heights of many tens or even hundreds of feet. Dunes of this type have been given the obvious name of *climbing dunes* (Fig. 12-18).

Dune sands and other wind-blown sand deposits are fairly easily recognizable in ancient rocks. The tendency of sands to accumulate on lee slopes at an angle of repose gives to wind-accumulated sands a high-angle cross-bedding. Furthermore, in most wind deposits the cross-bedding is quite irregular as a result of constant changes in wind direction. Thus, Fig. 12-19 shows a typical outcrop of wind-blown sand of Jurassic age (approximately 150 million years old) in the plateau area of western Utah. The only major difficulty in the recognition of dune

Fig. 12-18. Dunes "climbing" the cliffs of the Oregon coast. The sand is blown to high elevations by the onshore winds. (Photo by J. J. W. Rogers.)

sands based on their cross-bedding is the problem of confusing them with stream sands, which also have cross-bedding. The distinction is difficult on the basis of cross-bedding alone, but other evidence may be diagnostic (e.g., the presence of fossil fish). Although most dunes are composed of sand-sized grains of quartz, some are composed of grains of other minerals; for example, the White Sands area of New Mexico is composed of gypsum.

Fig. 12-19. Ancient dune structures exposed in Zion Canyon, Utah. (Photo by J. J. W. Rogers.)

We may mention briefly one other widely distributed type of wind-deposited material. As we shall see in the next section, the northern hemisphere has recently undergone a period of repeated glaciation. The advance of large continental ice-sheets obviously has an extreme abrasive action on the underlying rocks, and the result is the development of a large quantity of rock flour or finely divided dust. As a result, when glaciers melt they tend to leave behind vast accumulations of extremely fine material. This material is, of course, subjected to wind transportation and may be widely distributed. Dusts which have formed in this manner occur in the United States over large parts of the central and southern Middle West and are referred to by the name *loess* (Fig. 12-20). Other types of deposits of wind-blown dust are generally not successfully recognized in the geologic record. The

Fig. 12-20. Vertical cliffs in loess at Vicksburg, Mississippi. (Photo by H. B. Stenzel.)

problem is one of determining features of fine-grained rocks which can be examined sufficiently accurately to enable geologists to decipher the conditions of formation. It has been proposed that fine grains of quartz sand in limestones, and particularly reef deposits, in west Texas may have been blown to the depositional site by wind suspension. The evidence for such a proposal is largely negative and is based simply on the fact that no one can figure out any other way to get quartz sand into a basin in which 99 percent of the sediments are limestones or fine-grained shale.

GLACIERS

Glaciers are large bodies of moving ice. Today they are restricted to the polar regions or the tops of the highest mountain ranges. Thus it is

Fig. 12-21. Glacier flowing out of Greenland Ice Cap at coast. (Photo by Austin S. Post, University of Washington.)

possible to find valley glaciers in the Andes, nearly on the Equator, and in the Himalayas, the Alps, and the northern Rocky Mountains, to mention some of the locations within nonpolar areas. In the polar regions, too, we may encounter glaciers filling the deep valleys of mountain ranges, but here we may also encounter the broad ice sheets which cover hundreds of thousands of square miles with thicknesses of ice which, in many cases, have never really been measured. The entire central portion of Greenland consists of an ice cap ranging from 5000 to 10,000 feet thick, with its upper surface rising slowly from the margins to the center (Fig. 12-21). This cap gradually flows outward down the slope of its surface and emerges in a series of valley glaciers which commonly end at the lower altitudes of the coast. In the Antarctic continent, a central plateau of ice is surrounded by a mountainous margin, and from the plateau, valley glaciers issue down onto the broad ice shelves which fill the major sea indentations into the continent. In contrast to Greenland, the central part of the Antarctic ice cap, which is approximately at the South Pole, is actually lower than the margins.

In the recent geologic past, i.e., the last one million years, restriction of glaciers to polar regions and exceptionally high altitudes was not invariably the rule. We shall see in a later part of this section the evidence which quite conclusively demonstrates that broad ice sheets, similar to the Greenland ice cap, once extended over large portions of North America, Europe, and northern Asia. Farther back in the geologic record is evidence of glaciation in many other portions of the earth.

Mechanism of ice flow

Before discussing the nature of glaciers and their geological effect, we should mention briefly some of the problems encountered in trying to determine the mechanism by which ice flows. Freshly fallen snow is extremely porous, and indeed, 10 inches of snowfall may be the moisture equivalent of only about one inch of rain. As the snow sits on the ground, however, it becomes buried under more snow, compacted, hardened, and loses porosity. During the compaction process, the individual snowflakes tend to recrystallize, much as a limestone does when it is converted into marble by a metamorphic reaction. The reason for the recrystallization is the same in the two cases, namely that the coarser-grained material has a smaller surface area than fine-grained material and thus has a lower total energy. The compaction process, therefore, proceeds through several stages to the development of a solid and rather coarsely crystalline ice. Obviously the ice cannot form without a considerable overburden of snow to cause compaction, and it is generally considered that approximately 200 feet of reasonably hard-packed overburden must be present before ice will form.

Once several hundred feet of snow and ice have accumulated, the ice that has formed is capable of moving in a down-slope direction under the influence of the overburden. Apparently one of the major mechanisms by which ice moves is recrystallization; that is, ice crystals are dissolved at one point and either precipitated to form new crystals elsewhere or simply added on to the original crystal somewhat down slope. This process of flowing by recrystallization is at least moderately well understood from the study of the crystallographic orientation of ice crystals in a glacier. Ice is a hexagonal crystal with a structure broadly similar to that of quartz, and by optical methods it is possible to determine the orientation of the various crystallographic axes. In general, the axes of ice crystals in glaciers show a preferential orientation typical of minerals which have recrystallized under the pressure of some directed stress.

Glaciers move at rates that are surprisingly fast for solids, generally on the order of several inches per day. The front of a glacier in which the ice is flowing at a rate of 20 ft/yr, however, does not move forward that number of feet each year. The rate of forward movement depends not only on the rate of flowage but also on the rate of accumulation of new snow and ice at the foot or on the rate of melting of the glacier back toward its source.

Fig. 12-22. Small glacier on Ellesmere Island, Canada. Note spreading of ice as it is released from narrow valley. Lobe is surrounded by a small moraine. (Photo by Austin S. Post, University of Washington.)

Valley glaciers

Let us turn now to a discussion of valley glaciers. A typical one as shown in Fig. 12-22 extends from a rather steep head through a broad and somewhat sinuous valley to its foot at the valley floor. The glacier is almost certainly occupying the valley of a former stream except where it has spread out on the flat area in front of the mountain range. Otherwise the thicknesses of snow and ice needed to accumulate in order to begin glacial movement could hardly have been possible. The glacier, however, has considerably straightened the former stream valley for the simple reason that glacial ice cannot flow around corners as easily as streams can. Ice, furthermore, is capable of pushing much greater amounts of material out of the way than is running water. At the toe

Fig. 12-23. Toe of Forno Glacier, Swiss Alps. Ice has retreated up the valley by melting and has left the jumbled debris of the foreground. (Photo by B. C. Burchfiel.)

of most glaciers the evidence of melting is, of course, obvious (Fig. 12-23). In some places at the base of a glacier, small streams may have cut channels whose heads are somewhere back in the glacier itself, and melt water coming out of these streams commonly carries large amounts of ground-up rock flour formed by the movement of boulders in the base of the glacier over the rock floor.

The surface of a glacier is invariably cut by numerous open gashes called *crevasses* (Fig. 12-24). These crevasses are formed by irregularity in the rate of flow of different portions of the glacier. Thus, crevasses are abundant near the side and generally extend from the side back uphill into the glacier itself. The cracks have this orientation because the central portion of the glacier is flowing more rapidly than the sides, which are influenced by frictional drag along the valley walls. You may demonstrate that tensional cracks should have this orientation by holding a pack of cards on the end in one hand and shoving laterally along the other end of the pack with the other hand. The head of a valley glacier has commonly partly pulled away from the end of the valley, leaving an open space which is obviously another tensional feature.

The margins of a valley glacier are the site of accumulation of large amounts of rock and debris which has fallen off the

Fig. 12-24. Crevasses on the Saskatchewan Glacier, Canada. (Photo by M. F. Meier, U.S. Geological Survey.)

Fig. 12-25. Medial moraines on Barnard Glacier, Alaska, formed from lateral moraines of tributary glaciers. (Photo by Austin S. Post, U.S. Geological Survey.)

valley side. Material that is deposited together by any form of glacial action is commonly referred to as a *moraine,* and these marginal strips of moving sediment are referred to as *lateral moraines.* It is common for glaciers to join each other just as tributaries join other streams, and where they join, the lateral moraines at the inside of the junction tend to fuse together and may travel down the center of the larger glacier as *medial moraines.* These types of moraines are shown in Figs. 12-25 and 12-26.

All of the material brought down by a valley glacier is ultimately dumped in the zone of melting at its foot. The accumulated material forms a vast pile of chaotically jumbled rocks of all sizes and of all types which are encountered up the valley. This material deposited at the foot of the glacier is referred to as an *end moraine* (Fig. 12-27). Much of the fine material from a glacier is, of course, washed out of the moraine deposits by melt water from the glacier or by normal rain water.

Fig. 12-26. Lateral moraines (light gray) left by retreating glacier on Mt. Hood, Oregon. (Photo by Austin S. Post, U.S. Geological Survey.)

Fig. 12-27. Terminal moraine in U-shaped Dinwoody Valley, Wyoming. (Photo by M. F. Meier, U.S. Geological Survey.)

This finer material is deposited farther down the valley and may form exceptionally thick deposits, owing to the tremendous supply of sediment from the glacier. Material distributed in this way by melt water from glaciers is referred to as *outwash*. In some places, glaciers may carry enormous boulders and then, upon melting, leave these boulders on top of rocks of totally dissimilar character. These boulders are called *erratics* (Fig. 12-28) from the fact that they do not correspond to the underlying rocks.

Fig. 12-28. Concussion marks on boulder (pencil shown to gauge size). The marks on this glacial erratic were made when rocks in glacial ice were dragged against the boulder. (Photo by J. W. Teeter.)

The recognition of a valley which formerly contained a glacier but does not do so now actually presents relatively little difficulty. The combination of moraine deposits, erratics, and outwash is generally a fairly good indication of the previous existence of a glacier up the valley. Furthermore, the bare rock floor under the former glacier may be grooved or striated by the action of boulders carried in the base of the ice as it scraped along. The most significant feature of glaciated valleys, however, is the broad, smooth cross section which is totally unlike that produced by normal stream activity. Normal stream valleys commonly have a pattern approximating that of a V, particularly if they are formed in high mountain ranges and thus are presumably in an early stage of evolution. Glaciated valleys, however, more commonly have cross sections which may be approximated as U's. The U-shape results from the greater effectiveness of the ice in moving material out of the way and generally causing valley deepening and smoothing. A typical example of a U-shaped valley is Yosemite Canyon, which is shown in Fig. 12-29.

In some places the floors of glaciated valleys are quickly buried when streams reoccupy them after the glacier has retreated. The reason is that the glacier generally pushes itself so deeply into the floor that a stream reoccupying it finds itself well below normal grade. Thus, the stream tends to deposit material quite rapidly in order to reach a higher elevation and higher gradient.

Fig. 12-29. Yosemite Valley, California. The U-shape and sharp truncation of the sides are characteristic of glaciated valleys. (Photo by Sarah Ann Davis, California State Division of Mines.)

The heads of glaciated valleys have characteristic rounded or bowl-like shapes. This is the area from which the ice first started in its flow down the valley, and for reasons not fully explained, the head areas become broadly hollowed out. These bowl-like areas are referred to as *cirques,* and a typical example is shown in Fig. 12-30. A mountain range which has undergone glaciation by a number of different valley glaciers may have quite a striking appearance as the result of development of cirques along the entire crest of the range. The crest becomes sharpened by this cirque development, and the ridges between adjacent cirques may be very thin and exceptionally steep. Note, for example, the sharpness of ridges and peaks in Fig. 12-25.

Continental glaciers

Continental glaciers are similar to valley glaciers in many respects. The mechanism of flowage of ice is clearly the same, and the deposits formed around the margins and within the glaciers are very similar to those of valley glaciers. It is, however, necessary to introduce a few additional terms to account for the types of deposits which are characteristic of continental glaciers but not mentioned in the preceding discussion. The introduction of terms is something which we do with reluctance because the major object of a study of geology is to understand processes. Nevertheless, language must be learned if people are to communicate with each other, and thus some terms are unavoidable.

Either a continental glacier or to a lesser extent a valley glacier, as it flows over the earth's surface, may accumulate large quantities of rock and other debris at its base. This material may in places be plastered against the floor, and the glacier will then simply override it. In this

Fig. 12-30. Small, abandoned cirque in the San Juan Mountains, Colorado. (Photo by T. H. Foss.)

Fig. 12-31. Drumlin in North Dakota. Ice movement was from right to left. (Photo by Saul Aronow, U.S. Geological Survey.)

Fig. 12-32. Esker in Minnesota. (From W. S. Cooper, *The History of the Upper Mississippi River in Late Wisconsin and Postglacial Time*, 1935, University of Minnesota Press.)

way it is possible for the glacier to form mounds several hundreds of feet high and up to a mile or so in length. Just as dunes have a shape which offers a minimum resistance to air flow, so these deposited mounds, called *drumlins*, have a shape which offers minimum resistance to the overriding ice (Fig. 12-31). The side of the drumlin in the direction from which the ice is flowing has a broad gentle slope, whereas the front part of the drumlin has a very steep slope. The sides are rounded off to a "hydrodynamic" smoothness. These drumlins may occur singly, or they may cluster together in groups of aligned knobs.

Another type of glacial deposit occurs as a highly sinuous ridge, in some places with heights measured in terms of tens of feet and extending for distances of many miles. The material in such a ridge is a water-

Fig. 12-33. End moraine in North Dakota. (Photo by Saul Aronow, U.S. Geological Survey.)

Fig. 12-34. Irregular glaciated topography in North Dakota. (Photo by Saul Aronow, U.S. Geological Survey.)

worked mass of broken, angular rock fragments and sand and is obviously of glacial origin. These sinuous bodies are called *eskers* (Fig. 12-32) and apparently represent deposits from melt-water streams at the base of a glacier. They have the winding shape of streams, which is completely uncharacteristic of moving ice, and they almost certainly develop after major glacial flowage has stopped.

A continental glacier, similar to valley glaciers, advances in a series of intermittent steps and then retreats in the same fashion. Thus it forms a series of moraines which may either be overridden or left behind in sequence as the ice either advances or retreats. The furthest moraine for any period of glaciation is called an *end* or *terminal moraine* (Fig. 12-33), and the other deposits are simply referred to as moraines. Glaciers may also scatter large amounts of debris across any area over which they have advanced or retreated. In front of a continental glacier there is generally a large amount of fine material which has been washed out of the glacial debris and distributed rather widely. This material, as in the case of valley glaciers, is called *outwash*. A term which is commonly used for all deposits made by the ice itself is *drift* (Figs. 12-34 and 12-35).

We are now in the position of being able to investigate the reasons why geologists assume that there has been a considerable period of glaciation in the recent past. Actually it has been possible to subdivide the glacial periods in North America and also in northern Europe into four distinct stages of advance and intervening retreat. The evidence, in general, is the existence of outwash deposits, moraines, drift of all types, eskers,

Fig. 12-35. Glacial till, showing jumble of boulders and rock flour. (Photo by Saul Aronow, U.S. Geological Survey.)

drumlins, and other features which can be proven by study of currently existing valley glaciers to be typical products of glacial activity. That is, features such as moraines, outwash plains, and to a certain extent eskers and other glacially shaped features can be found in valleys from which glaciers have retreated within the time of man's observation. Thus deposits of these types can be proved to have been formed by glacial action. Similar deposits in central North America, however, are so widely distributed over a landscape which obviously has been so flat for extensive periods of time that it would be impossible to attribute them to a number of local valley glaciers; it is, therefore, necessary to propose the existence of ice sheets similar to that which covers Greenland today.

Other types of evidence for these continental ice sheets consist of the presence of broad, flat surfaces of fresh rock in which there are large grooves apparently formed by the rubbing of boulders carried in the base of the glacier over the rock surface. In some cases, the boulders appear to have skipped or "chattered" over the surface and have left a series of small cracks much as a hammer might make if hit repeatedly on the rock surface (Fig. 12-28).

The presence of four distinct stages of glaciation in North America may be demonstrated by a variety of means. One excellent method is the finding of several series of moraines lying on top of each other and separated from each other by periods of deep soil formation (Fig. 12-36). Each moraine must represent an interval of glaciation, and each period of soil formation must represent a time in which glaciers had retreated sufficiently far for plant life to resume normal activity and for soil-forming processes to take place. It is possible, also, in some places to find major trends of terminal or other moraines cut off or intersected by other sequences of moraines. Again, in this case, it is apparent that the transected moraines represent an early period of glaciation and have been superseded by materials deposited at some later date. By using such evidence as described above, it has been possible for geologists to depict the recent glacial history of the United States in considerable detail.

Fig. 12-36. Soil (dark) overlain by light till in Wisconsin. The soil is formed on earlier glacial deposits. (Photo by Robert F. Black.)

The effects of continental glaciation are found not only within the glaciated area but also outside of it. The large amount of crushed material developed by glaciers is distributed not only in outwash plains but, as mentioned earlier, also by wind. The fine dust that has spread widely by winds may form exceptionally thick beds, and beds of this type have been found throughout much of the south-central part of the United States. As discussed in the section on wind transportation, this wind-deposited glacial material is called *loess,* and the stratification of different loess deposits may also be an indication of several periods of glaciation.

Another effect of large-scale continental glaciation is that of tying water up on the land surface and thus reducing the level of the ocean. In the last stage of glaciation, the Wisconsin stage, it appears that the sea level around the world was lowered approximately 600 feet. The evidence for this lowering is found by exploration of the sea bottom, which shows former atmospheric exposure of rocks now at depths of several hundreds of feet. Thus, soil zones, stream valleys, and other typical terrestrial features are now buried beneath several hundreds of feet of water. At any one place such burial might be attributed to a simple downwarping of the coast line, but where this occurs over the entire world, then it is apparent that we are dealing with a distinct change of sea level rather than local movement of the land itself.

Many of the sediments which occur in shallow water today have formed either during this period of low sea level or have been greatly affected by the sudden dumping of glacial debris at the end of the last continental glaciation. It is for this reason, among others, that the present condition of the bottom sediments of the ocean is probably atypical of that of other times in the geologic past. This renders the examination of ancient sediments in the light of a strict uniformitarianism concept a little risky.

Another major effect of continental glaciation is the climatic effect. Though we are not concerned in this book with the paleontological evidence concerning the evolution of life and the changes in forms of life throughout geologic history, we may mention that cold-weather organisms obviously lived much farther south in the recent geologic past than they do now. Furthermore, certain animals, such as the mammoth, existed only during glacial and immediately postglacial times and have now disappeared.

Ancient climates

The cause of continental glaciation is a major problem for geologists. A large number of possibilities have been suggested, including variations in the energy output of the sun and variations in the carbon dioxide content of the earth's atmosphere. The theory concerning carbon dioxide is that a lowered carbon dioxide content would tend to promote the formation of glaciers by permitting the earth to cool off. Carbon dioxide in the atmosphere is capable of absorbing the infrared (heat) radiation from the earth and preventing it from going back into space. Thus, when the carbon dioxide content is high, the earth should be relatively warm, and when it is low, the earth should be relatively cool. It then remains to establish some mechanism for causing a variation in the carbon dioxide content of the atmosphere. This, unfortunately, has not been satisfactorily done.

Variations in the earth's climate have long attracted the attention of geologists. In rocks of the ancient past, the climate must, of course, be inferred by the nature of the rocks themselves, and fortunately it is possible to do this with a fair degree of accuracy. For example, the finding of glacial deposits in the geologic record signifies the presence of a climate cold enough to form large bodies of ice. It is also possible to detect the reverse. It is known, for example, in recent seas that coral reefs can form only in areas extending north and south from the equator to relatively low latitudes. By analogy, and here the analogy is only approximately accurate, we can assume that such reefs in the past must have developed in an area of warm water. In similar manner, coal beds presumably have formed only in areas of mild, or perhaps tropical, climates. Coal is the result of the accumulation of plant material in an essentially swampy environment, and such environments would not be expected to persist over broad areas except in temperate regions.

It is possible, then, to take such materials as coal, coral reefs, and glacial deposits and, for any particular time in the geologic past, to plot these on a present map of the earth. One such plot is shown in Fig. 12-37, where we see an extremely interesting situation. The belt of warm-weather deposits for this period is extended at a very high angle to the present Equator and, indeed, goes into the present Arctic regions. At this same time, glacial deposits formed in locations which today are tropical to temperate. We can, therefore, plot the position of the earth's pole for this particular period of the earth's history, and if we make maps of this type and plot pole positions for sequential periods of the earth's history, we will find that the apparent position of the pole wanders considerably and continuously over the earth's surface. The position of the pole for various dates is shown in Fig. 12-38, and it will be seen that the pole position progresses rather smoothly up to its present location.

This progression of the locations of the pole may also be verified in part by studies of the direction of magnetization of ancient rocks. The method is based on the fact that when rocks containing iron minerals are formed by crystallization in a magnetic field, the direction of polarization of the minerals is controlled by the position of the magnetic field. Although the total magnetization of most rocks is extremely small, it is possible in this manner to determine the orientation of the magnetic pole at the time of formation of rocks such as granite, iron ores, or even sediments containing a large amount of hematite in the cement. This method is subject to the difficulty of the destruction of the direction of the magnetization by later events, but in many cases the original directions seem to have been preserved.

Since the magnetic pole of the earth appears to occupy a position generally close to the actual pole of rotation, the location of the magnetic pole is presumed to be roughly equivalent to the location of the earth's rotational axis. As mentioned previously, some of the magnetic measurements verify the measurements made from climatic study and indicate that the pole of the earth has wandered in the manner shown in Fig. 12-38.

The mechanism of polar wandering is a bit obscure. Certainly the

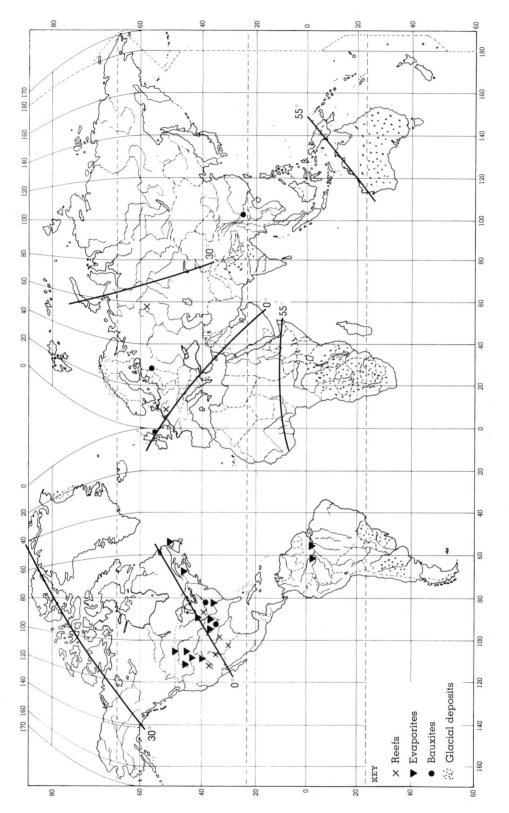

Fig. 12-37. Indices of ancient climates. The locations of climatic indicators are shown together with latitude lines determined by paleomagnetism for this period approximately 350 million years ago. Note the correspondence between the two lines of evidence. (Replotted from N. D. Opdyke in S. K. Runcorn, ed., *Continental Drift*, Academic Press, New York, 1962, p. 54.)

KEY

× Reefs
▼ Evaporites
● Bauxites
⋰ Glacial deposits

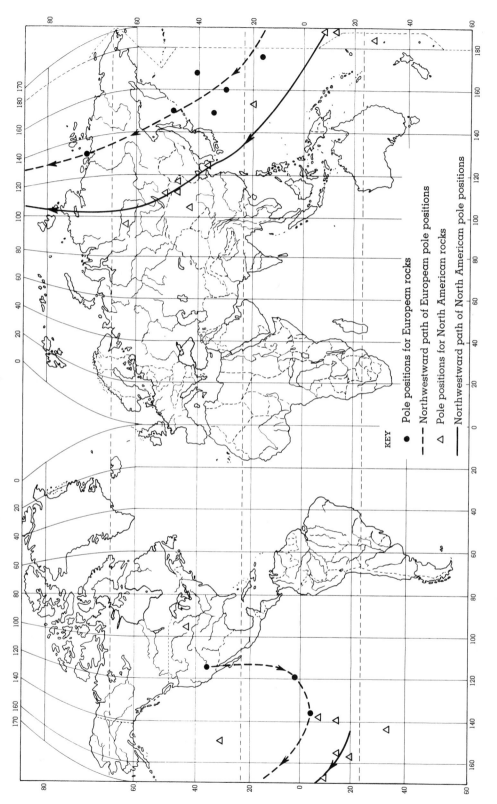

Fig. 12-38. Positions of poles of various ages as determined by paleomagnetic studies of rocks in Europe and North America. The discrepancy in locations for the same age indicates relative movement of the continents. (Replotted from S. K. Runcorn, in *Polar Wandering and Continental Drift* [A. C. Munyan, ed.], *Society of Economic Paleontologists and Mineralogists Special Publication 10*, 1963.)

KEY

● Pole positions for European rocks
--- Northwestward path of European pole positions
△ Pole positions for North American rocks
— Northwestward path of North American pole positions

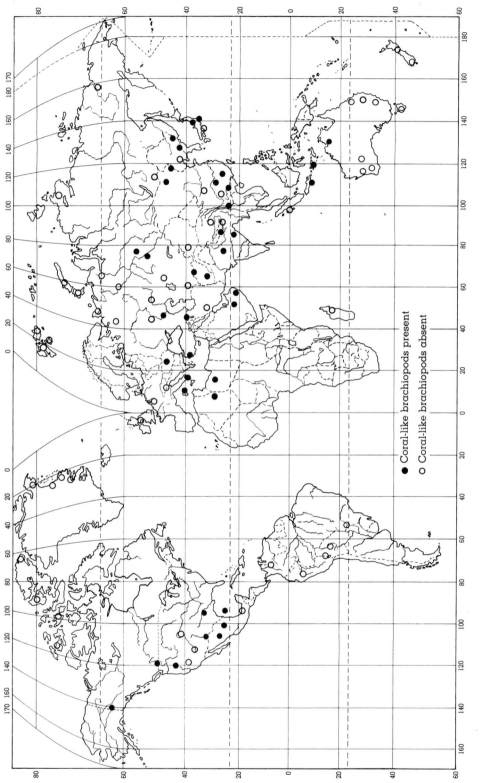

Fig. 12-39. Distribution of two types of coral-like brachiopods in rocks approximately 300 million years old. These organisms are presumed to be restricted to warm water by analogy with modern corals. Their absence from high southern or northern latitudes suggests that the Equator and continents occupied the same relative positions that they have today. (From F. G. Stehli, *American Journal of Science*, vol. 255, 1957.)

● Coral-like brachiopods present

○ Coral-like brachiopods absent

axis of rotation of the earth has not changed its position. The earth's angular momentum is extremely large, and there seems to be no reasonable outside force which could cause it to shift. What may have happened is that the crust of the earth, resting on a relatively fluid lower layer, shifted independently of the lower layer. Thus, although the orientation of the earth's mantle and core have always remained exactly the same in space, the orientation of the crust may have changed from time to time. Relative to the crust, therefore, the pole of the earth has migrated in a fairly continuous fashion. The evidence used to prove the hypothesis of polar wandering has also been used by some geologists to disprove the hypothesis that the continents have shifted relative to each other through geologic time (Fig. 12-38). We shall refer to this hypothesis and some of the related evidence in more detail in Chapter 14.

Before leaving the subject of polar wandering, we should mention the fact that some evidence seems to refute the possibility of relative changes in pole positions. Figure 12-39, for example, is a map of the distribution of certain types of brachiopods in rocks of Permian age (about 300 million years ago). In a loose sense, brachiopods can be considered ancient equivalents of modern clams, and the best available evidence indicates that the brachiopods mapped in Fig. 12-39 lived in reasonably warm water. It is significant, therefore, that the belt of brachiopod-bearing rocks parallels the present equator. This evidence, if accurate, indicates that the present equator is in the same position as the Permian equator, which is obviously at variance with the concept of polar wandering and the Permian pole position shown in Figure 12-38.

CHAPTER 13 THE OCEANS

◀ Erosion of coastline. (Photo by Meyer Liebowitz; courtesy of New York *Times*.)

It may seem paradoxical that we have spent virtually the entire book discussing the land areas of the earth, whereas the oceans cover 71 percent of the earth's surface. The reason for such concentration on the land surface, however, is that geologists, just like other people, tend to discuss those things which they know best, and it has obviously been easier to study the land than to study the ocean. The oceans cover 136 million square miles of the earth's surface with an average depth of 12,500 feet. Thus there is in the oceans a total of 321 million cubic miles of water representing essentially all of the water on the earth's surface.

Neither the location of oceans nor their depths are distributed uniformly. The Pacific Ocean occupies nearly an entire hemisphere and is roughly twice the size of the Atlantic. As we shall see in Chapter 14, this unequal distribution of the oceans has led to some major theories concerning the distribution and possible fragmentation of continents. In addition to a concentration of ocean water in the Pacific hemisphere, most of the oceanic areas are in the southern hemisphere, and the continents tend to be clustered together in the north.

SEA WATER

The composition of sea water varies from place to place but is remarkably constant over much of the earth. Naturally, close to land, in bays or off the mouths of large rivers, the water tends to become diluted. The diluted water, which may range in composition anywhere from the fresh water of lakes and rivers to the normal salt content of ocean water, is called *brackish*. A chemical analysis of the major constituents of ocean water is given in Table 13-1. This table shows clearly that sodium and chloride are the major ions dissolved in sea water. The total amount of dissolved material in sea water is usually reported in terms of an equivalent weight of sodium chloride. This concentration is termed *salinity* and is generally referred to in parts of dissolved salt per thousand

TABLE 13-1. AVERAGE COMPOSITION OF SEA WATER

	parts per million
SiO_2	6
total Fe	0.01
Ca	400
Mg	1350
Na	10,500
K	380
HCO_3	25
SO_4	885
Cl	19,000

parts of water by weight, and the concentrations are expressed as "parts per thousand" ($^o/oo$); for example, $35^o/oo$ equals $3.5^o/o$. We have already seen in Chapter 9 that the total amount of sodium chloride in sea water could be supplied by the current rate of addition from river waters in a period of time much shorter than the age of the earth. Therefore, the salt in the oceans must be undergoing a recycling movement in which some of it is extracted into evaporite sediments and some is recycled by spray-drying through the atmosphere.

Geologists have investigated the difficult question of determining changes in composition of sea water throughout time. One method of doing this is to investigate the nature of diagenetic changes in sediments at various times of the earth's history. These changes, which represent adjustment of the sediment to chemical equilibrium in the environment of sea water, are presumably sensitive to the composition of the water. As yet no conclusive results have been obtained. Most geologists conclude, on the basis of analogy between ancient organisms and modern ones, that the composition of sea water cannot have varied too greatly from its present concentration during at least the last few hundred million years of geologic history. It is noteworthy that the ionic strength and composition of human blood is very similar to that of sea water. It is virtually impossible, however, to prove that organisms through time have not adjusted to changing salt concentrations, and thus the paleontological approach to an investigation of sea water cannot be very definitive.

At the present time the oceans are probably far more restricted in area than they have been in most periods of geologic time. The only exception to this statement would be those periods in which major continental glaciation occurred, and as we mentioned in Chapter 12, the last glaciation appears to have lowered sea level by approximately 600 feet. The evidence for this present restricted distribution of the oceans is contained simply in the record of marine sediments covering the continental areas, added to the fact that no geophysical studies have found evidence of continental-type crust beneath modern oceans. With the exception of the central portions of the shield area, the entire North American continent has been flooded repeatedly. In the midwestern part of the United States there has been an accumulation of several thousands of feet, in places several tens of thousands of feet, of dominantly marine sediments. Most of these sediments appear, from their fossil contents and the general properties of the rocks, to have been formed in shallow water, probably in depths of not more than a few hundred feet. Despite this shallowness, this amount of water spread over all of the continental areas of the world at the same time represents an enormous flooding, and paleontological and other evidence of dates indicates that flooding in many cases was essentially synchronous on a world-wide basis.

The source of the water for world-wide flooding is a major problem. Were the oceans at the time of continental flooding simply more shallow and thus more widely distributed? Geophysical evidence, such as is presented in Chapters 3 and 4, indicates that such a marked change in the relative elevations of continents and ocean basins is unlikely, although we shall see later in this chapter that the last major continental flooding coincides with the upwarping of a part of the ocean floor in the western Pacific. Was there even less ice on the earth during these periods of flooding than there is today? This is a possibility, of course, but unfortunately a complete melting of the ice in the Antarctic and in the Greenland ice caps and on the Arctic Ocean itself would only serve to raise sea level by approximately 200 feet, which is clearly not enough to cause the flooding of broad continental areas. Did the earth during periods of major continental flooding simply have a smaller continental area, thus reducing the total amount of water needed for almost complete inundation? This, again, is a possibility, but within the past few hundred million years the continents do not appear to have undergone any major growth, and it seems unlikely that the amount of ocean water needed for flooding would ever have been much less than it is today. The simple truth is that if the earth is today in a period of isostatic equilibrium, which it appears to be, it is very difficult to move continents up and down in such a manner as to cause flooding without supplying large quantities of additional water; there seems to be no good source for the water.

There is no question that the amount of water on the earth's surface has increased throughout geologic time; the simple addition of water vapor from volcanoes would insure such an effect. Under these conditions, however, since there appears to be no ready method for removing water from the earth's surface once there, we must conclude that the total amount of water on the earth's surface today represents at least as much as, and probably more than, was available in the past. On this basis, the ancient flooding becomes even more difficult to understand. In short, the mechanism of past continental flooding is a major geologic problem, and to date no one has proposed a really plausible solution for the question.

WATER MOVEMENTS

The term "restless" has been applied to the sea for many years and is indeed appropriate. The oceans are never quiet. Water moves in response to a variety of forces, generating tides, waves, and currents. In this section we shall investigate some of the types of water movement and the reasons for them.

Tides

Ocean tides are caused both by astronomic forces and wind. Astronomic tides form in response to the attractive effect of the moon, and to a lesser extent the sun, on ocean water; the effect of the moon is shown diagrammatically in Fig. 13-1. The rotation of the earth causes the moon to be opposite any

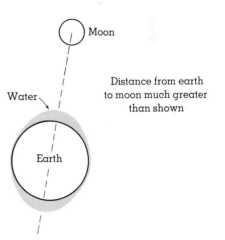

Distance from earth to moon much greater than shown

Fig. 13-1. Effect of the moon on tides. Gravitative attraction of the moon for both the oceans and the solid earth causes high tides closest to and farthest from the moon.

Fig. 13-2. Partially submerged tidal flats in Bay of Fundy, Canada. (Photo by G. DeV. Klein.)

Fig. 13-3. Tidal flats of Bay of Fundy, Canada. Enormous portions of this estuary are alternately exposed and covered by tides with ranges measured in tens of feet. (Photo by G. DeV. Klein.)

point on its surface approximately every 24 hours. The "approximately" must be added because the moon itself is revolving around the earth, and for that reason there is not a perfect 24-hour cycle. The attractive gravitational force of the moon on the easily movable ocean water causes a piling up of the water at a point nearest the moon on the earth's surface. As the earth continues to rotate, the water piled up at one point is released and tends to subside to a more normal height. High tides also occur at a point on the other side of the earth opposite the moon, because here the attractive force of the moon is a minimum, and the centrifugal force imparted to the water by the earth's rotation has unrestricted effect. High tide, then, occurs at a point closest to the moon and at a point 180 degrees around the earth. Low tides occur at points 90 degrees around the earth from the closest point to the moon.

Each point on the earth's surface, therefore, has two high tides and two low tides in each approximately 24-hour period. The process is complicated by the irregular shape of the ocean basins, and the complications generally affect both the sizes of the tides and their times of occurrence. For example, the funnel-like structure of the Bay of Fundy in Nova Scotia causes water to be piled up toward its head and permits tidal ranges of as much as 70 feet (Figs. 13-2 and 13-3). In some broad, flat coasts on the open ocean the tide range may be only 1 or 2 feet. For accurate surveying purposes, *sea level* is variously defined as the mean low tide, mean high tide, or possibly some average of low and high tides.

The effect of the sun on tides, though less than that of the moon, is easily shown by the sizes of *spring tides* and *neap tides*. Spring tides are exceptionally high tides which occur when the sun and the moon are in line on the same side of the earth; neap tides occur when the sun and moon are exactly opposite each other, and the tides are very small.

Many tides are controlled far more by winds than by astronomic forces. Along the coast of the Gulf of Mexico, for example, low tides are commonly caused in the winter by northern cold air masses known as

314

"northers" blowing toward the south and pushing water away from the land. The low water may persist for several days. Conversely, winds from the south may cause water to pile up on the shore.

Shoreline areas between low and high tides which are repeatedly flooded and uncovered by water are areas of extraordinary chemical and biological activity. The organisms which survive in such rapidly changing environments must be extremely hardy. Some are both air- and water-breathers. Others manage to seclude enough water within themselves so that their gills are, in effect, under water at all times, even when the tide is out. Many organisms survive by burrowing into the soft intertidal sediments which always remain wet (Fig. 13-4). Chemical activity is promoted by the alternate wetting and drying of the rocks. For example, a nail completely immersed in a glass of water does not rust as fast as a nail which is sprinkled lightly

Fig. 13-4. Snails on tidal flats in Bay of Fundy. (Photo by G. DeV. Klein.)

by water and has access to air at all times; oxidation is one of the important reactions which occurs in tidal sediments. The structures of sediments in this environment are also affected by the alternate wetting and drying (Fig. 7-3). Muds, for example, tend to crack into separate blocks upon drying, and the cracked sediments may be preserved if additional material is deposited on top of them before they have a chance to be thoroughly soaked again.

The width of the intertidal zone obviously depends on the slope of the surface. In some places on the relatively steep beaches of the western United States the distance between high and low tides may be only a few tens of feet. In other places, for example on the exceptionally shallow slopes around portions of the North Sea, the tide may advance and retreat for many miles.

Currents

Major circulatory systems of water in the oceans are called *currents.* Some, such as the circulatory system in the North Atlantic Ocean, are of such size that they rim the borders of the entire ocean. Other currents may be fairly small, such as the longshore currents which may be formed locally along irregular coast lines.

Before discussing the pattern of circulation of major currents it is necessary to explain the *Coriolis effect,* which has already been mentioned briefly in Chapter 2. The Coriolis effect is simply the result of forces applied to a body by a spinning object (Fig. 13-5). The earth rotates at a steady rate from west to east, and the velocity of rotation, obviously, is dependent upon latitude. The speed is highest at the Equator, where

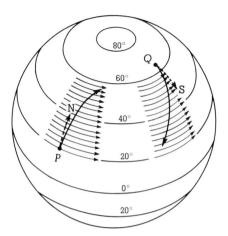

Fig. 13-5. Coriolis effect. Objects moving north or south are deflected, as shown in the northern hemisphere. (From A. N. Strahler, *The Earth Sciences*, Harper & Row, New York, 1963.)

the radius of rotation is largest, and diminishes to zero at the axis of rotation (at the Poles). Consider, now, a body of water moving southward in the northern hemisphere. The water has a speed from west to east imparted to it at its place of origin by the spin of the earth. As the body moves south, it will pick up some additional speed, but because of slippage between the solid earth and the water, the velocity of the water will not become as large as that of the earth beneath it. As a result, the water mass moving south tends to drift westward as the earth spins more rapidly toward the east. The reverse of this relationship is, of course, true for a body of water moving north, and in the southern hemisphere the reverse of everything is true. Thus consider a point of high pressure in the northern hemisphere from which the water is moving radially outward. As the mass moves, the westward drift of the southerly moving water and the eastward drift of the northerly moving water tend to give the whole water body a clockwise rotation.

The exact opposite direction of rotation is formed around centers of low pressure towards which fluids are moving. Thus, around the eyes of hurricanes or tornadoes, which are low-pressure centers, the movement is counterclockwise in the northern hemisphere. In the southern hemisphere, hurricanes have a clockwise rotation.

The direction of movement of major ocean currents is controlled largely by winds. In the case of the Gulf Stream and related currents in the North Atlantic Ocean, for example (Figs. 13-6*A* and *B*), the impulse for a westerly water drift in low latitudes is caused by prevailing westward-blowing winds in equatorial regions (the trade winds—see Chapter 2). Upon reaching higher latitudes (approximately 30 to 50 degrees) the prevailing westerlies, which blow eastward, cause the northern part of the current to move toward the east, thus completing a general clockwise rotation.

Though the rotation of the Gulf Stream and other major currents is primarily controlled by wind, other forces have secondary effects. The Coriolis force, for example, reinforces the tendency of currents to rotate clockwise in the northern hemisphere and counterclockwise in the southern hemisphere. The high speed of the Gulf Stream along the east coast of Florida (where it is called the Florida Current) results in part from the fact that prevailing equatorial winds have piled water up into the Gulf of Mexico so that sea level averages 19 inches higher on the west coast of Florida than on the east coast; this high water pressure from the Gulf of Mexico enhances the rate of flow tremendously.

The effect of large currents, such as the Gulf Stream, is enormous. The relatively mild climate of northern Europe is dependent solely on the fact that the Gulf Stream brings warm southern waters into northern latitudes and thus gives Europe a much milder climate than is experi-

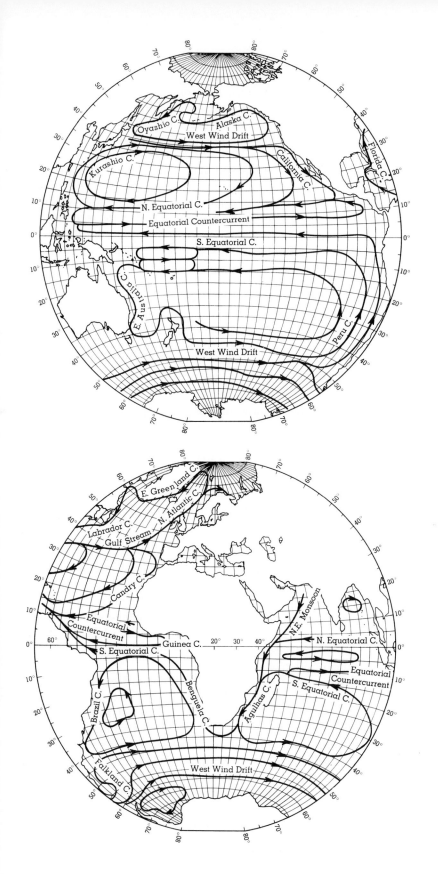

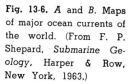

Fig. 13-6. *A* and *B*. Maps of major ocean currents of the world. (From F. P. Shepard, *Submarine Geology*, Harper & Row, New York, 1963.)

enced in equivalent latitudes elsewhere, for example in Labrador and Newfoundland. The Gulf Stream moves at a speed of approximately 3 miles per hour as it passes the eastern coast of the United States and has a width up to 50 miles. The juncture between waters of the Gulf Stream and waters of the open Atlantic is an extremely sharp one, and very little mixing occurs. The waters of the Gulf Stream have temperatures averaging 5 to 10 degrees higher than those of the Atlantic, and they can readily be recognized by simply trailing a thermometer over the side of a ship.

Major currents tend to generate small countercurrents. For example, the clockwise rotation of the Gulf Stream promotes the development of counterclockwise-rotating bodies of water in the extreme northwestern part of the Atlantic Ocean. This counterrotation tends, in part, to bring Arctic water down the east coast of North America, and these cold waters penetrate to the Middle Atlantic States. The ability of the Gulf Stream to bring warm weather to northern Europe is countered by the ability of the Japanese current in the Pacific to bring cooler weather to the west coast of the United States. The cold water characteristic of beaches off the Pacific Coast is largely a result of the Japanese Current (labeled Kurashio and California Currents in Fig. 6A).

Waves

Waves are the most obvious forms of movement in oceans. In actuality, waves are nothing more than cyclical alternations in the level of water at any particular point, and no net lateral movement occurs except where they approach land. Wave motion in water is similar to that in the solid earth (discussed in Chapter 4) with the exception that water is not sufficiently rigid to maintain its own shape. If water were rigid, and we placed a cork on the surface of the ocean without any currents and observed its position as various waves went past it, we would find that no net movement had occurred at all. As a simple analogy of this type of wave motion, you can take a garden hose, stretch it out full length, grasp one end, and give a sharp upward jerk. What you will see then is a wave passing down the length of the hose such that the elevation reached by any point is roughly the height to which you had originally jerked the end. This translation of the wave down the hose, however, has not succeeded in moving the hose in the direction in which the wave appears to be moving. In fact, after the wave has passed, everything is in exactly the same position as it was before.

The lack of rigidity of water renders this simple analogy a bit imprecise. Water tends to flow down the sloping surface of a wave, moving forward as the wave crest approaches some point and then backward after the crest has passed by. Thus an individual particle in a water wave tends to have an orbital motion, with the movement greatest at the surface and decreasing with depth. Fig. 13-7 shows the paths followed by water particles in waves.

Waves in the open ocean may become extremely large. Depths from trough to crest (the *wave height*) are commonly measured in feet but may, in periods of storm activity, be measured in tens of feet. Distances between wave crests (the *wave lengths*) are measured in terms of many tens or hundreds of feet. Although the wave itself is expressed only on the surface of the water, the movement extends to some depth which is dependent on the height of the wave. It is generally found that quiet water is encountered below depths of 100 feet and perhaps shallower. The depth below which motion is virtually absent is entitled *wave base;* in geologic practice wave base is commonly defined as the depth below which bottom sediments are not moved by wave activity.

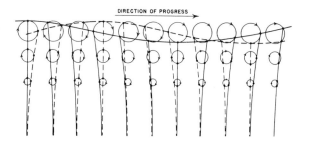

DIRECTION OF PROGRESS

Fig. 13-7. Orbital motion of particles in a standing wave. Particles follow the paths shown as the wave crest passes. Note that the size of the orbit diminishes downward. The near-vertical lines join particles in equivalent positions in the wave. (Reproduced from *U.S. Naval Oceanographic Office Publication No. 604,* 1951.)

As a wave approaches land the purely orbital motion of the water particles in it is impeded by the sea bottom. Specifically, the backward motion of the particles (in a direction opposite to that of the advancing crest) is hindered, and the particles show a net movement toward the shoreline. As an example of this effect, you may drop a marble into a soup bowl filled with water. The marble will cause oscillatory waves to spread outward from the point of impact, and until the lip of the bowl is reached there will be no translational movement of the water particles. At the edge of the bowl, however, there will be considerable splashing as the water moves up the side. In the ocean this change to net forward movement occurs where the bottom becomes shallow enough so that it is within the range of water undergoing wave movement. Ultimately, the drag of the bottom on the water is so great that the top of the wave is moving much faster than the bottom. At this point, water crashes forward in the form of *breakers,* and the zone in which breakers are developed is called the *surf zone.* The frothing together of water and air in the breakers gives them a white appearance. In the open ocean breakers cannot form, although on windy days the tops of waves may be sufficiently blown about to cause a slight frothing effect, and the waves are then called *white caps.*

Seismic sea waves or *tsunamis,* often inaccurately called *tidal waves,* are immense waves which are caused by earthquakes. There is generally only one significant wave crest, but wave heights of 100 feet have been observed, and on flat coasts water may penetrate many miles inland, causing enormous destruction. The first indication of the approach of a seismic sea wave is generally a pronounced withdrawal of water from the shore, and this advance warning has been valuable in saving many lives.

Where waves approach land they may be refracted in a variety of ways, much as light waves are refracted by a prism (Fig. 13-8). Consider, for example, a rocky headland jutting out into the ocean between two bays. Waves approaching from the open ocean will obviously run into this headland first; thus there will be a relative slowing of waves in the neighborhood of the headland and a comparatively higher speed of waves

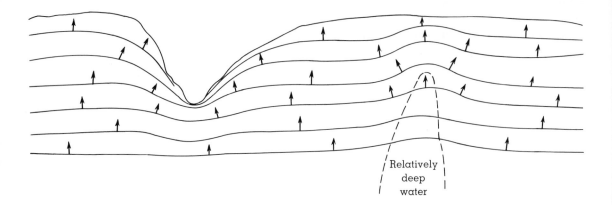

Relatively
deep
water

Fig. 13-8. Diffraction of wave crests by bottom topography and shoreline features. Waves travel faster over deep water, and wave energy is dispersed away from coasts opposite a local deep area. Conversely, wave energy is concentrated on headlands, and wave crests are diffracted toward them.

in the central portion of the bays. These effects can be approximated by rolling a pencil along a table and then suddenly putting your finger in front of one end. The pencil will tend to rotate around the point where it is stopped, and in like manner the crests of waves tend to rotate around the sides to the central part of the bay. This effect tends to concentrate the wave energy at the headland and leave only a small amount of energy for direct contact with the coast at the middle of the bay. Since waves can cause erosion just as other types of running water (Fig. 13-9), the headland should be worn away more rapidly than the bay, and the result of such refraction should be to smooth the coast to a straight profile.

As another example of refraction, we may consider waves approaching a coast over a bottom of irregular depth. Over a shallow ridge the waves are obviously slowed down, whereas over relatively deep water the waves can maintain their normal speed. The result is similar to that caused by a headland, namely wave activity tends to be concentrated at the coast opposite the ridge, and water piles up on the coast at this point. Similarly, there is a dispersal of wave energy from the coast opposite the deep water (Fig. 13-8).

Fig. 13-9. Wave-cut indentation (notch) in limestone cliff on Okinawa. The notch is slightly above the platform exposed at low tide. (Photo by E. A. King.)

One effect of wave refraction is to cause water to pile up on the coast at one spot and to be in comparatively short supply at another. As a result the water tends to flow from the place where wave activity is concentrated toward the places where the activity is least. This creates a *longshore current,* so named because it represents a body of water moving laterally along the shore. Longshore currents can also be created simply by wave crests striking a coast at an angle without any irregularities in the coastline. These currents generally move on the order of 1 to 5 miles per hour and transport an enormous amount of sedimentary material, such as beach sand, along the coast. One of the principal objects of the construction of breakwaters, in fact, is to cause sediment carried by longshore currents to be deposited on the up-current side of the breakwater. The construction of the breakwater also prevents sediment from being delivered to beaches below it and may permit erosion of these beaches. The water of longshore currents must, obviously, move out to sea at some point, and this commonly occurs where two currents moving in opposite directions meet. The resultant outflow of water can be exceptionally strong and is generally called a *rip tide,* although it is not actually a tide.

Turbidity currents

The water movements which we have discussed thus far are those concerned solely with water itself. There is, however, another type of current, known as a *turbidity current,* in which a concentrated mixture of mud, fine sand, and perhaps even coarser material forms a slurry with water. Under the force of gravity this slurry may move rapidly down slopes, in much the same manner as a mud flow on land (Fig. 12-9). The densities of turbidity currents may be quite high, with specific gravities on the order of 1.5 not at all uncommon. Naturally, the currents move along sea or lake floors and may distribute sediment rather widely. Turbidity currents, in fact, have been invoked as one major mechanism for the distribution of relatively coarse sedimentary material out into the deep ocean basins where normal current activity is insufficient to move large particles. Some geologists feel that a major mechanism for the movement of sediment in the oceans is the development of turbidity currents in shallow waters near continents and then a down-slope movement of the sediment-laden water into the deeper basins.

Turbidity currents may be studied quite readily in the laboratory, and indeed you may make one easily by mixing up a slurry of mud and water and pouring it down the side of a water-filled bowl. Deposits formed from intermittent

Fig. 13-10. Sandstone showing graded bedding from coarse material at the base to fine at the top. (Photo by E. F. McBride; from the *Journal of Sedimentary Petrology,* vol. 32, 1962, p. 50.)

Fig. 13-11. Turbidity current of mud-laden water formed where the Colorado River enters Lake Mead, Nevada. (Photo by Bureau of Reclamation, U.S. Department of the Interior.)

turbidity currents of this type have a rather characteristic structure known as *graded bedding* (Fig. 13-10). In such bedding the individual beds have coarse particles on the bottom and finer material toward the top. Bedding of this type is characteristic of the graywacke deposits of geosynclines, and some geologists feel that a large portion of the typical geosynclinal sedimentary rocks has resulted from turbidity-current distribution of sediment from shallow waters into the greater depths presumably characteristic of such environments.

Turbidity currents can be found in lakes or in any other body of water (Fig. 13-11). They are the underwater equivalent of the mud flows characteristic of relatively arid regions on land. Mud flows on land are commonly formed by the saturation of a mass of loose sediment by a sudden rain storm, causing the resultant mixture to flow at relatively high speeds, as much as 15 to 20 miles/hr, down small canyons or over broad slopes. Speeds reached by turbidity currents in the oceans may be quite high. The earthquake of 1929 near Grand Banks, Newfoundland, initiated a turbidity current from sediments on the upper slope of the shallow banks. Apparently the loose sediments on the slope were in a comparatively unstable condition. These sediments, mixed with water, traveled rapidly down the slope of the Grand Banks into the open ocean after they were "triggered" by the earthquake. The speed of this particular turbidity current could be traced fairly well by the fact that the current cut several Transatlantic cables at a number of points, and the positions of cutting and time of cutting could be measured accurately. Speeds of up to 50 or 60 miles/hr have been proposed for this particular turbidity current, although some geologists have felt that such high speeds are unreasonable for anything moving under water.

Density differences between two masses of water can be caused in ways other than the incorporation of sediment. Water reaches its maximum density at 4° C. One of the major currents in the ocean consists of water cooled in the Arctic and Antarctic regions which sinks to the bottom and spreads toward the Equator along the ocean floor. Bottom waters in both the Atlantic and the Pacific oceans are consistently at a temperature of 4° C.

OCEANIC LIFE

Since we have discussed the ocean waters and their movements, we must now turn to one more geologic agent before describing the products of marine processes. This other agent is the vast body of life which occurs within the oceans. We are not in a position to enter into a discussion of marine biology, but it is appropriate to make a few comments about the geologic effects of marine organisms, both plant and animal.

Obviously, one of the most important contributions of marine organisms to the geologic record is simply their shells. Most invertebrate animals which secrete hard shells build them of calcium carbonate, either as calcite or another crystalline form, aragonite. It is difficult to estimate the percentage of ancient limestones which consist of the hard parts of marine organisms, but it probably amounts to 80 to 90 percent (Fig. 7-4). Not only do whole shells and pieces of shells form the vast bulk of many limestones, but also the fine-grained matrix of many limestones may in part have resulted from the grinding up of shells or the accumulation of fine particles from organisms which cannot now be identified.

The hard parts of marine organisms accumulate in deep sea sediments as well as in shallow-water limestone. Many of the fine-grained sediments on the floor of the open ocean consist dominantly of the remains of some tiny animal or plant. The major contributing animals are Radiolaria

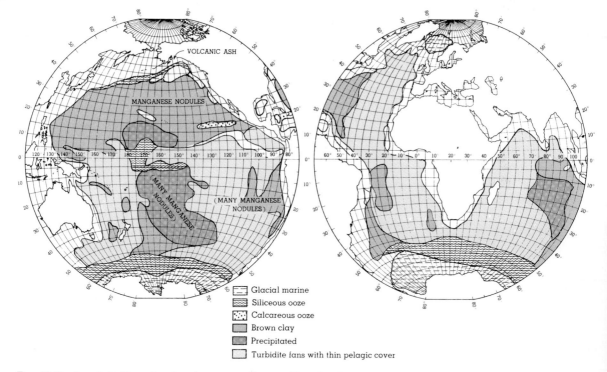

Fig. 13-12. *A* and *B*. Map of major deep-sea sediments. The glacial marine sediments are materials washed out of melting ice. Siliceous and calcareous oozes are composed almost entirely of the hard parts of tiny organisms. Brown clay is probably largely debris from the continents, whereas precipitated material is chemically deposited on the sea floor. Turbidite fans are wedge-shaped deposits of turbidity currents. (From F. P. Shepard, *Submarine Geology*, Harper & Row, New York, 1963.)

(single-celled organisms which secrete a spiny shell of silica) and certain calcium-carbonate secreting Foraminifera; the major plant contributors are silica-secreting diatoms. All of these organisms are single-celled, have diameters of fractions of a millimeter, and float or swim freely in the open ocean, where they are a dominant source of food for larger animals. After death the hard parts settle on the ocean floor, and although the rate of deposition is exceptionally slow, the absence of sediment from other sources permits the formation of large areas of almost pure deposits of these organic remains. These fine-grained deposits are called *oozes* (Figs. 13-12*A* and *B*).

Reefs

One of the most dramatic forms of calcium carbonate accumulation is the coral reef, so named because of its characteristic corals. The bulk of the reef, however, is generally constructed of calcium carbonate secreted by marine algae. Modern reefs are restricted to water in which the temperature is above 68° F., and they have a latitude restriction in that they occur only within about 30 degrees of the earth's Equator. The reef-forming corals and other animals cannot grow in cold water, and the algae which contribute to the growing reef must have the year-round light of the equatorial regions. The coral reef is formed by growth of a colony of organisms, with younger forms developing on the skeletons of older ones. Thus a meshwork of calcium carbonate is developed. The reef builds up from a base in shallow water (the organisms cannot live below the zone of light penetration) and ultimately reaches sea level, where it becomes a barrier to wave activity (Fig. 13-13). The tendency of reef-forming organisms to grow most vigorously in active, wave-agitated water makes the outer edge of the reef grow most rapidly. The meshwork of corals and other branching organisms is filled in by calcium carbonate deposited either organically or possibly by inorganic precipitation.

Fig. 13-13. Reef at outer edge of Bahama Banks. Deep water is to the right. (Photo by E. G. Purdy.)

Reefs range from very small patches, five or so feet in diameter, to the enormous Great Barrier Reef of the northeastern coast of Australia. The Great Barrier Reef extends laterally for a distance of 1250 miles. The general characteristics of both the small and the large reefs, however, are roughly the same.

The most picturesque development of coral reefs is around the islands of the South Pacific (Fig. 13-14). Here, reef formation generally starts on the flank of some volcanic island, and initial reef growth may start rather close to the shoreline (Fig. 13-15). In the past several thousand years, however, since melting of ice from the last major glaciation, sea level has risen several hundreds of feet.

As it has risen, the reefs have attempted to grow straight upward, and the drowning of the volcanic islands and previous reef growth has thus put the present reefs some distance offshore from the main island. It is also possible, of course, that relative sinking of the island has occurred, thus accentuating the rise of sea level. In some cases the volcanic top of the island has disappeared completely, thus leaving merely a circular fringe of coral reef. The fringes, whether surrounding islands or not, are called *atolls*. The interior floor of the atolls is generally partially filled in by calcium carbonate deposited in the relatively quiet water of the lagoon.

It is important for geologic purposes to be able to distinguish reef-front deposits from reef deposits and sediments formed in the quiet waters back of the reef. Reef fronts toward the open ocean are characteristically littered by blocks of the reef which have broken off in storms. Back-reef deposits form in quiet waters sheltered by the reef and are thus comparatively fine grained and contain fragile organisms which could not survive in the more active forereef environments. Typical features of reef and associated deposits are shown in Fig. 13-16. In the geologic record reefs are commonly found to form along the margins between relatively shallow and comparatively deep water. Apparently, here the requirements for the growth of organisms such as corals are most easily met. Such requirements include a shallow base exposed to warmth and light and a supply of nutrients from the deeper waters. In such places, proliferation of animal and plant colonies can take place rapidly (Fig. 13-17).

Other organic effects

Organisms may affect sediments without their remains being necessarily preserved in the rocks. In areas in which marine circulation is restricted, for example, organisms tend to die without be-

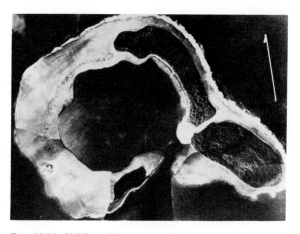

Fig. 13-14. Ifaluk atoll, western Pacific, as seen from the air. The white areas are coral reef deposits. The atoll has a diameter of about 2.5 miles. (Uncontrolled photo mosaic by the U.S. Navy. From J. I. Tracey, D. P. Abbott, and T. Arnow, *Bernice P. Bishop Museum Bulletin 222*, 1961.)

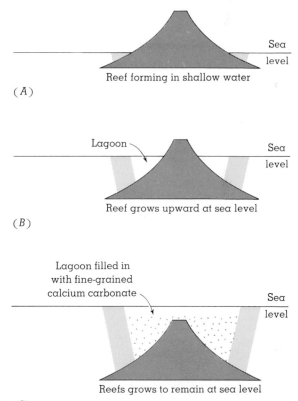

Fig. 13-15. *A* to C. Growth of coral reef and atoll. Reef is just beginning to form around exposed volcanic island in Figure *A*. As island subsides and/or sea level rises, reef grows upward and outward, ultimately resulting in a near-circular atoll.

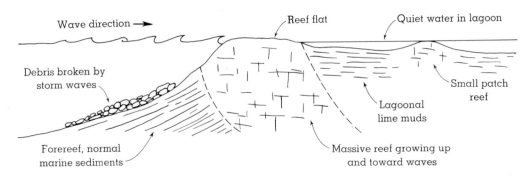

Fig. 13-16. Major portions of a reef.

Fig. 13-17. Guadalupe Peak, West Texas. This mountain is formed of reef limestone overlying stratified, fore-reef, basin sediments. (Photo by Muldrow Aerial Surveys Corporation.)

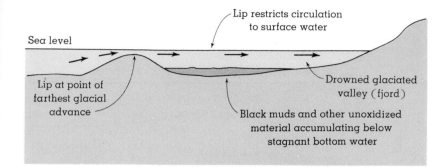

Fig. 13-18. Cross section of Norwegian fjord showing development of stagnant bottom water, owing to restricted circulation.

ing destroyed by later processes. Where current activity is reasonably high, the supply of nutrients and oxygen is sufficient to support animals on the sea bottom which eat the remains of other animals. Where the water becomes sufficiently stagnant that these bottom-dwelling, scavenging animals cannot live, organisms which die in the overlying water settle, decay, and accumulate. The result is the formation of conditions in which sedimentary material is reduced by the oxidizable organic compounds. Ferric compounds are reduced to the ferrous state, hydrogen sulfide is produced in large quantities, and unoxidized organic residues may accumulate. Such conditions may lead to the formation of black shales, which are characterized by the presence of carbonaceous material and, in some cases, pyrite. A typical modern equivalent is the black mud of the Norwegian fjords (Fig. 13-18). The fjord is essentially a drowned, glaciated valley; the outer edge of the fjord, past the limit of major glacial advance, is comparatively shallow, and this lip prevents the sea water from circulating freely in the fjord. The bottom of the fjord, then, is a site of accumulation of decayed organic matter.

Scavenging organisms which have an effect on bottom sediments may be as important by their presence as by their absence. Many primary sedimentary features are destroyed by these organisms by their pushing across or through the deposited material. One of the major animals which destroys bedding and other sedimentary features is a small marine worm which lives on organic matter in the sediments. It has also been shown in Fig. 7-14, *A* to *C,* that boring clams can be destructive of primary sedimentary features.

SUBMARINE TOPOGPAPHY

At one time it was thought that the sea floor was almost completely flat. This idea has now been abandoned, although some broad plains have been found on which the relief appears to be quite small. The abandonment of the concept of a flat sea floor is caused by the development of echo sounding devices. In the absence of echo sounding, depths had to be measured by throwing a weighted line over the side of a boat. Throwing the line over is not particularly difficult, but hauling it back in is pretty tedious in 12,000 feet of water. Thus before it was discovered that sound waves could be bounced off the bottom and their

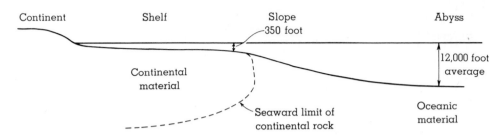

Fig. 13-19. Diagrammatic section of continental shelf and slope and oceanic abyss.

travel times recorded to give water depths, the number of soundings was exceptionally small.

Broadly speaking, the oceans may be divided into three portions (Fig. 13-19):

1. The *continental shelf* is simply an extension of the continents out under the ocean. The shelf generally has a rather gentle slope of much less than one degree. Sediments formed on it have been derived almost wholly from streams and other continental sources, the water is agitated, and in the upper portion, light reaches the sea floor. The shelf around the Atlantic Ocean extends, in general, out to distances of many tens or perhaps hundreds of miles off the coast. Around the Pacific Ocean, however, the shelves tend to be rather limited, and the slopes off the continental edges are steeper. The outer edge of the continental shelf is commonly at a water depth of about 350 feet.

2. The *continental slope* is the border between the shelf and the deep sea. The margin between the continental slope and shelf is really the geologic edge of the continent, and it is here that crustal continental structures give way to crustal oceanic structures. The angle of the continental slope is larger than that of the shelf but rarely exceeds 3 to 5 degrees.

3. The continental slope extends downward to *abyssal plains* which in all oceans are at an average depth of about 12,000 feet. Where the abyssal plains are not punctuated by other localized topographic features they are comparatively flat. It is on the abyssal plains that the various deep-sea clays and oozes accumulate. Some of the clays are simply muds which have been carried out from the continents and, being fine-grained, have been swept into the deep oceans before finally settling. Some of the material around the margins of the plains and the continental slopes has probably been brought down the slopes by turbidity currents. Some of the muds in the open ocean are apparently formed almost solely by the accumulation of different types of organisms and are called *oozes*. Calcium carbonate is absent from many deep-sea deposits, because the low temperature and high pressure of the waters permits sufficient solubility of carbon dioxide to dissolve the calcite. In some regions, however, a considerable accumulation of a calcite-secreting Foraminifera may occur.

A recent map of deep-sea muds and oozes has already been presented (Figs. 13-12*A* and *B*).

Ridges (rises)

One of the major features discovered rather recently in oceanic exploration is the presence of a number of *ridges* (also known as *rises*) which extend throughout all of the oceans and which may be interconnected with each other. The most widely known of these ridges is the Mid-Atlantic Ridge, which is so-named because it extends down the middle of the Atlantic Ocean and very effectively follows the midpoint between continents regardless of the irregularities of the continental coast lines. This ridge extends many thousands of feet above the normal 12,000-foot level of the abyssal plains, and at some places it rises above the ocean surface as small volcanic islands. The topography of the ridge is quite rugged, much like the ordinary mountain range that we see on land, and it is obviously quite different from the topography in other abyssal areas. It has recently been proposed that the various oceanic ridges are linked together to form a broad network shown in Fig. 13-20. Some geologists feel that this network follows a series of fault zones along which movement has caused construction of topographic high areas. Other geologists have disputed not only the existence of major faults along these ridges but also the evidence which supports the idea that the ridges are completely connected.

In addition to being topographically high, the mid-oceanic and other ridges have a number of additional features in common. Associated with most of the ridges are faults which are clearly shown topographically on the sea floor and also can be recognized as the locations of seismic activity. The nature of the movement on these faults has not been definitely established, but they may be analogous to the normal faults characteristic of uplifted areas on land, such as the plateau region centered around

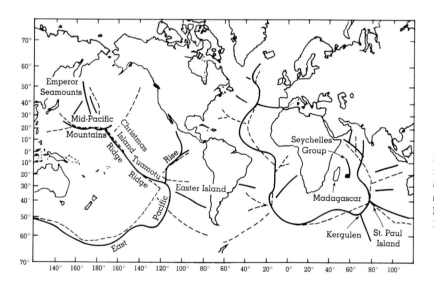

Fig. 13-20. Crests of submarine ridges and rises (solid line) compared with geometrical median line (dashed line). Median line is constructed as being equidistant from the 1000-meter depth contour around the continents. This depth contour conforms closely to continental outlines except in areas shown by dotted shading. (From H. W. Menard, *Experientia*, vol. 15, 1959, p. 205.)

Nevada. The ridges are also loci of volcanic activity. Much of the lava is erupted under water, but in some places islands have been built above sea level. Despite the importance of these properties, probably the most significant feature of the oceanic ridges is the fact that they represent areas of high crustal heat flow.

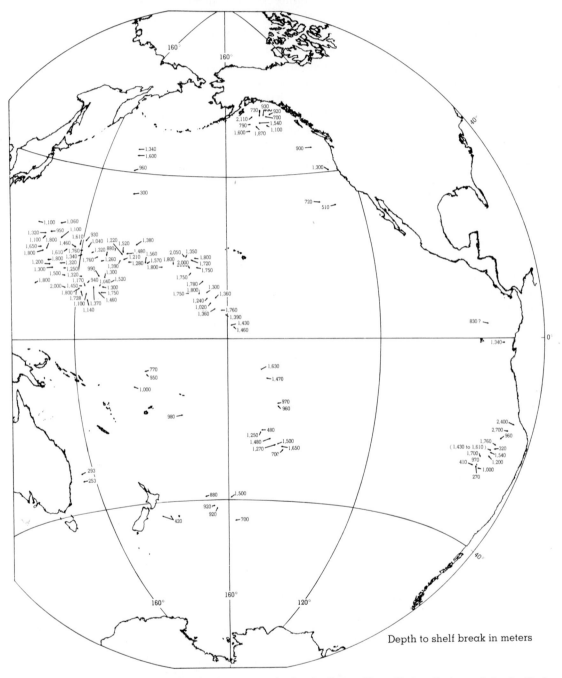

Fig. 13-21. Depth of guyots in the Pacific Ocean. (From *Marine Geology of the Pacific* by H. W. Menard, Copyright © 1964 McGraw-Hill Book Company. Used by permission of McGraw-Hill Book Company.)

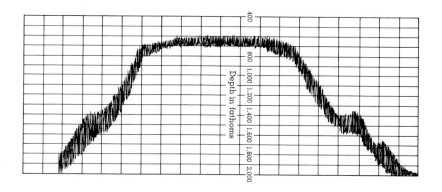

Fig. 13-22. Depth record (by fathometer) of a typical guyot. (From H. H. Hess, *American Journal of Science*, vol. 244, 1946.)

The quantity of heat flowing out through crustal rocks is calculated by methods outlined in Chapter 5. In general this heat flow is constant in both oceanic and continental areas throughout the world, but along oceanic ridges the heat flows are abnormally high. These high heat flows are almost certainly caused by high temperatures in the mantle immediately underlying the ridges. We shall see in Chapter 14 that one likely cause of an upwelling of high-temperature rock in the upper mantle is a convection current which brings material from the base of the mantle to the top.

Oceanic ridges are apparently not permanent features of the crust. It can be demonstrated, for example, that a major ridge, called the "Darwin Rise" after Charles Darwin, existed in the western Pacific about 75 million years ago but has since disappeared. The evidence for this rise consists mainly of the finding of large number of broad, flat-topped submarine mounds grouped in a generally elliptical pattern throughout the Pacific Ocean west of Hawaii. The locations of these mounds and the depths to their tops are shown in Fig. 13-21. Mounds of this type have been found in all oceanic areas, though they are most concentrated in the western Pacific, and are called *guyots* (Fig. 13-22). They have the general shape of volcanic islands from which the tops have simply been shaved off.

The origin of guyots has been a topic of considerable discussion. It appears obvious that the only agent in the ocean capable of cleaning off a flat surface several miles across is wave activity, and waves obviously do not extend to depths of several thousand feet. Guyots, therefore, must have been at or near the surface at some time in their history. This conclusion has recently been reinforced by the finding of shallow-water fossils of approximately 75 million years in age on the top of some of the Pacific guyots.

Returning now to the Darwin Rise, if the guyots of the western Pacific have been uplifted to the zone of wave action (i.e., sea level), and if all of them have been uplifted at about the same time 75 million years ago, it is necessary to hypothesize a broad ridge through the region at this time. It is, in fact, possible to contour this ridge rather accurately by the

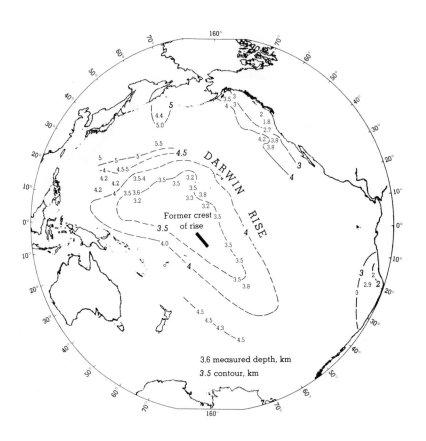

Fig. 13-23. Reconstructed depth contours of Darwin Rise in western Pacific. This map is based on data given in Fig. 13-21 and is constructed as explained in the text. (From *Marine Geology of the Pacific* by H. W. Menard, Copyright © 1964 McGraw-Hill Book Company. Used by permission of McGraw-Hill Book Company.)

following process. At the present time, the ocean floor between the guyots is essentially a flat abyssal plain. Therefore, the depth of the guyot tops below the sea surface must represent the depth of sinking of the ridge, and these depths must also equal the elevations of the ridge above the abyssal plain when the ridge existed. There are, of course, certain irregularities caused by differential sinking of different guyots, but the general pattern of the ridge can be portrayed with remarkable clarity (Fig. 13-23). It is interesting to note that the date of maximum elevation of the Darwin Rise, as determined by the shallow-water fossils on the guyots, coincides with the last major flooding of continental areas by shallow seas.

Volcanic islands and arcs

One of the interesting features of the oceanic regions is the presence of volcanic islands. As already mentioned, a series of these islands occurs along the Mid-Atlantic Ridge starting with Iceland in the north. The characteristic development, however, is in the Pacific Ocean. A volcanic island simply represents the extension of a submarine volcano above water level. Considering that the volcanic accumulation must be built up from a sea floor which has a depth of approximately 12,000 feet, and considering that the slopes on the sides of volcanoes are generally in the

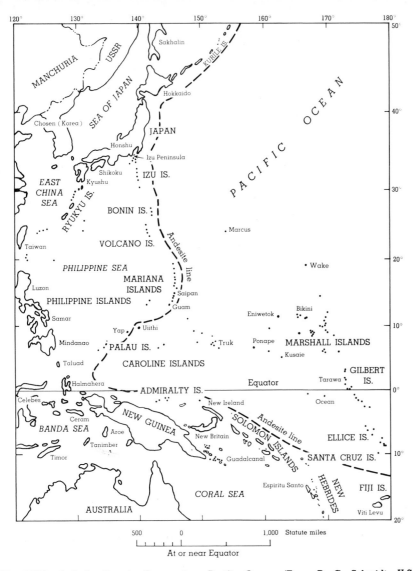

Fig. 13-24. Andesite line in the western Pacific Ocean. (From R. G. Schmidt, *U.S. Geological Survey Professional Paper 280-B,* 1957.)

range of 15 to 30 degrees, the total volcanic accumulation necessary for the construction of an island just a few miles in diameter is obviously immense.

The islands of the central Pacific contain volcanic rocks which differ from the rocks of arcs and land areas bordering the Pacific. Volcanic suites on the margins of the Pacific Ocean consist of basalts, andesites, and rhyolites with quite distinct chemical properties, such as an extremely low content of potassium. The rocks of the central Pacific are primarily basalts with some unusual differentiates, most of which are comparatively enriched in potassium. The transition between these two suites of rocks is quite abrupt, and the dividing line is commonly referred to as the *andesite line* (Fig. 13-24). Owing to immense difficulties of obtaining valid samples, it has not yet been possible to compare the volcanic rocks of continental areas with those of the central Pacific or of the marginal zone just outside of the andesite line. Thus the complete geologic significance of this line of separation is unknown.

Islands around the margin of the Pacific Ocean, landward of the andesite line, are characterized by the arcuate form which chains of these islands commonly show. Start, for example, with Alaska and look westward along the bend of the Aleutian Islands. Look at the arcuate form of the Japanese Islands and then at the arcs which are formed by several other sets of islands extending south of Japan along the western border of the Pacific Ocean. These arcs are hardly a geologic accident and must have some rational explanation for their origin. It has been pointed out, for example, that a plane intersecting the earth's surface at an angle would form an arc along the intersection. The shape of the arc would depend on the angle of inclination of the plane. Thus it is possible that the arcuate form of these volcanic chains is, in some way, related to the development of a reasonably straight fault surface.

If we examine the arcs in more detail, and in particular make soundings in the oceans surrounding them, we will find a very persistent deep trench on the seaward side of the arc. This trench, commonly known as a *foredeep,* is the deepest part of the ocean. In fact the Marianas Trench, in the western Pacific, reaches a depth greater than 35,000 feet, which is thus far the deepest encountered. In general, trenches have depths some 10,000 to 15,000 feet below those of the normal abyssal plains.

If we make gravity surveys across the island arcs, we shall discover several other important features. The main feature is that the arc has a broad negative gravity anomaly. That is, in the region of the arc, light rock extends to much greater depth than it should if isostatic compensation had been achieved. The arcs are, in short, out of isostatic balance and are obviously kept that way by some continuing crustal stress.

Exceptionally interesting studies of subcrustal structure have been made in the Japanese Islands. One result of these studies has been a map of the foci of earthquakes, that is, the actual centers at depth, and the results are shown in Fig. 13-25. It is virtually impossible to escape the idea that some sort of seismically active feature extends down under Japan from its east coast back toward the Asiatic mainland. It is interesting to note that the volcanic rocks of Japan can also be zoned in an east-west fashion with

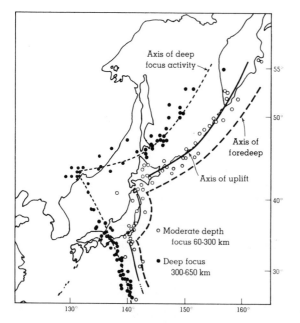

Fig. 13-25. Depth of foci of earthquakes near the Japanese island arc. (From H. H. Hess, *Geological Society of America Bulletin,* vol. 59, 1948.)

progressive changes in composition and mineralogy from the east to the west. Presumably, the surface which extends under Japan is a fault zone and is the source from which lavas are derived for eruption at the surface, and it is certainly logical that different types of basalts may be derived at different depths in the subcrust.

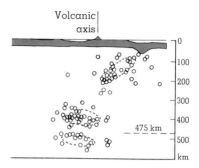

Fig. 13-26. Cross section of island arcs south of Japan, showing location of earthquake foci. There is a tendency toward clustering in three groups, with increasing depth away from the foredeep in front of the arc. (From H. H. Hess, *Geological Society of America Bulletin*, vol. 59, 1948.)

Similar features to those of the Japanese Islands have been proposed for other island arcs, including those consisting solely of volcanic material in the central ocean (Fig. 13-26). Here, however, is an area in which considerably more detailed work must be done before a complete interpretation of arc structure is available. The highly tentative conclusion that we can reach at the moment, however, is that these volcanic arcs represent some sort of compressional movement in which a broad fault plane develops, and the crust out in front of the overriding block is bent down in the form of a foredeep. The whole compression causes the shoving of surface rock down into the subcrust and produces the negative gravity anomalies. This picture oversimplifies a number of details which we have not been able to discuss here, but it is a valid first approximation.

Features precisely similar to the island arcs are not found in the Atlantic Ocean, although there are broad similarities in two arcs which join, respectively, the North and South American continents and the South American and Antarctic continents. The Caribbean Islands, starting with Cuba and extending out around the Antilles, represent an extension, in the north, of structural trends from Central America. In the south, as the arc swings back around, the structural trends join with those in northern Venezuela. Thus, although the topographic link between North and South America is through Panama, the geologic link may actually be more accurately described as passing through the Caribbean Islands. Interestingly enough, a similar arc occurs at the southern tip of South America. Here South Georgia and other islands swing in a broad loop through the Atlantic Ocean and connect with the northern tip of Graham Land Peninsula in the Antarctic. In the Caribbean area the typical foredeeps are present as in the Pacific Ocean, and many of the islands are highly volcanic. Other types of rocks, however, do occur on these islands, and there is partial similarity between the general geology of the Caribbean Islands and the geology of the Japanese arc. The geology of the arc between South America and the Antarctic is not well known and certainly merits considerable study.

Submarine canyons

Another important and puzzling topographic feature of the ocean floor is the submarine canyon. These canyons are simply deep valleys cut in the continental slope but extending, in some cases, back into the shelf. The valleys have every appearance of being typical of stream valleys on

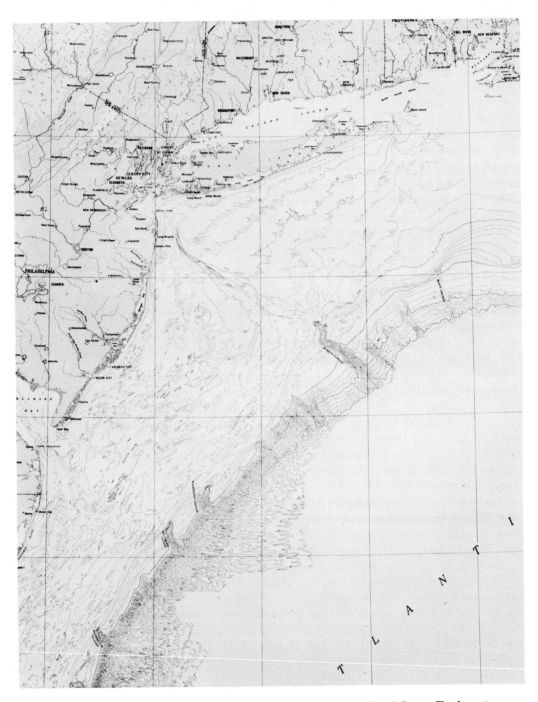

Fig. 13-27. Submarine canyons off the east coast of the United States. The largest canyon clearly extends to the mouth of the Hudson River, but most are confined to the outer edge of the continental shelf and the slope (steep contours). (From A. C. Veatch and P. A. Smith, *Geological Society of America Special Paper 7,* 1939.)

land, but they extend to depths of many thousands of feet. Figure 13-27

shows a map of the submarine canyons off the east coast of the United States. It is immediately apparent that the canyons are generally opposite the mouths of large rivers. This fact has given rise to several lines of speculation. One theory holds that the sediments derived from the rivers tend to form vast piles of debris on the shelves off the river mouths. This debris is relatively unstable and may, under proper conditions, possibly with the aid of a triggering effect, became a major turbidity current. The turbidity currents would, presumably, flow directly down the shelf and slope and would ultimately reach the abyssal plains. Many geologists feel that these turbidity currents, moving rapidly and carrying a great deal of sediment, are capable of eroding the canyons in a manner almost identical to that in which streams cut valleys on land. Certainly, turbidity currents must flow down the canyons on occasion, but whether they are effective in causing erosion has been a topic of considerable dispute.

Another theory is that the submarine canyons were formed by erosion when the continental margins were above sea level. In part, the margins may have been elevated relative to the sea by the lowering of sea level during the recent glaciation. The canyons, however, extend below the maximum 600-foot lowering of the glacial period. Thus an additional elevation of the margins must have taken place if they were truly eroded in this fashion. There is no evidence that this has occurred, although the possibility has been accepted by some geologists. The idea of elevating the continental margins so as to permit subaerial erosion also runs into the problem of finding a mechanism by which the margins could be raised.

SHORELINES

Thus far we have discussed the sea floor and, in particular, the deep ocean. Let us turn now to a consideration of those features that are developed along shorelines and which, in general, are better known than those of the deep sea. The shoreline areas, in fact, are one of the most thoroughly studied geologic areas on the earth; this is partly because they represent the interaction between marine and land environments and, therefore, are interesting in a theoretical sense.

Beaches

One of the characteristic features of shorelines is the sandy beach, although beaches are found along only a small portion of the North American coastline. Beach sand has been accumulated either from material carried by longshore currents or from offshore sediments and has been driven up onto the shore by wave activity. The inward rush of a wave generally brings a considerable amount of sediment with it. The backward rush is less effective because of loss of water by soaking into the loose beach sand; this prevents the wave from taking back as much material as is brought to the beach. Under these conditions, provided there is a sufficient supply of sediment, beaches are rather continuously

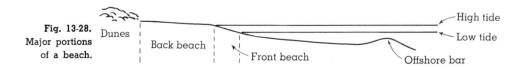

Fig. 13-28. Major portions of a beach.

Dunes | Back beach | Front beach | Offshore bar | High tide — Low tide

built outward. The typical beach (Fig. 13-28) has a fairly steeply sloping front portion and a more gently sloping back portion, ending commonly in a group of sand dunes. The steeply sloping area, or *foreshore,* represents the area of tidal activity. The top of the foreshore is the mean high-tide level, and the more gently sloping *backshore* commonly receives very little water. The subdivision of the beach into these two portions is characteristic only of those beaches which are actively being built outward and not of those beaches which, because of lack of sediment supply, are being eroded.

Bars

Wave activity does not necessarily bring sand all the way up to the beach fringing the shoreline. On shallow shelves, incoming breakers may form sufficiently far out so that sand is churned up in them and may be deposited in long parallel ridges somewhat off the actual coastline. These ridges commonly build up near or above water level, particularly if the sand supply is large. Ridges of this type, whether islands or below sea level, are referred to as *bars* or *offshore bars* (Fig. 13-29). Where these bars are laterally extensive, they may form islands to restrict wave activity and thus develop quiet-water embayments between the bar and

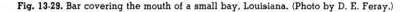

Fig. 13-29. Bar covering the mouth of a small bay, Louisiana. (Photo by D. E. Feray.)

Fig. 13-30. Small delta formed inside of a lagoon by tidal waters washing through an opening in the bar. Texas coast. (Photo by R. R. Lankford.)

Fig. 13-31. Hook on Louisiana coast. (Photo by D. E. Feray.)

the land (Fig. 13-30). These embayments are commonly called *lagoons.*
By gradual infilling with sediments, which cannot be reworked owing
to the absence of current and wave activity, these lagoons may be converted into swamps.

A special type of offshore bar may be developed across the mouths of
bays by the action of longshore currents sweeping sand across the mouth
of the bay. The deposition is caused in part by wave activity and in part
by initial accumulation of sediment in the relatively quiet bay waters.
Bars which extend in this fashion are commonly referred to as *spits.*
In some places, currents flowing into the bay from the open ocean may
cause the end of the spit to curve around, and such a curving spit is called
a *hook* (Fig. 13-31). On a very large scale, the tip of Cape Cod is a hook.

Erosional features

Thus far we have discussed the construction of beaches along coastlines. It should be recognized, however, that where coastal topography is
fairly steep and waves can pound directly against cliffs, then erosion will
occur rather than deposition. The eroded coastline may be a fairly
chaotic place, with a jumble of boulders and rocks offshore, possibly
caves at the base of the cliff, and slumping and other destructional
features in the neighborhood of the cliff face (Fig. 13-9). On occasion
it is possible for waves to plane off portions of the coastline, and these
flat surfaces may be exposed by later elevation of the coast or retreat of
sea level. Such flat surfaces formed in this fashion are referred to as
marine terraces or *wave-cut terraces* (Fig. 13-32).

Fig. 13-32. Series of wave-cut terraces on San Clemente Island, California. (U.S. Navy
Photograph by R. S. Dietz; from *Geological Society of America Bulletin,* vol. 74, 1963.)

Fig. 13-33. Norwegian fjord. This is a drowned glaciated valley. (Photo courtesy of Norwegian National Travel Office.)

The characteristic properties of shorelines are highly dependent on whether the shore has undergone a recent emergence or a recent submergence. Movement of a shoreline outward from its original position can be caused either by deposition, by uplift of the land, or by retreat of sea level. Along such shorelines it is common to find constructional features such as beaches, bars, etc. The reason for the abundance of these constructional features is that the emergence of the sea floor has produced a flat topography both landward and seaward of the shoreline. The elevated shallow-water sediments are also a prime source of beach and bar material and are easily reworked by advancing waves to form deposits closer to the shoreline. Another common feature along emergent shorelines is a swamp formed by the poor drainage developed on the flat former sea floor.

Submergent shorelines tend to be quite rugged (Fig. 13-33). Obviously, the drowning of a normal hilly or mountainous topography brings oceanic waters up against rocky slopes and causes erosion to be the predominant activity. Quite a number of small offshore islands may be formed by simple isolation from their former mountain range. The typical example of a drowned coastline is that of eastern Maine, where deep embayments, offshore islands, and a rugged shoreline without a sandy beach are the rule. Despite the simple examples given here, it is not always easy to determine the dominant mode of formation of drowned shorelines.

CHAPTER 14 SOME MAJOR
EARTH PROCESSES

◀ Section through fossil in rock. (Photo by D. F. Toomey.)

$\mathbf{N}$ow that we have outlined the major aspects of geology, we are in a position to inquire about the major processes which have caused the development of continents, ocean basins, mountain ranges and other large features of the earth's surface. In Chapter 5 we outlined a possible mechanism by which continental material has separated from the remainder of the earth and the possibilities for an increase in the amount of continental material during the course of geologic history. In this chapter we shall discuss whether or not the continents have formed in the position which they now occupy relative to each other or whether their positions have changed throughout the later part of geologic history. We shall also inquire into the mechanisms and causative forces of major movements of areas of continental or subcontinental sizes. By these major movements we mean *orogeny,* the general process of the construction of mountains (see Chapter 10), and *epeirogeny,* the more mild undulation of continents relative to sea level.

Another question of major geologic importance is the relationship between the development of organic life and the inorganic evolution of the earth. This relationship is discussed in this chapter together with an evaluation of the uniformitarianism concept.

CONTINENTAL DRIFT

The idea of continental drift was first proposed by Alfred Wegener in 1910. He was impressed by the similarity between the coastlines of South America and Africa and the geologic similarity of such areas as South Africa, South America, the southern peninsula of India, and Australia. Since his time a considerable number of additional arguments have been invoked to prove that these continents were once connected and have drifted apart at some reasonably late time in the earth's history. Ex-

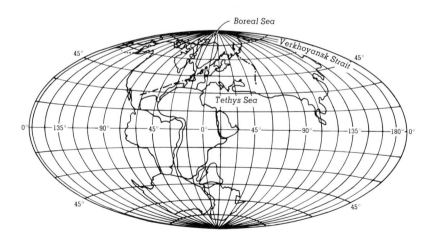

Fig. 14-1. Positions of continents prior to continental drift. (From J. T. Wilson, *Nature,* vol. 198, 1963.)

345

actly what this time might be is uncertain, although some have even suggested that it was as recent as 75 million years ago. Figure 14-1 shows a reconstruction of a possible major continental area before fragmentation, and the paths which the various pieces must have followed in order to become the present continents can easily be deduced. Some of the major lines of evidence introduced as proof of a drift of this type are as follows:

1. The similarity in coastlines of South America and Africa. As mentioned in Chapter 13, it is not proper to consider only the present coastline marked by sea level; it is necessary to consider the coastline as marked by the edge of the continental shelf, where true continental structures apparently are bordered by true oceanic structures. Figure 14-2 shows a reconstructed map in which South America and Africa are placed together along the line of the continental margins. The fit is quite remarkable.

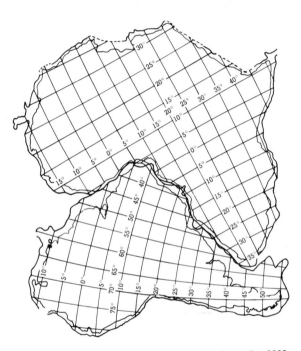

Fig. 14-2. Fit of Africa and South America along the 2000-meter depth contour. This is a spherical projection which removes the distortion caused by flat maps. (From S. W. Carey. Reproduced with permission from *Geological Magazine*, vol. 92, 1955, p. 198.)

2. The dissimilarity between the Atlantic and Pacific oceans. Geophysicists have disagreed as to whether or not there are major dissimilarities in the crust underlying the Atlantic and Pacific oceans, and we are not in a position here to enter the controversy. Nevertheless, the lands bordering the Pacific and Atlantic oceans are obviously quite different. The Pacific, for example, is rimmed by island arcs and exhibits general volcanic activity and earthquakes. With the exception of the Caribbean arc and the arc at the tip of South America, island arcs, earthquake activity, and volcanic activity are absent from the land bordering the Atlantic Ocean. Furthermore, the number of islands in the Atlantic Ocean is considerably smaller than in the Pacific despite the presence of the Mid-Atlantic Ridge, whose configuration alone indicates some relationship to the surrounding continents. Also, in the Atlantic Ocean the continental shelves are broad, and the coastlines behind them are generally flat for considerable distances. Note, in particular, the flat areas of the eastern United States and the eastern part of South America. These gently sloping coastal and underwater areas contrast markedly with the abrupt mountainous coasts and steep shelves in the Pacific Ocean, particularly on the west coasts of South and North America. This type of evidence could be used to support the idea of continental drift on the basis that the Pacific represents a true primordial oceanic struc-

ture, whereas the Atlantic has until recently been overlain by continental material.

3. Geologic similarity of the continents. A number of geologists have felt that the geologic features of South America, Africa, Australia, Antarctica, and the southern portion of India are sufficiently similar that they could be fitted together. For example, orogenic belts of various ages are matched together to show a possible configuration of the different continents before drifting occurred (Fig. 14-3).

4. Paleontologic evidence. One of the problems facing both paleontologists and modern biologists is explaining the similarity of animals and plants in widely separated parts of the world. The similarities and differences can be used to demonstrate the presence or absence of connections between these separate areas. For example, the native mammals of Australia are all marsupials, which differ from true mammals in a number of ways, such as raising their young in pouches. Marsupials are extremely rare in the rest of the world, with the exception of a few isolated groups such as the opossums of the southern U.S. On the basis of this evidence it may be assumed that Australia and the rest of the world were connected in some way at the time that marsupials began to evolve; this

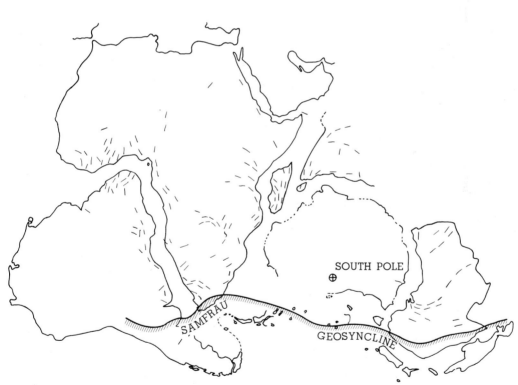

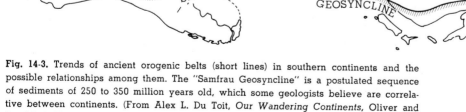

Fig. 14-3. Trends of ancient orogenic belts (short lines) in southern continents and the possible relationships among them. The "Samfrau Geosyncline" is a postulated sequence of sediments of 250 to 350 million years old, which some geologists believe are correlative between continents. (From Alex L. Du Toit, *Our Wandering Continents*, Oliver and Boyd Ltd., Edinburgh, 1937, p. 58.)

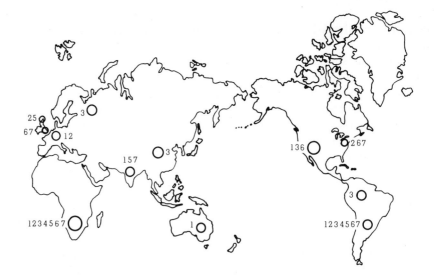

Fig. 14-4. Distribution of certain amphibians and reptiles during the Triassic Period (approximately 200 million years ago). Each number refers to one particular group of animals, which is present where the number occurs. Note the correspondence between Africa and South America. (From E. H. Colbert, *American Museum of Natural History Bulletin 99,* 1952.)

connection, however, was severed before the evolution of mammals at a somewhat later date.

On the basis of similar reasoning, the maps shown in Figs. 14-4 and 14-5 are extremely interesting. The various families of tetrapods (an

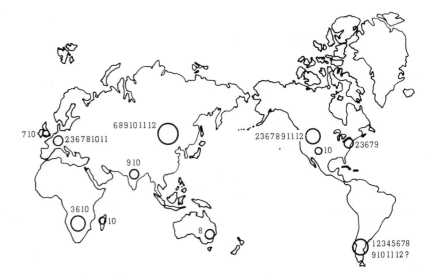

Fig. 14-5. Distribution of certain reptiles during the Cretaceous Period (approximately 75 million years ago). Presentation similar to that of Fig. 14-4. Note the lack of correspondence between Africa and South America. (From E. H. Colbert, *American Museum of Natural History Bulletin 99,* 1952.)

extinct form of reptile) living in South Africa at two different periods in the earth's history are numbered. The same numbers indicate the presence of these identical families in sediments of the same age elsewhere. Obviously, the similarity between the tetrapods of South America and South Africa is very large in the Triassic Period (about 200 million years ago) and very small in the Cretaceous Period (about 75 million years ago). Possibly the continents split apart between those two periods.

5. Paleoclimatic evidence. As discussed in Chapter 12, it is possible to map ancient climatic zones on the basis of such features as glacial deposits, coal, and other rocks and fossils. In some paleoclimatic studies it has been concluded that there has been variation in the location of the earth's climatic belts because of polar wandering without relative movement of the continents. In fact, if ancient climatic zones can be mapped on the basis of continents in their present positions, then relative movement is impossible (e.g., Fig. 12-39).

Some types of climatic evidence, however, have been used to demonstrate the existence of a continent in the southern hemisphere which has later fragmented as described above. The major line of evidence is the presence of glacial deposits and glacially striated surfaces in Permian rocks (300 million year age) in South America, South Africa, India, and Australia. These areas are so widely separated now that it seems impossible for glacial climates to have spread over all of them at the same time, and it is likely that these land areas were closer together at the time of glaciation.

Paleoclimatic evidence in favor of continental drifting has already been shown in Fig. 12-37. This figure was given largely to demonstrate the relationship between paleomagnetic measurements and climatic indications of Pole and Equator positions obtained from rock properties. In the figure, however, note that the position of the Equator found for each of the continents differs from that for the other continents. This difference means that the continents are not now in the same position relative to each other that they occupied at the time the rocks being studied were formed. Shifts in relative positions obviously signify drift.

6. Paleomagnetism. In Chapter 12 we mentioned the fact that some paleomagnetic studies verified the possibility of polar wandering. It is also possible to interpret the evidence as demonstrating the concept of continental drift. Figure 12-38, in fact, may be interpreted as such evidence. The pole positions obtained from different continents for the same period of time are not identical, thus indicating movement of the continents not only with regard to the pole but also with respect to each other. Not all geologists, however, accept the validity of the data on which Fig. 12-38 is based, and the comparative importance of polar wandering and continental drift has not been established. It is important to note, of course, that the two theories are not wholly exclusive of each other.

The evidence which we have given for continental drifting comes largely from studies in the southern hemisphere. Indeed, until recently geologists have been reasonably well split between those who preferred the idea of continental drifting, and who were primarily concentrated in the southern hemisphere, and those who did not believe in drift, and who were primarily concentrated in the northern hemisphere.

One argument which has been used against the possibility of continental drifting is that there does not seem to be any readily determinable mechanism by which the drifting could have occurred or a force which could have caused it. An argument of this type, though commonly used, is not really very worthwhile. The fact that no mechanism or force has been described does not mean that it cannot exist. Furthermore, the geologist who makes use of this type of argument puts himself in the position of having to demonstrate that such a force and mechanism not only has not been thought of but actually cannot exist.

OROGENY

The construction of mountain ranges involves movements on a smaller scale than those of continental drift, but the forces required may be even larger. That movement occurs is demonstrated by the shrinkage of the crust required in at least a small area by the folding and thrusting which characterizes orogeny. Whether the crust as a whole shrinks is a difficult question, and actually the intrusion of igneous rocks and other adjustments may be sufficient to counteract the shortening effect of the thrusting and folding. The forces necessary to cause mountain-building may be greater than those necessary to cause drifting, if drifting has occurred, by virtue of the fact that the folding, thrusting, and shoving upward of rocks may be a more difficult process than a simple lateral sliding of a continental mass. Although some geologists have proposed that continental drifting is a mechanism by which mountain ranges are formed, others have felt that the drifting may be a sufficiently "quiet" process that very little, if any, observable deformation occurs within the continents.

Any mechanism that is proposed to account for major mountain-building must explain the whole cycle of geosynclinal downwarp, sedimentary accumulation, vulcanism, the thrusting and folding which ends the sedimentation period, the development of mountain roots, and perhaps post-orogenic processes such as normal faulting and additional vulcanism (Chapter 10). The mechanisms proposed may also have to account for another major geologic observation, namely that of the distribution of mountain-building in space and time.

Sediments of many geologic periods seem to have been deposited in areas of complete crustal stability, and evidence of deformation during these periods is virtually absent on a world-wide basis. This fact plus the fact that certain widely separated mountain ranges, such as the Appalachian Mountains in the United States and the Ural Mountains in Russia, seem to have formed at virtually the same time has led geologists to propose the concept of a periodicity of mountain-building (Fig. 14-6). The idea is that pulses of major orogeny occur on a world-wide scale at roughly the same time and that these are interspersed with periods of crustal stability. The argument encounters two major difficulties, neither of which is irrefutable, but both of which pose a very serious question.

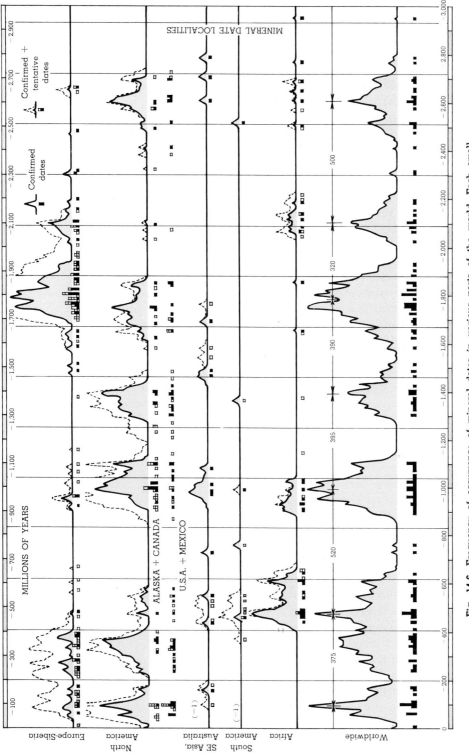
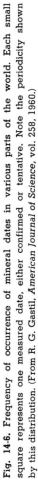

Fig. 14-6. Frequency of occurrence of mineral dates in various parts of the world. Each small square represents one measured date, either confirmed or tentative. Note the periodicity shown by this distribution. (From R. G. Gastil, *American Journal of Science*, vol. 258, 1960.)

The first problem is that the absence of orogenically deformed material during certain periods does not necessarily mean that deformation was not occurring at these times. Deformed areas, being uplifted, are obviously subjected to erosion with much greater intensity than areas of flat-lying sedimentary rocks at an elevation closer to sea level. Thus the absence of evidence of deformation in certain periods may have resulted from the simple erosion of the rocks deformed at these times. Another possibility for the absence of deformed rocks in the older geologic periods is their being covered by the rocks of later periods.

The possibility of covering by later deposits is a partial answer to the other major objection to a simple periodicity of mountain-building. This objection is that if the various periods of mountain-building within the last billion years are plotted, as shown in Fig. 14-6, it is possible to hypothesize that the time intervals between them become shorter as we approach the present. This "speeding up" of the orogenic cycle is, of course, a possibility, though it is not one which geologists like to invoke. It is conceivable that the apparent acceleration simply results from the erosion of evidence of former orogenies or perhaps a covering of former orogenically deformed rocks. Naturally, the erosion and covering would be more effective for the older orogenies. The balance of evidence at the moment seems to indicate that there is some periodicity of orogenic activity. It is distinctly possible, however, that this conclusion is based solely on insufficient evidence, and orogenic activity may actually be reasonably continuous throughout geologic time.

We have already mentioned the fact that continental drifting has been considered by some people to be a major source of orogenic forces, although others feel that the drifting was sufficiently "quiet" so that no deformation took place. We can now consider two other theories which have been proposed to account for orogenies. The first theory, and at first sight the most appealing one, is the possibility of a continually *shrinking earth*. The shrinkage, presumably, would take place because of loss of heat and resultant cooling of the earth, and under conditions of this type the earth's crust might be considered to shrivel up much like the skin of a dried prune. The shriveling, of course, would not take place unless the crust was solid and the underlying material was effectively a liquid. In this case the shrinkage attendant upon loss of heat would withdraw support from the base of the crust. The withdrawn support would then cause the crust to be in a position of supporting itself as a hollow shell; thus, lateral stresses would be directed throughout the earth's crust parallel to the surface.

One line of reasoning that has been used to substantiate the possibility of a shrinking crust is the present distribution of major mountain ranges on the earth. Effectively, there are two broad bands of mountain ranges. One of these is the Andes–Rocky Mountain chain along the western coast of North and South America. This is essentially a north-south trending chain which extends over a distance of approximately 9000 miles. The other major chain of mountains extends from the Himalayas westward through Northern Iran, the Alps, the Pyrenees Mountains between Spain and France, and is in line with the orogenic activity in the

Caribbean area. These two mountain chains are approximately perpendicular to each other. The reason that the perpendicularity of the two broad belts favors the possibility of a shrinking earth is that if a sphere is to shrink and still maintain itself as a sphere, then it must shorten itself in equal amounts along two great circles perpendicular to each other. This is a difficult concept to demonstrate physically, but if you wish to try, cut a tennis ball into two mutually perpendicular semicircles and squeeze them together. The argument against such evidence is first, that the mountain-building episodes were not all concurrent in these various areas; and second, that if the earth's crust is going to shrivel like the skin of a prune, then it should do so roughly equally at all spots and not preferentially along two circles. Shrinkage along two broad bands means that stresses in the crust must be distributed from the entire distance around the earth until they are finally relieved by buckling in one point. This postulates a much greater degree of strength for the earth's crust than is normally thought to be possible. Another argument against the possibility of a shrinking earth is that the earth may actually not be cooling off at all. The amount of radioactivity within the earth is large enough to indicate that there may be an actual increase in temperature from the heat given off by radioactive processes or at least a thermal balance.

A second major mechanism which has been proposed to explain the origin of mountains and the events which preceded final deformation is *convection currents*. Convection currents in the mantle of the earth can be expected, by virtue of the fact that the hotter, inner part of the mantle must become, as a result of its high temperature, less dense than the cooler, outer part. The density inversion would cause a convective overturn such that there would be a down-flow of the cooler and denser material and up-flow of the hot material. The cooler material, upon reaching the lower part of the mantle, would then be heated up sufficiently to become less dense than the material now above it; thus the process would repeat itself. Geometrically, the convection current would look something like a water fountain, with upward flow in the center and downward flow around the edges.

Whether or not convection currents are continuous or intermittent, the movement of such currents must cause a drag along the lower part of the crust. The drag is exerted in a direction from the point of rise of the hot material to a point at which the cold material is moving downward. The process is very difficult to diagram in three dimensions, and Fig. 14-7 shows merely a two-dimensional representation of a laboratory model. The action of the two convection cells shown in Fig. 14-7 causes the crust to be dragged together and, at least in the initial stages, downwarped. The downwarped area presumably fills with sediment which is crushed and deformed as the convection cells continue to

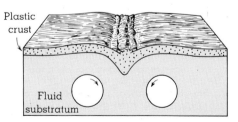

Fig. 14-7. Model showing development of down-warped, deformed belt by rotating drums. In nature the drums would be analogous to convection currents below the crust. (From D. T. Griggs, *American Journal of Science*, vol. 237, 1935.)

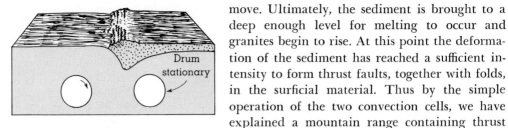

Fig. 14-8. Model similar to that of Fig. 14-7, but with one stationary drum. (From D. T. Griggs, *American Journal of Science*, vol. 237, 1935.)

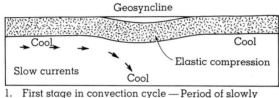

1. First stage in convection cycle — Period of slowly accelerating currents.

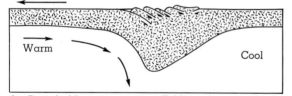

2. Period of fastest currents — Folding of geosynclinal region and formation of the mountain root.

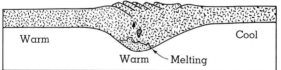

3. End of convection current cycle — Period of emergence. Buoyant rise of thickened crust aided by melting of mountain root.

Fig. 14-9. Sequence of development of mountain-building phases. (From D. T. Griggs, *American Journal of Science*, vol. 237, 1935.)

move. Ultimately, the sediment is brought to a deep enough level for melting to occur and granites begin to rise. At this point the deformation of the sediment has reached a sufficient intensity to form thrust faults, together with folds, in the surficial material. Thus by the simple operation of the two convection cells, we have explained a mountain range containing thrust faults, folds, granitic intrusions, uplifts, and roots; this range has all of the requisites for the normal mountain ranges that have been determined from purely geologic mapping.

It is not necessary that two cells operate together; one operating alone is perfectly adequate to cause the deformation, at least in a somewhat asymmetrical sense (Figs. 14-8 and 14-9). Thus the operation of one convection cell may cause thrust faults and overfolds all to tilt in the same direction, which we have seen to be common in mountains such as the Appalachians. The fact that the theoretical results of a process such as convective drag match so closely with the actually observed geology is a point in favor of the theory but does not necessarily prove the theory. The presence of some sort of convective overturn can be presumed with a high degree of confidence from simple geophysical calculations; the effectiveness of such a process in causing the type of deformation shown in Fig. 14-9 is obviously an entirely different question.

In Chapter 13 we discussed the features shown by mid-oceanic ridges and concluded that such ridges must be underlain by abnormally hot material in the upper mantle. It seems likely that the ridges may be the sites of upward currents in convection cells. Figure 14-10, for example, is a hypothetical diagram of convection cells in the South Pacific. Note the median ridge at the point of the rise and the Andean deformation where the current plunges downward under the margin of the South American

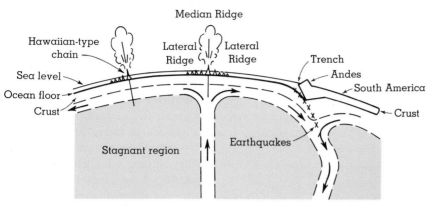

Fig. 14-10. Hypothetical relationships of crustal features in east-central Pacific Ocean to convection currents in the mantle. The median ridge is the East Pacific Rise, as shown in Figure 13-20. (From J. T. Wilson, *Nature*, vol. 198, 1963.)

continent. The fault shown in the diagram under the western margin of South America has been demonstrated to be present by location of earthquake foci.

We mentioned, above, the possible periodicity of orogenic processes. Such periodicity may indicate a periodicity in the activity of convection currents. On the other hand, if orogeny really is continuous through geologic time, the continuity may indicate a continuity of convection currents. We have, in short, constructed a rather flexible theory, and the best thing we can say about the flexibility is that we should not hold it against the theory. We should mention here that the long-lived radioactive isotopes could provide a continuous source of energy for continuous orogeny.

EPEIROGENY

After our discussion of the causes of orogeny it may seem to be a simple matter for us to construct some explanation for the causes of epeirogeny. Epeirogeny is defined as simply a small-scale relative motion of land and sea level over broad regions which thus brings about the repeated flooding and exposure of continental areas that has characterized so much of geologic time. Expressed more plainly, it would seem that if geologists are willing to consider seriously the rather peculiar ideas expressed in the first part of this chapter for the origin of mountains and the possibility of continental drift, then they certainly should not have any difficulty finding some sort of mechanism which would account for the smaller-scale variations of epeirogeny. Actually, the mechanism of epeirogenic movements is even less certain than that of orogenic movements. The problem in the explanation of epeirogeny is that there seems to be no good way to determine whether or not the continents are actually sinking somewhat in the subcrust during periods of flooding or whether sea level is simply rising with no relative movement between continents and the subcrust. As we mentioned in Chapter 13, there is also the problem that if the continents have been repeatedly flooded, there must have been some relative movement of the crust underlying the oceans in order to push the water up and let it back off. It is impossible to contend that the flooding and exposure are related to major and repeated changes in the quantity of ocean water on the earth, because that quantity must have been increasing at a slow though steady pace throughout much of geologic time.

The repeated nature of the epeirogenic movement is extremely well illustrated in a series of sediments in the mid-continent of the United States. Here, during several tens of millions of years, the sediments formed have alternated repeatedly from land-laid swamp sediments through shoreline sands to offshore marine shales and limestones and then back again to land-laid sediments, with the cycle repeating itself several times. This alternating cycle, which clearly demonstrates a relative change in sea level at any one point, is referred to as a *cyclothem* (Figs. 14-11 and 14-12). The alternation of marine, coastal, and nonmarine rocks in cyclothems demonstrates the fact that the earth's crust in the mid-continent portion of the United States has been sufficiently unstable, that it has been flooded and exposed a large number of times. The actual number of periods of flooding is variable from place to place since the crust did not remain completely flat, and therefore different portions were inundated at different times.

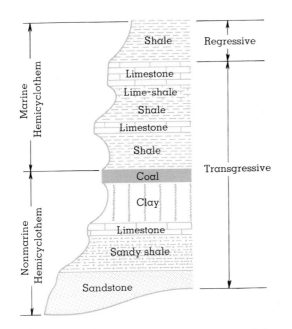

Fig. 14-11. Portions of a typical mid-continent cyclothem. (From J. M. Weller, 1963, *Stratigraphic Principles and Practices,* Harper & Row, New York, 1963.)

GEOLOGIC EFFECTS OF ORGANISMS

It is difficult to imagine what the earth would be like if organic life had not developed on it. Animals and plants have made major contributions to the rocks of the earth's surface and to processes which have taken place on the earth's surface. Without organic life, for example, there would be no soils, few or no limestones, no oil or coal, and practically no way in which the vast majority of the rocks of the earth's surface could be dated. Actually, however, the absence of life would have caused far greater changes than just those few mentioned above. The entire balance of oxygen and carbon dioxide in the earth's atmosphere depends very largely upon the metabolic processes of both animals and plants. Oxygen and carbon dioxide, in turn, affect the weathering of rocks, the solubility of calcium carbonate, the precipitation of iron from waters, and many other processes. In this section we

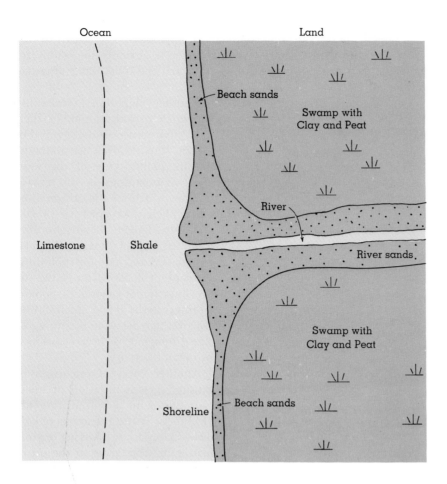

Fig. 14-12. Map showing geographic and geologic relations at one time during the deposition of a cyclothem. Rocks are sequentially covered by other rocks as the shoreline shifts back and forth.

shall try to indicate some rather specific effects which the total mass of living material has had on the geologic evolution of the earth.

Organisms may affect sediments in two ways, one direct and one considerably less direct. The direct effect of organisms upon sediments comes from the contribution of organic materials to the sedimentary rocks. In most cases the preserved organic remains are the hard parts of the organisms, such as shells or bones, but in some cases the soft parts may be preserved in decayed fashion in the form of petroleum, coal, or disseminated organic molecules. The indirect contribution of organisms to the geologic record comes from the ability of both plants and animals to modify the environments in which they occur.

As a very simple example of modification of the environment by organisms, we may consider the formation of quiet-water, shallow, lagoonal areas behind reefs (Fig. 13-13). The reef blocks wave activity and prevents the development of currents or other water movements in the shallow areas to the leeward of the reef crest. Such effects can easily be identified in the geologic record because of the preservation of the reef. In many cases, however, the quiet-water areas may be produced by such organisms as marine plants or grasses. The entrapment of fine-grained muds in such grassy areas may lead to the formation of abundant fine-grained rocks, and the complete disappearance by decay of the grassy or other plant material would render it virtually impossible for geologists to understand the manner in which the quiet-water area had developed.

Fig. 14-13. Limestone with structures similar to those found in modern algal mats that cause the accumulation of fine-grained calcium carbonate. (Photo by D. F. Toomey.)

Another important mechanism by which organisms modify their local environment is the removal of carbon dioxide from sea water by marine plants. One of the most effective organisms in this regard is algae, which use the carbon dioxide in their photosynthetic process and thus deplete the neighboring water of carbon dioxide (Fig. 14-13). This reduction of carbon dioxide content in the water causes the precipitation of calcium carbonate. In this case the actual precipitation reaction may be a purely inorganic one although it has been occasioned by organic activity.

Another effect of organisms in causing the modification of materials added to a sedimentary environment is the reduction of oxidized materials by decaying organic matter in some areas of the ocean floor. In areas of restricted circulation, as discussed in Chapter 13, oxygenated waters are not supplied to the sea bottom, and the accumulation of animal remains may cause the complete depletion of oxygen and the formation of some organic-reducing material. In most sediments where there has been extensive reduction, the reducing agents are preserved, at least to a limited extent, in the form of coaly or oily residues. In some cases, however, these organic remains may have been destroyed by later activity and only their effect on inorganic material can be observed. An example of such reducing action might be a widespread shale bed in which all of the iron was in the ferrous state.

The evolution throughout geologic time of different animals and plants is a subject beyond the scope of this book. We can, however, mention briefly some of the salient aspects of this evolution from the standpoint of the materials which are synthesized by organisms to form their skeletons. Approximately 600 million years ago, at the beginning of what is known as the Cambrian period, marine rocks suddenly began to contain large amounts of preservable shells and other solid organic remains. In Precambrian times these preserved organic materials are rare at best, and in most rocks they are completely absent. At first glance it would seem that this is the time when organisms first began to develop. The vast diversity of different forms of organisms present at the start of the Cambrian, however, renders such an explanation highly unlikely. It appears mandatory that there must have been in Precambrian times a widespread evolution of different types of animals and plants so that the diverse flora and fauna of Cambrian times could have existed. Granted this assumption, the sudden appearance of hard parts of animals in the Cambrian sediments must coincide with a sudden development of the ability of organisms to synthesize hard parts. One of the extremely important, and as yet totally unanswered, geologic questions is the cause of this sudden development of synthetic ability.

The types of materials synthesized by animals and plants have undergone changes throughout the course of geologic history. If we discount uncommon materials, the three major types of skeletal minerals are phosphates, which are organic phosphatic complexes (including bone and chitinophosphatic material); silica, generally in the form of opal (an amorphous variety of SiO_2); and calcium carbonate, either in the form of the common mineral calcite or its polymorph aragonite. All three of these materials have been synthesized by some form of animal or plant throughout post-Precambrian geologic history. There have, however, been changes in the types of organisms which have most abundantly used the materials. Chitinophosphatic material, for example, was synthesized by animals of all types in the earliest evolutionary period. Gradually during the course of time most animal groups lost the ability to synthesize this material, and now only a few types of organisms are capable of producing it; the most common occurrence is in the bony portions of fish, mammals, and reptiles.

Changes in the synthesis of silica have been somewhat different than those in the synthesis of chitinophosphatic materials. In the early stages of the evolution of organic hard parts, silica was secreted primarily by animals living on the sea floor. Among such animals were sponges and other related forms. In more recent geologic times, however, the extraction of silica from sea water to produce hard parts has been accomplished almost completely by organisms within the near-surface waters of the ocean. Floating and swimming plants, such as diatoms, or animals, such as the single-celled radiolaria, now are the primary agents for utilizing the silica of sea water, and most bottom-dwelling organisms synthesize calcium carbonate.

Calcium carbonate in one form or another is secreted by more organisms than any other type of skeletal material. Some types of organisms produce largely calcite, some largely aragonite, and some produce both. The precipitation of calcium carbonate can be hypothesized as occurring either as a simple inorganic crystallization from solution, or it can be visualized as occurring within a complex organically controlled environment. The production of calcium carbonate by removal of carbon dioxide from sea water by algae, discussed just above, is an inorganic form of precipitation. Nevertheless, in most cases it appears that the calcium carbonate is produced in a chemical environment whose nature is determined very highly by the organism itself. As evidence of this statement, there is the fact that inorganic precipitation should yield a rather direct relationship between the concentration of various minor elements in sea water and the concentration of minor elements in the corresponding marine shells. Thus, for example, if two shells were taken from marine environments having widely different concentrations of some specific element (e.g., strontium), then the concentrations of strontium in the shells should be proportional to the concentrations of strontium in the sea water at each locality. Experiments of this nature have been performed, and the data on naturally occurring shells indicates that an equilibrium of this type is not established (Table 14-1). The absence of such equilibrium is explainable in one of two ways:

TABLE 14-1. RATIO OF STRONTIUM TO CALCIUM IN SHELLS OF ORGANISMS LIVING IN CONTACT WITH SEA WATER

material	Sr/Ca
sea water	$20.0 \cdot 10^{-3}$
oysters	$2.0 \cdot 10^{-3}$
snails	$3.6 \cdot 10^{-3}$
barnacles	$5.0 \cdot 10^{-3}$
stony corals	$20.5 \cdot 10^{-3}$

SOURCE: From Robert C. Harriss (personal communication).

1. It may be considered that the dominant factor controlling the chemistry of the marine shells is some sort of kinetic precipitation process, the effect of which naturally destroys any simple equilibrium relationship.

2. The equilibrium relationship which is established between the precipitated shell and its surrounding environment is an equilibrium within an environment which is vastly modified by the animal itself. That is, the calcium carbonate is secreted virtually within a medium that is established by the organism rather than within a medium consisting of almost unaltered sea water.

The problem can be stated fairly simply, but the mode of solution is not easily determinable. The exact mechanism by which marine organisms precipitate shells of calcium carbonate is almost completely unknown.

PALEOTEMPERATURES

One of the interesting uses to which organically precipitated calcium carbonate can be put is the establishment of the temperature at which it was precipitated. Several methods have been proposed for doing this, two of which are of major significance and can be discussed here. It can be shown experimentally that the ratio of the oxygen-18 isotope to the vastly more common oxygen-16 isotope is variable in both marine shells and in different types of water on the earth's surface. Rainwater, and consequently lake and river water, contains a far higher proportion of the oxygen-16 than of the oxygen-18, simply because the heavier H_2O^{18} is less easily distilled from the ocean than the lighter H_2O^{16}; thus the lighter molecule becomes concentrated in the vapor over the ocean, which ultimately leads to rain. Within the oceans themselves, however, the ratio of O^{18} to O^{16} is comparatively constant. In precipitation, a mechanism somewhat the reverse of the distillation process occurs. Here the heavier oxygen-18 is preferentially absorbed within the calcium carbonate lattice. The ratio of O^{18}/O^{16} in the calcium carbonate to the ratio in the sea water is dependent upon temperature. This ratio decreases with increasing temperature, thus signifying a relatively smaller percentage of O^{18} in shells grown at high temperatures.

Experimentally, it is easily possible to precipitate calcium carbonate with different ratios of O^{18}/O^{16} at different temperatures. From the experimental curves, then, the temperature of precipitation of naturally occurring shells can be calculated on the assumption of a particular O^{18}/O^{16} ratio in sea water. The experimental data to establish calibration curves are shown in Fig. 14-14, and the use of a calibration curve to determine the temperatures of formation of marine shells of considerable age is shown in Figs. 14-15 and 14-16.

Another method for the utilization of calcium carbonate to establish paleotemperatures is the ratio of aragonite to calcite in a shell. Aragonite, being the unstable polymorph of calcite, can form only where its development is occasioned by some kinetic process. In general, unstable minerals are formed where the process leading to their development is rapid, thus preventing the establishment of a true chemical equilibrium.

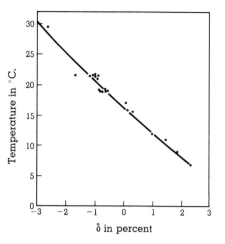

Fig. 14-14. Isotopic temperature scale. The horizontal scale is based on an arbitrary standard and shows the amount of O^{18} which a carbonate shell contains above or below the O^{18} of the standard. Temperatures may be read from the graph assuming a constant O^{18}/O^{16} ratio in the sea water in equilibrium with the shell. (From S. Epstein, et al., *Geological Society of America Bulletin*, vol. 64, 1953.)

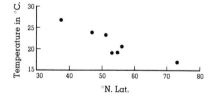

Fig. 14-15. Temperatures measured for a period of time approximately 100 million years ago at outcrops of correlative rocks at different latitudes. Each point is an average of several oxygen-isotope measurements. Note decreasing temperature toward high latitudes. (From H. A. Lowenstam and S. Epstein, *Proceedings of XXth International Geological Congress*, Mexico, 1959.)

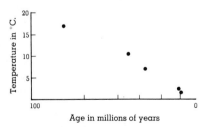

Fig. 14-16. Temperatures measured in rocks of east Greenland during the last 100 million years. Each point is an average of several oxygen-isotope measurements. (From H. A. Lowenstam and S. Epstein, *Proceedings of XXth International Geological Congress*, Mexico, 1959.)

We expect that carbonate shells precipitate more rapidly in warm water than in cold waters because of the lower solubility of carbon dioxide in the warm waters. The observed variations in aragonite/calcite ratios in single species of organisms collected in a variety of water temperatures confirms this assumption; that is, the warm-water forms have a higher aragonite/calcite ratio than the cold-water forms. It is necessary in such studies to calibrate individual species, because different species synthesize shells with vastly different aragonite/calcite ratios at the same temperature. In ancient shells, unfortunately, it is not possible to detect actual aragonite because, owing to the instability of the mineral, all ancient shells have inverted completely to calcite.

We have now discussed a number of current problems facing people who are interested in the interaction between the biologic environment and the inorganic portion of the earth. Organisms play a large part in the production of sediments and modification of environments, but exactly how large a part is not certain. Some types of sediments are thought by some geologists to be organically derived and by others to be inorganically derived. There is always the question of whether organisms occur in some location because of their environment or whether an organism can modify an environment to make it more favorable to itself. The study of paleotemperatures and the establishment of even better techniques of determining them is an extremely important geologic task. It may be possible, for example, to establish fluctuations in sea-water temperature through geologic time to correlate with evidence of various types of climates established over the earth and ultimately to derive a complete climatic history of the earth. All of these investigations of the effects of organisms on the geologic record must be carried out within the framework of paleontological studies of the evolution of different types of organisms.

EVALUATION OF UNIFORMITARIANISM

In Chapter 1 we indicated the necessity of the concept of uniformitarianism to the geologic sciences. Unless we can consider the earth and the processes occurring on it at present to be similar to those of the past, then it would be almost impossible to determine the nature of the past. It is impossible to observe at the present time the direct formation of such features as granitic rocks or to see the type of material which comprises the subcrust. Therefore, it is necessary to infer the nature of those materials and to determine the processes leading to the formation of rock such as granite on the basis of indirect observations of the material as it now exists. Nevertheless, even such indirect inferences as these would be extremely difficult if the general aspects of the theory of uniformitarianism were not accepted. In this book we have discussed the various methods by which an application of the study of the present condition and processes of the earth's surface can be used to decipher geologic history. It is now appropriate that we investigate very briefly the validity of this theory in the light of the more detailed knowledge we have accumulated in the past thirteen chapters.

There are two drawbacks to an absolutely strict interpretation of uniformitarianism. One of the problems confronting geologists is the existence of sedimentary rocks quite unlike those which are forming at the present time. Among these rocks are dolomite, certain varieties of limestone, and the Precambrian "iron formations" composed of silica and magnetite. It is not difficult to conceive of an origin of certain types of highly fossiliferous limestone in shallow seas over the continental shelf area, despite the fact that these seas do not exist today. Their presence in the past is attested to by the appearance of marine sediments in areas around the central continental shield. Accounting for the presence of dolomite is somewhat more difficult. Although dolomitization of fairly recently deposited limestones has been observed, for example, in borings in some of the South Pacific atolls, modern equivalents of the typical bedded dolomites with ages of several hundred million years are not being produced now. Even more difficult is the problem of accounting for such highly unusual rock types as chemically precipitated, interbedded quartz and magnetite (iron formation). It is virtually impossible for sediments of this type to be produced in modern oceans, and certainly no examples have been found.

The presence of sediments which are not, and possibly could not, be formed today makes it necessary to interpret the concept of uniformitarianism a little more broadly than we might be led to do otherwise. It is possible that the composition of ocean water has changed through geologic time, although as discussed in Chapter 13, no major changes are apparent. It is possible that such rocks might be formed from the modern ocean water if conditions were sufficiently changed on the earth to cause precipitation. Exactly what these conditions might be are a little difficult to imagine, but this difficulty does not render the possibility unworthy of consideration.

Another difficulty for geologists who wish to interpret the history of the earth in terms of the present geological condition is the fact that the recent history of the earth appears to have been rather different from the normal. Within the last million years several major glaciations have occurred; thus the rate of glaciation has been unusually high in the recent geologic past. Uniformitarianism only requires that glaciation take place throughout geologic time. The continents at the present time are almost completely exposed, and the epeirogenic epicontinental seas of the past are largely missing. Along with this comparatively high topographic position of present continents is a marked climatic zonation, an acceleration of erosion and the consequent supply of large quantities of debris to the oceans, and the intense volcanic activity around the margin of the Pacific Ocean which provides an additional major source of sedimentary material. There is also the possibility that the continents have drifted apart in the fairly recent geologic past, and thus the former land connections between various continental areas have been severed.

From the standpoint of the sedimentary petrologist, perhaps the most serious of these abnormalities on the present earth's surface is the large quantity of clastic sediment which is being supplied to the continental shelf and near-shore areas. This clastic sediment masks and completely overshadows, in most places, the typical carbonate deposits which characterize most previous geologic periods. Thus the student of modern sediment is, at least in part, studying a suite of materials which is not wholly identical to those of the past. For this reason it is not possible to attempt a direct matching of current sedimentary sequences with the sequences of ancient rocks. The modern sedimentationist finds it necessary to use recent sediments to determine, in conjunction with studies of the environment in which they are deposited, those features of the environment which have had a direct control over the types of sediments being deposited. In short, a student of modern sediments wants to know *why* a particular type of clay mineral is being deposited in a certain area and is comparatively unconcerned about whether this clay deposit will be followed by a bed of sand or by additional clay. Presumably, if the environmental conditions which have controlled the formation of a particular type of sediment can be fully outlined, then these conditions must have existed more or less similarly in the formation of a comparable sediment in the past. The sequence of events in the past and the geographic position of the deposited sediments may have differed markedly from the history and position of the modern deposit, but if the principles controlling deposition are understood, then an accurate geologic interpretation can be made.

The point of the above discussion is that uniformitarianism implies mainly that the modern geologist has an opportunity to discover those principles which have led to the formation of rocks in the past. It does not mean that the exact processes of the present are to be found in the past or that in ancient rocks there will be direct correlatives of sediments being deposited today. In some cases, to be sure, direct correlations and even identity of modern and ancient processes can be established without too much difficulty, although in many cases this establishment is not possible. By assuming that the basic laws of physics and chemistry have remained unchanged throughout geologic time, we can interpret modern sediments and other geologic features in terms of modern processes, so that it is possible to reconstruct a geologic history of the earth through the use of the uniformitarianism principle, and this is all that geologists are interested in.

Another apparent difficulty in the direct application of the theory of uniformitarianism is the fact that the nature of the animal and plant life on the earth's surface has changed throughout geologic time. This evolution has brought extinction to many types of organisms and the development and flourishing of new types. It is conceivable that the organisms occurring in the past would affect their environment differently than the organisms existing at the present time. Actually, this difference appears not to be the case. The reason is that organisms which have evolved only recently have almost direct counterparts in the past. The modern clams, for example, occupy environmental positions very similar to those occupied by a wholly different group, the brachiopods, in earlier geologic history. Modern algae, which are major contributors to the formation of coral reefs, had both animal and plant counterparts in the past. Apparently, at any time in the earth's recent history, there have been animals and plants occupying most of the environmental positions which are now filled by newer types; the correspondence is not perfect, of course, particularly during the earliest stages of life on earth.

ECONOMIC
GEOLOGY: GEOLOGIC
ASPECTS

The preceding chapters of this book have been devoted to a discussion of the basic principles of the geologic sciences. We have tried to describe both the surface and the interior of the earth and to indicate the methods by which the descriptive facts have been obtained. On the basis of these facts, we have then tried to outline the history of the earth in its broad aspects and demonstrate the mode of formation of individual geologic features. Now, having shown what we know and think about the earth, it is time to discuss what we can do with the earth. For this purpose we turn in the last two chapters to a discussion of the principles of economic geology. This chapter discusses the geologic aspects of the occurrence, mode of formation, and production of economically important geologic material. The next chapter discusses the economics of these materials.

In addition to food, man needs a source of energy, a source of materials with which to build things, and a source of water in order to live. Civilization is constructed upon these four items. At the present time the principle sources of energy are oil, coal, and running water. In the future we may add to these sources both nuclear energy from reactors using thorium and uranium, nuclear fusion, and solar energy. The materials which man needs can be subdivided into the metallic ores, including copper, lead, zinc, iron, and aluminum; and the nonmetallic materials, such as limestone for cement, clay for ceramics, salt, and a whole variety of other substances. Mankind's current supply of water is contained partly in rivers and lakes and partly in underground water, and we shall discuss the geologic principles of the occurrence of ground water in this chapter. An additional future source of water may be the oceans, if a fully economic method is developed for removing the salt.

ENERGY

Oil

Oil occurs almost exclusively in sedimentary rocks. In fact, the major petroleum deposits of the world occur in basins of extremely thick accumulation of sediment. This association apparently results not only from the fact that sedimentary rocks provide a logical place for oil to accumulate but also because the oil forms in sediments.

The term *oil* refers to naturally occurring liquid hydrocarbons. Associated gaseous hydrocarbons are referred to as *natural gas*. The major components of oil are the aliphatic hydrocarbons such as *n*-octane, with the formula shown below:

$$CH_3-CH_2-CH_2-CH_2-CH_2-CH_2-CH_2-CH_3$$

Some of the aliphatic hydrocarbons form closed rings with loss of the two end hydrogens. Another type of hydrocarbon which occurs in some petroleum accumulations is aromatic material such as benzene. The aromatic hydrocarbons are characterized by ring structures with some double carbon-carbon bonds in which the various carbon atoms are linked circularly to each other as shown in the formula for benzene:

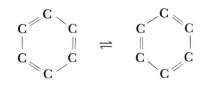

The typical crude petroleum is a mixture of a great many compounds with formulas similar to those shown here. In addition, crude oil may contain such elements as sulfur or nitrogen in small amounts. The dominant characteristic of oil, however, is the lack of oxygen. This reduced state makes the oil oxidizable and accounts for the ability of petroleum to be burned and to yield energy. A typical reaction by which petroleum combines with oxygen and gives off heat is shown below.

$$C_7H_{16} + 11O_2 \longrightarrow 7CO_2 + 8H_2O + \text{HEAT}$$

ORIGIN. The exact mode of formation of petroleum has puzzled geologists for many years. Two facts, however, point almost inescapably to the conclusion that oil is formed by the decay of animal, and possibly some plant, remains in a reducing environment in sedimentary deposits. One fact is the virtual restriction of petroleum to marine sedimentary rocks. The second fact is the detection of small amounts of hydrocarbons, similar to those found in petroleum, in some recently deposited sediments formed in areas in which current activity and oxidation are absent. One easily observed example of such hydrocarbon production is the small bubbles of methane which are generated in many swamps, and which commonly bear the name "marsh gas" or "swamp gas." In some swamps these bubbles can be seen coming up through the water and can easily be lit with a burning match. On occasion, the gas appears to ignite spontaneously, and many of the ghost stories told by people passing through swamps at night probably are initiated by little flames of methane seen burning in the distance. It is, however, a long way from methane to the long chain of highly polymerized hydrocarbons which characterize the typical crude petroleum. The exact mechanism of this polymerization process is uncertain, although recent experiments in organic geochemistry have shed a good deal of light on the problem.

MIGRATION. An investigation of the chemical processes leading to the formation of oil answers only a part of the question relating to the development of petroleum deposits. Most oil is simply not produced from the rocks in which it formed. This statement can be demonstrated in two ways. First, most petroleum deposits occur in relatively "clean" (uncemented) quartz or quartzofeldspathic sandstones which could never have contained enough organic material to form the amount of petroleum which they now hold; and second, the rocks which are now forming and which appear to contain small amounts of hydrocarbon capable of developing into oil are generally rocks which are not characteristic of reservoirs for petroleum deposits. Most of the rocks in which oil appears to be forming in modern sediments are fine-grained, somewhat shaly, and could not be effective as reservoirs. Oil, therefore, must migrate from its source to a suitable reservoir rock in which it can flow easily enough to be produced through an oil well. This migration of oil from source to reservoir is obviously a topic of considerable interest to geologists. If the mechanics of migration are fully known and if source rocks can be identified in sedimentary sequences, then it may be possible to predict the occurrence of reservoir rocks and hence the location of economic petrolum deposits.

The movement of oil in water-soaked sediments is affected by three major factors, namely: the immiscibility of oil in water, the lower density of oil relative to water, and the fact that oil does not adhere to or wet silicate sedimentary particles as well as water does. Presumably, therefore, in any sequence of water-saturated sediments, there will be a tendency for oil under the influence of gravity to move upward through the sedimentary section or up-dip along a tilted sedimentary bed in which the movement is relatively easy. This movement under the influence of gravity, however, is impeded by the tendency of water to surround the sedimentary particles and to isolate small drops of oil in the center of pores, as shown in Fig. 15-1. In most cases, therefore, major accumulation of oil probably requires some movement of the water through the rock in addition to the oil. Such movement

KEY

■ Oil

Water

Fig. 15-1. Oil and water in pores of sandstone.

would, of course, be necessary in cases in which the oil had moved in some manner other than in an upward direction. In this fashion the oil and accompanying gas move through the sedimentary column until they reach some place where they can accumulate to form an oil pool in suitable rock.

RESERVOIRS. The rock in which accumulation occurs is called a *reservoir rock,* and the geologic structure or feature which permits such an accumulation is called a *trap.* The necessary requirements for a reservoir rock are high porosity, high permeability, and sufficient volume to contain enough oil to be worth considering. Porosity, as discussed in Chapter 7, is simply the void space between sedimentary grains. In many sediments the individual grains are packed together sufficiently loosely that void spaces of up to 30 or even 40 percent may occur (Fig. 15-2). The typical sedimentary rock, however, contains a porosity far less than this, largely because of the precipitation of chemical cements or the development of a clay cement in the pores. In some cases cementation may be so great that the porosity is effectively destroyed. Disregarding the effects of cementation, porosity increases as the irregularity of the grain shapes increases. Thus, in a shale containing tabular and irregularly shaped grains, the porosity may be as much as 50 percent; in a sandstone with the pore space not reduced by cementation, porosities are commonly on the order of 20 to 25 percent.

Fig. 15-2. Artificial sand showing porosity between grains. A thin section has been cut to show this sand after impregnation of the loose material in plastic. Magnification approximately 100 times. (Photo by J. J. W. Rogers.)

The other requirement for reservoir rock, *permeability,* is the ability of a material to flow through the rock. A rock without porosity is obviously impermeable, but rocks with high porosity may also have exceptionally low permeability. For example, a highly vesicular basalt in which the individual holes are completely isolated from each other might have an extremely high porosity but virtually no permeability. In like fashion, a shale has a very low permeability, although the porosity is generally quite large. In the case of the shale, low permeability results from the extremely fine-grained nature of the rock and the fact that any flowing fluid must move through exceptionally small openings between individual grains. The common permeable rocks are relatively uncemented sandstones, and it is generally in sandstones that the combination of porosity and permeability is sufficient to develop an effective reservoir (Fig. 15-3).

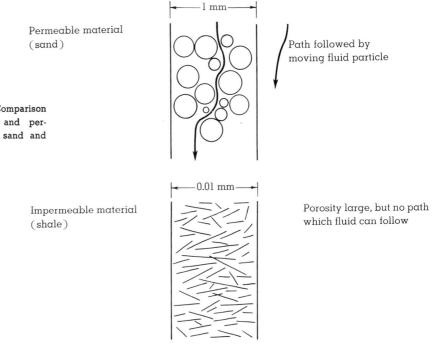

Fig. 15-3. Comparison of porosity and permeability of sand and shale.

Permeable material (sand)

|← 1 mm →|

Path followed by moving fluid particle

Impermeable material (shale)

|← 0.01 mm →|

Porosity large, but no path which fluid can follow

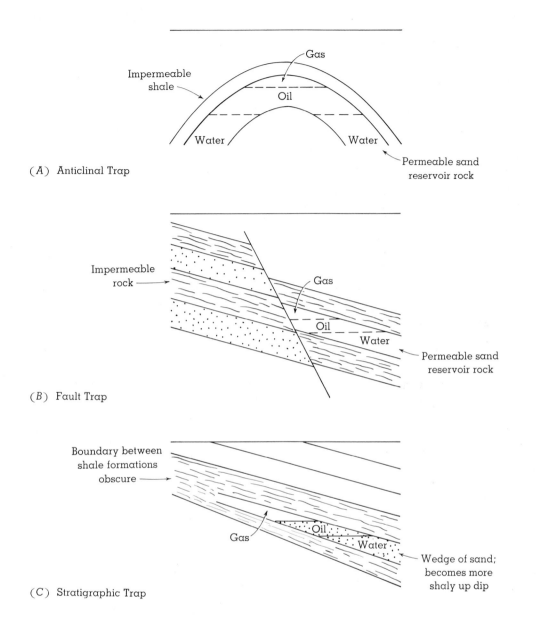

(A) Anticlinal Trap

Impermeable shale

Gas

Oil

Water   Water

Permeable sand reservoir rock

(B) Fault Trap

Impermeable rock

Gas

Oil

Water

Permeable sand reservoir rock

(C) Stratigraphic Trap

Boundary between shale formations obscure

Gas

Oil

Water

Wedge of sand; becomes more shaly up dip

Fig. 15-4. Three common oil traps.

TRAPS. A reservoir rock will not accumulate oil unless the oil is stopped from further migration by some form of trap. One of the most common forms of trap is the simple anticline in which a permeable and porous sandstone is overlain by a relatively impermeable shale or other type of rock through which the oil cannot move. The accumulation in this case results from the tendency of the low-density oil to be trapped between the water and the overlying impermeable rock. A typical example is shown diagrammatically in Fig. 15-4A, in which the gas, water, and oil occur in a simple sequence of specific gravities, and the whole material

371

is confined under an impermeable shale bed. The anticlinal trap has accounted for much of the oil that has been produced, and the early days of oil exploration were dedicated largely to the anticlinal theory of accumulation.

Anticlines are, however, not the only structures which trap oil. Figure 15-4*B* also shows an example of a fault trap, in which the beds are truncated by a fault that either brings an impermeable layer into a position above a permeable reservoir rock or, perhaps, confines the reservoir by the development of an impermeable fault gouge. The gas and oil occur next to the fault in sediments which are dipping away from the fault. A wide variety of traps are broadly referred to as stratigraphic traps, one type of which is illustrated in Fig. 15-4*C*. Here the up-dip portion of a permeable formation becomes impermeable through the admixing of clay or perhaps some other cementing agent. The oil and gas accumulate along the zone between the permeable and impermeable portions of the formation. Stratigraphic traps are obviously more difficult to detect in the subsurface than are traps formed by anticlines or faults, and exploration for them has been developed far more slowly than the mapping and geophysical techniques for the determination of structural traps.

One of the most important features which has led to the development of structural traps is the salt dome. A cross section through a typical salt dome is shown in Fig. 15-5. The development of such a dome results from the fact that salt beds which occur within the stratigraphic section are less dense than shales, sandstones, and other materials deposited on top of them. Being less dense and relatively plastic, the salt is in an unstable position and tends to flow upward. The process may be similar to the upward flowage of magma, and indeed, the structures that are developed in the flowing salt are very similar to those which have been found in batholiths. It is uncertain exactly at what point a salt dome will begin to form in the rocks overlying the original salt bed, but when upward flowage starts, it appears to take place quite rapidly and to develop an

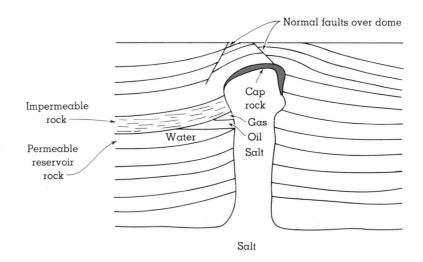

Fig. 15-5. Cross section through typical salt dome. Domes may extend tens of thousands of feet above the original salt layer.

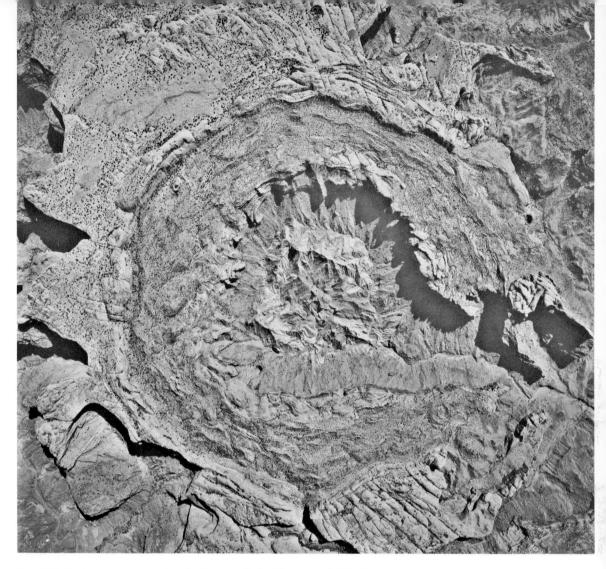

Fig. 15-6. Surface expression of salt dome in Utah. (Courtesy of U.S. Department of Agriculture.)

elongated finger of salt above the source. If the salt dome approaches the surface, it may cause a small mound to form or disrupt the drainage pattern of the area (Fig. 15-6). In a very few instances salt domes have punctured the surface, and the salt has flowed slowly out onto the ground. In most cases, however, the salt dome is not observed on the surface and can be found only by geophysical techniques. The low density of the salt, of course, makes it easily detected by simple gravity measurements (Chapter 3).

As the salt flows upward and punctures the surrounding beds it causes the development of several types of structural traps. In part the upward flowage of the salt causes the formation of normal faults around the side of the dome, and these faults may lead to the accumulation of oil. In part the salt dome causes an upward bowing of the sediments and creates an anticlinal or domal structure over the salt. Oil actually occurs rather rarely at the anticline at the top of the dome but more commonly in the up-turned beds around the flanks. As the salt pushes its way upward through the sedimentary sequence, the high pressures on the top of the dome tend to cause solution of the salt in the ground water. This solution leads to the accumulation of an insoluble residue consisting of calcium sulfate and related minerals which form a *caprock*. In some cases the sulfate is reduced to sulfur by bacterial action, and a great deal of sulfur is recovered from salt dome caprocks.

Oil occurs in carbonate rocks in a variety of ways. Some types of carbonates, notably reefs, have an original porosity, owing to an incomplete in-filling of the spaces between skeletal organic remains. Porosity may also be caused by fracturing, and the brittleness of limestones makes them fracture readily. Another major method of developing porosity is by dolomitization of original limestone. Dolomitization of hard limestones causes porosity, because the mineral dolomite is denser than calcite. Thus a replacement of calcium ions by magnesium ions causes shrinkage of the lattice, and if the replaced material is confined between other hard sediments so that overall volume shrinkage cannot occur, then pore spaces must be formed. Dolomitization of soft sediment, however, cannot cause porosity owing to volume shrinkage of the whole rock. Although oil is produced from all types of carbonate rocks, the most important production has been from reservoirs developed in ancient reefs. Reefs are favorable for the accumulation of oil partly because of their original porosity, partly because they are commonly dolomitized, and partly because the rocks deposited around the reef may be less permeable and thus form an impervious cap over the porous reef.

Sedimentary rocks are formed under a variety of tectonic and environmental conditions, and oil is not found in all of them. Most of the oil produced in the world has been developed from relatively thick basin-like accumulations of sediments on the continental shelf areas or in the more shallow portions of geosynclines. In general, oil is absent from rocks formed subaerially and is found, thus far, rather rarely in typical geosynclinal rocks. In order to develop, oil apparently needs both marine organisms and the general environmental conditions of marine sediments and also needs relative tectonic stability. Perhaps oil can be formed in geosynclinal sediments but is easily destroyed by later deformational activity.

Coal

Coal is best defined as solid, carbon-bearing, naturally occurring material. Whereas petroleum consists mainly of hydrocarbons, coal consists largely of either pure carbon or carbon in some sort of oxidized carbohydrate or similar substance. The exact organic compounds which occur in coal are even more difficult to identify than those which occur in oil. The difficulty is enhanced by the fact that most of these materials are insoluble and thus hard to examine. In a broad sense, coal is distinguished from oil in a chemical fashion by its content of oxygen and by the presence of pure carbon in some varieties of coal.

ORIGIN. Despite the chemical uncertainties, the geologic process for the formation of coal is comparatively clear. Coal starts to develop by the decay of plants under moist but essentially subaerial conditions. The typical environment for the initiation of development of a coal bed is a swamp in which plant material accumulates without the complete oxygenation which might occur in a forest or other well-drained soil (Fig. 15-7). This swampy accumulation of plant material undergoes gradual compression and removal of the moisture and oxygen of the typical plant materials until, at the highest possible grades of coal development, the remains may be reduced to almost pure carbon. As the original plant material is exposed to higher pressures and temperatures, the coal changes to a series of different grades much as a metamorphic rock changes to different mineral assemblages.

The lowest grade of coal is simply an accumulation of woody and plant remains which has decayed only partly and in which, in many cases, the individual plants are readily distinguishable. This generally brownish material is called *peat* and is used for fuel in areas where better-developed coal is not available. Swampy areas in which peat is accumulating are commonly referred to as *peat bogs*. Greater burial and increase in temperature on the peat causes its conversion to a type of coal which is generally called *bituminous (soft coal)*. Bituminous coal is black or dark brown, somewhat soft and crumbly, not particularly shiny when broken, and is characteristic of the coal beds developed in most areas except those of considerable orogenic activity. The highest grade of coal development is the rock called *anthracite (hard coal)*, which is very hard, shiny, has a smooth fracture, and consists largely of pure carbon. The reduction of the organic material to carbon removes from the coal materials which do not burn completely and thus renders the anthracite essentially smokeless.

The effect of burial and the general orogenic and metamorphic conditions on the formation of coal is easily seen in the coal areas of Pennsylvania. In the west, toward the shelf from the geosynclinal deposits, the coal is primarily bituminous. Toward the east, where geosynclinal activity and later deformation and metamorphism have been more intense, the grade of the coal gradually increases until anthracite is developed.

The fact that coal beds are generally formed in swamps has given stratigraphers a method for determining approximately the positions of ancient sea levels. Coastal swamps are obviously very close to sea level, and the finding of an extensive bed of coal developed from such coastal swamp environments provides a reference point for sea level in ancient sediments. Thus, in the cyclothems which we discussed in Chapter 14, coal beds commonly occupy a position just above sea-level deposits and were formed at a time just prior to the encroachment of the sea during a marine flooding. The coal bed, therefore, is the top of the nonmarine sequence of sediments and just underlies the base of the marine sequence.

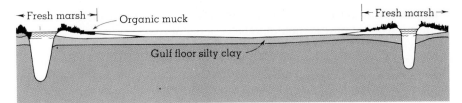

(A) Initial development of distributaries and interdistributary trough

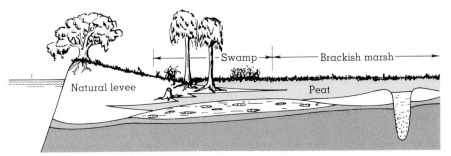

(B) Enlargement of principal distributary and its natural levees — creation of marshes in trough

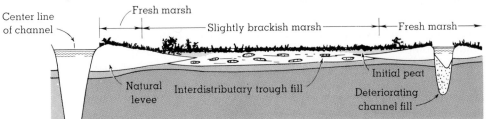

(C) Maximum development of distributary and its natural levees — creation of swamp as levee subsides

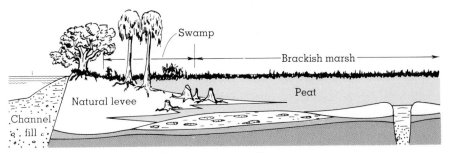

(D) Deterioration of distributary — advance of swamp over subsiding levees

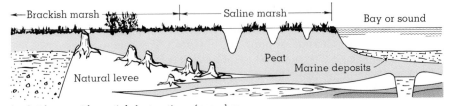

(E) Continued subsidence with partial destruction of marshes

Fig. 15-7. Stages in accumulation of peat on a deltaic plain. (From H. N. Fisk, in H. R. Gould and J. P. Morgan, *Geological Society of America Field Trip Guidebook for 1962 Annual Meeting*, published by Houston Geological Society.)

Naturally, if swamps are formed at a time when waters are receding from the land areas, then the coal beds overlie the marine sediments and underlie land-laid sediments. Some peat and coal accumulations are developed in fresh-water lakes and bogs, and such formations obviously are not indicative of sea level.

Radioactive materials

The possibility of using radioactive materials in reactors to produce power has recently aroused a great deal of interest. The two naturally occurring elements suitable for this purpose are uranium and thorium. The radioactive decay of these elements has been discussed briefly in Chapter 1. At each step in the decay series energy is produced, and we have already discussed in Chapter 14 the possibility that this derived energy may be leading to a heating up of the earth. In reactors the energy is produced by a complex sequence of nuclear reactions which will be discussed in slightly more detail in Chapter 16.

In order to construct nuclear reactors it is necessary to have a source of raw material. Uranium is not particularly difficult to locate as a result of its tendency to accumulate in fairly concentrated deposits. Uranium occurs in nature as pitchblende, having a formula somewhere between UO_2 and U_3O_8, and as a series of complex uranates containing the UO_2^{++} ion. Uranium occurs in pitchblende in a number of vein deposits identical to those of the typical metals such as lead and zinc, and it also occurs in sedimentary rocks in association with peat or woody or coaly material. In some places in eastern Utah and western Colorado, logs which contain immense quantities of uranium have been found in sandstone beds. The uranium was absorbed at some time during the period from approximately 100 million years ago until the present day. The exact origin of the pitchblende in these coaly or woody deposits is not certain, but in a few types of land-laid sediments, such as those of the eastern Utah area, these deposits may be exceptionally rich. Uranium developed at the surface generally occurs in the form of one of the complex uranates. These minerals are invariably bright yellow or bright green, and the UO_2^{++} ion in them has resulted from the oxidation of the uranous ion under surface conditions. In some cases the complex uranates can be mined profitably, but in many deposits they are simply easily detected indicators of pitchblende, which is more difficult to recognize. The tendency of uranium to be concentrated by geologic processes, particularly those which permit oxidation on the surface, allows a comparatively easy exploration for uranium deposits.

In contrast to uranium, thorium is not concentrated by surface processes, and thus the detection of reasonable economic concentrations of thorium is quite difficult. Some vein deposits of thorium oxide have been found, though these are generally small. In some beach sands or river sands containing large quantities of comparatively dense minerals, thorium occurs along with other materials such as rare earth elements, chromium, and titanium. At the present time, however, the potentially largest source of minable thorium appears to be certain types of highly siliceous and alkali-bearing granites. Some rocks of this type may have as much as 50 or more parts per million thorium, and the exploration process is generally one of locating a body of sufficient size and sufficient concentration. Although this concentration is exceptionally low in comparison with that of most materials which are obtained as metals, the comparative ease of separation of thorium during recovery processes may make the deposits at least marginally profitable.

METALLIC ORES

Hydrothermal deposits

Most metals are obtained from ores which appear to have been formed by a process known as *hydrothermal deposition*. A hydrothermal deposit is one which has been formed by the precipitation of minerals from comparatively hot water or other fluids. The evidence for such hydrothermal deposition of metallic minerals is as follows:

1. Most, though not all, ore deposits occur in areas of intrusive igneous activity. Most deposits are formed in areas of mountain-building, and the hydrothermal ores almost invariably occur in the neighborhood of intrusive igneous rocks which were formed during the orogeny.

2. It is possible to determine the temperature at which some minerals have formed. This geothermometry can be done in a variety of ways. One method, for example, is to obtain a mineral which undergoes a transformation from one crystal structure to another structure at some particular temperature and pressure and which may remain metastably in the high-temperature form at low temperatures. We have already dis-

TABLE 15-1. SOME TEMPERATURE INDICES FOR GEOTHERMOMETRIC STUDIES OF ORE DEPOSITS

Melting points of pure minerals

realgar (AsS)	320° C.
galena (PbS)	1115

Inversion points of pure minerals between two crystal structures

chalcocite (Cu_2S)	105° C.
microcline-sanidine	~700
low quartz–high quartz	573

Dissociation

pyrite (FeS_2) — pyrrhotite (FeS_x) + $(2 - x)$ S   690° C at 1 atm of S vapor

Exsolution

microcline and albite	~660° C.
chalcopyrite ($CuFeS_2$) and sphalerite (ZnS)	350–650(?)

Destruction of color caused by radiation damage at low temperature

fluorite (CaF_2), various colors	250–400° C.
smoky quartz	250–300

SOURCE: Data from E. Ingerson, Methods and problems of geologic thermometry, 50th Anniversary Volume of Economic Geology, 1955.

cussed one example of metastability in Chapter 6, namely the retention of a high sodium content and high-temperature crystal structure in the quickly-cooled potassium feldspars of volcanic rocks. If metastable high-temperature minerals are present in an ore deposit, they presumably indicate that the deposit at one time had been above the inversion temperature. Without going into the numerous mineralogical details concerning the temperatures of formation of different minerals, we can say that many minerals in ore deposits appear to have developed at temperatures in the range of 100° to 300° or 400° C. (Table 15-1).

3. Certain definitely igneous deposits have characteristics similar to those of ores. For example, minerals such as galena and sphalerite, the common ores of lead and zinc, have been found in some typical igneous pegmatites, and there appears to be every gradation between pegmatite deposits and hydrothermal deposits containing quartz, feldspar, and metallic ores. This pegmatite association leads to the hypothesis of hydrothermal deposition even for the many lead and zinc deposits which are not related to observable igneous activity.

The conclusion that metallic ores have been deposited by a type of hydrothermal process does not imply anything concerning the exact chemical nature of the hydrothermal fluid. Because of the ability of this fluid to permeate widely through different types of rocks, most geologists feel that the hydrothermal solution must be a very dilute, watery material in which the content of the various sulfide minerals is exceptionally small. Other geologists have pointed to the extremely low solubility of typical sulfides in water (the solubility product of lead sulfide at 25° is 10^{-28}); this low solubility has led them to hypothesize a hydrothermal fluid which contains water and a highly concentrated slurry of sulfides held in a solution or suspension by some chemical process as yet not fully understood. Regardless of the nature of the hydrothermal fluid, however, it is reasonably clear that it originates at some time during the later stages of magmatic differentiation and proceeds into wall rocks from the granite intrusives. It is possible to find ore deposits in areas not occupied by granite, and such fluids may have been derived in a slightly different manner from those in igneous wall rocks.

Hydrothermal fluids form two types of deposits as their temperatures decline. *Vein deposits* are tabular bodies which are commonly

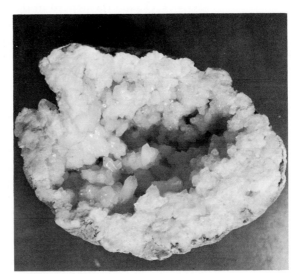

Fig. 15-8. Crystals filling cavity. These are quartz crystals growing into a cavity lined by amorphous SiO_2. The cavity is formed in a limestone, and the whole structure is known as a geode. (Photo by J. J. W. Rogers; courtesy of S. H. Stow.)

Fig. 15-9. Replacement veins of sulfide ore (dark stringers and some shiny specks) in a granite. (Photo by J. J. W. Rogers.)

developed around some sort of planar structure such as a fault, joint, or possibly a bed which is highly receptive to ore minerals. In some cases vein deposits are formed by precipitation of the various minerals in open spaces left by faulting or jointing (Fig. 15-8). It is not necessary, however, that open spaces exist for the formation of veins, and in many deposits the ore minerals seem simply to have replaced the preexisting wall-rock material (Fig. 15-9). The mechanism of this replacement process is not clear, but essentially it seems to be a simultaneous solution of the preexisting rock and deposition of the replacing minerals. All of this apparently occurs in a fluid which pervades the rock and occupies positions along grain borders and in pores. Certain types of rocks are more readily affected by hydrothermal solutions than others. For example, limestones, being comparatively more soluble than quartz, are commonly mineralized, whereas surrounding sandstones and shales are not.

Not all ore deposits are developed in the form of tabular veins. In some places the ore minerals are simply distributed throughout a large area of rock, and the deposit in this case is called a *disseminated ore*. This distribution occurs commonly in receptive and soluble rocks such as limestones, but it may also occur in rocks which might not normally be considered capable of replacement.

In both vein and disseminated deposits, whether formed by replacement or open space filling, certain elements tend to occur together. The reasons for these associations are not entirely clear, although in some cases there is a chemical similarity of the elements. Silver and gold, for example, are commonly associated in deposits. In most cases the gold occurs as a native metal, and the silver forms a variety of complex sulfides with other elements. Lead and zinc generally occur together, the zinc invariably in the mineral sphalerite and the lead either as galena or as one of a numerous variety of complex lead sulfides. It is interesting that, although lead and zinc occur together in deposits, they do not form isomorphous series with each other, and in fact zinc does not occur in combination with any other metal in any naturally occurring mineral. Copper occurs in some deposits of the vein or disseminated type but most commonly is produced from slightly mineralized large bodies of igneous rocks. These bodies are generally relatively shallow granitic intrusions with a slightly porphyritic texture, and the ores are referred to as *porphyry deposits*. The copper is disseminated in small joint surfaces and cracks in the porphyries, and the widespread nature of the mineralization permits mining of ores down to a very small concentration. In many porphyry copper deposits, additional enrichment of the metal has been caused by surficial weathering.

In all hydrothermal deposits the minerals formed are not solely the sulfide ore minerals. Pyrite is a common accompaniment of hydrothermal mineralization and generally is of no economic importance. In addition to pyrite a great number of silicate minerals are commonly formed. Clays are abundant, possibly as a result of the alteration of preexisting anhydrous silicates to the hydrous clay minerals. Quartz is a common associate of hydrothermal deposits. The total amount of material other than an actual ore mineral itself which must be mined in order to obtain the ore is referred to as *gangue*. Naturally, it is important in developing an economic deposit to find one in which the percentage of ore is the highest and the percentage of gangue is the lowest.

Nonhydrothermal ores

Not all metals are obtained from hydrothermal deposits, although by far the greatest number of them are. Iron, for example, which is the metal mined most abundantly on the earth, is produced largely from sedimentary deposits. The typical sedimentary iron deposit consists of extensive beds of hematite with an average grade of about 50 to 55 percent Fe_2O_3. These hematitic beds have, in most cases, resulted from the oxidation and partial leaching of sedimentary deposits of chert and magnetite (iron formation). The type of sedimentary environment which could lead to the production of chert and magnetite is difficult to visualize. Most such deposits, however, are formed comparatively early in the earth's history and may have developed at a time when sea-water composition was different from that which it has now (Chapter 14). The chert and magnetite deposits may undergo either a surficial weathering or some sort of hydrothermal leaching after sedimentary deposition in which part of the silica is removed and the hematite is formed by the oxidation of magnetite. The leaching thus increases the percentage of iron and makes the ore highly profitable. The large iron deposits around the western edge of Lake Superior have been formed in essentially this fashion.

Another extremely important element in our technological society is aluminum. Although aluminum is the third most abundant element in the earth's crust, it is so widely disseminated among all types of rocks that economically minable concentrations of it are extremely rare. The only significant ore of aluminum is bauxite. As discussed in Chapter 9, bauxites are formed by tropical weathering of rocks comparatively impoverished in silica. Under these conditions, it is possible to develop alkaline solutions which leach silica out of the rocks and leave behind a residue enriched in aluminum oxides and hydroxides. Naturally if iron is present, then a laterite forms, and the mixture of iron and aluminum is economically undesirable. Although much of the world's aluminum ore is found in tropical regions, the extension of tropical climates to other areas in the geologic past makes it possible to find aluminum deposits much further north and south than the present extent of the tropics.

Another type of surficial deposit of metallic ores is the *placer*. Placers are concentrations of comparatively heavy minerals in stream or beach sands. The heavy minerals are accumulated in large concentrations because their greater density makes it impossible for them to be transported as readily as the lighter quartz, feldspar, and clays. The heavy minerals which are accumulated must also be stable under weathering conditions on the earth's surface and must be resistant to mechanical abrasion. Thus pyrite, although heavy and abundant, does not occur in placers because it oxidizes easily and is weathered to limonite or other iron hydroxides. A number of minerals, however, do satisfy the requirements for accumulation as placers. One of the most common is gold, and placer deposits have been immense providers of the metal. Platinum, being chemically similar to gold, also occurs in some placer deposits, though it is much more rare. Other minerals which occur as placer deposits and yield large amounts of ore are cassiterite, which is a major source of tin, and monazite, a phosphate of rare earths which is a major source of all of the various rare earth elements.

Before leaving the subject of metallic ores, we should mention the rapidly developing potentiality for obtaining metals from water. Magnesium, for example, is now produced almost wholly from the evaporation and purification of salts obtained from sea water. The process has almost completely replaced the production of magnesium from magnesite ($MgCO_3$) deposits or other deposits of minerals. Furthermore, the brines of some dry lakes in the western United States have been found to be exceptionally rich in certain highly soluble elements such as lithium and are now commercially exploited.

NONMETALLIC ORES

In the exploitation of metallic ores, the major objective is to obtain a mineral from which an individual metal may be removed by some sort of metallurgical or refining process. Many geological materials, however, are valued for their properties as rocks and minerals rather than for the material which they contain. A complete list of these nonmetallic ores is well beyond the province of this book, but a few of the more important ones should be mentioned.

The cement industry depends upon a source of calcium carbonate for the production of calcium oxide. Cement is simply a powdered mixture of calcium oxide and various calcium silicates which, in the presence of water, undergo a slow reaction yielding the development of a hard mass. In order to produce a suitable calcium oxide for the cement, however, it is necessary to find limestone of exceptional purity, for the presence of even small amounts of magnesium generally renders the material unusable. Thus, although limestones as rocks are comparatively common, the cement-producing limestones are relatively rare, and exploration for them is a major problem.

Another nonmetallic material which is valued as the mineral itself is salt. Salt is obtained from sedimentary beds, from salt domes, or by the evaporation of sea water. Most of the salt thus far produced has been from sedimentary deposits and salt domes, but of course this production may change in the future. Along with the production of salt from sedimentary deposits is the possibility of obtaining potassium from potassium chloride or other potassium evaporites deposited along with the sodium chloride. Most halite deposits do not contain potassium minerals, but those which do are valued for the content of potassium alone.

Clays are also extremely useful materials in a variety of industrial applications. The ceramic industry, for example, depends upon pure clays for the production of china ware and, on a more rough basis, the production of tiles, sewer pipes, and the like. Not all clays, however, are suitable for these various applications. In general, a pure clay formed by the weathering of a granite or a pegmatite is reasonably useful, but the typical clays of the ordinary marine shale are not suitable for ceramic purposes.

One of the major industries using rock is the quarrying industry. The production of polished or unpolished large blocks of rock for construction purposes is a dominant industry in some parts of the country. Naturally, for the construction of buildings it is important to obtain a rock which has a pleasing appearance, and certain quarries whose rocks are particularly decorative have become quite famous. Rock for construction purposes must not only be decorative but must also be free of joints, cracks, and a content of easily weathered materials. Thus, despite the preponderance of granite in the earth's crust, most granite bodies are nearly unusable for quarrying operations.

The list of materials valued as minerals and rocks is virtually endless. We should mention, however, the various types of gem stones such as diamonds, rubies, and sapphires and also the many other less valuable rocks and minerals which are used for ornamental purposes. We could also mention asbestos, a highly fibrous form of serpentine or amphibole, and talc, which is a hydrous magnesium silicate similar to ordinary clay minerals and which is used for both industrial and medicinal purposes.

GROUND WATER

Of the things which man obtains from the earth, food and water are obviously the most important. The easiest places from which to obtain water are lakes and rivers. Even in the earliest civilizations, however, it was found necessary to drill wells to make use of water in the ground. Now, much of the water used in civilized countries in obtained from underground wells.

Water underground occurs in the pore spaces of rocks. As we discussed in the portion of this chapter dealing with oil, in uncemented sandstones the pore space may occupy 20 to 25 percent of a rock, and in shales the porosity may be considerably higher. Water may be obtained, however, only from those rocks which have a reasonably high permeability together with a reasonable porosity. These reservoir rocks for water are called *aquifers,* and most aquifers consist of sandstones in which the cementation is comparatively small. Some limestones and other rocks, however, in which fracturing has occurred can be very productive of water. Rates of water movement may be quite high along fault or joint zones.

TABLE 15-2. COMPOSITION OF A TYPICAL GROUND WATER. DAKOTA SANDSTONE, NORTH DAKOTA

	parts per million
SiO_2	23
total Fe	4.8
Ca	136
Mg	35
Na + K	960
HCO_3	249
SO_4	1,260
Cl	734

SOURCE: Data from *U.S. Geological Survey Water-Supply Paper 1473*, 1959.

In composition, underground water ranges from essentially pure water to brines in which the salinity is higher than that of the typical ocean (Table 15-2). Although rainwater is very pure, in the ground it dissolves material with which it comes in contact, and the concentration of some elements may become quite high. One of the most common ions in solution in ground water is the bicarbonate ion; any water containing carbon dioxide from the atmosphere dissolves limestone with which it comes in contact, and thus the bicarbonate ion is produced in large quantities. Unless the underground water occurs in an area in which limestone and lime cements are ·absent, the solution of all types of minerals commonly produces a composition similar to that shown in Table 15-2. It may be interesting to compare this composition with that of normal ocean water (Table 13-1).

Source

Underground water is originally derived from rainfall. A raindrop falling on the earth's surface may become involved in one of four processes (Fig. 15-10). It may, for example, join surface "runoff" in the form of rills or sheet wash and ultimately enter rivers and pass on down to the ocean. The water may also simply evaporate, a process which predominates in regions of high temperature and low humidity. Another possible mechanism by which water is transferred back to the atmosphere is through absorption by plants out of the soil. During certain portions of their daily cycle, plants emit water from their leaves; this is essentially a type of evaporation through the medium of plants and can be extremely important in areas of considerable vegetation. If the water neither runs off nor is evaporated, then it must sink into the ground and ultimately become a part of the ground water at some depth. Water which runs off of a surface is not necessarily lost to ground water. Some streams, for example, provide a considerable amount of water into the ground by simple seepage into their banks. Other streams are receiving water from the ground by the reverse process, and the relationships

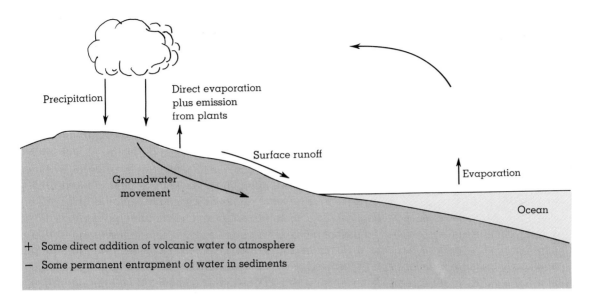

Precipitation

Direct evaporation
plus emission
from plants

Surface runoff

Groundwater
movement

Evaporation

Ocean

+ Some direct addition of volcanic water to atmosphere

− Some permanent entrapment of water in sediments

Fig. 15-10. Diagrammatic representation of hydrologic cycle. Water may be added to the cycle by volcanic gases or the weathering of hydrous minerals and may be removed from the cycle by entrapment in sediments.

between the streams and water movements in the ground will be discussed in the next section.

Another source of water is simply the sea water or other water entrapped in sediments at the time of their deposition. It is possible for rocks in which permeability is comparatively low to retain the sea water with which they were in contact at the time the fresh sediment was deposited. This type of water is called *connate*, and its composition naturally reflects the composition of the environment at the time of deposition of the enclosing sediment. In the preceding sentence we used the word "reflects" rather than "equals," because the sea water need not be in exact chemical equilibrium with the sediments which are deposited from it. Thus, over a long period of time, the connate waters may gradually dissolve some of the surrounding minerals, may precipitate on others, or may even create new ones. In this manner the composition of the connate water may change quite rapidly, and in some cases highly concentrated solutions are formed by continual solution of surrounding mineral grains.

Water table

One of the most important features related to the study of ground water is the *water table*. The water table is simply the level below which the ground is completely saturated with water and above which the pore spaces in the rocks contain not only water but also air. Water falling onto the ground or entering the ground from a stream or lake passes through this upper, unsaturated zone until ultimately it joins the water table at depth. The water moving downward to join the water table

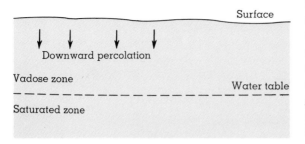

Fig. 15-11. Relationships between water table and vadose and saturated zones.

is called *vadose*. In the unsaturated, or vadose, zone the combined effect of air and water on the rock is generally quite high, and considerable oxidation and intense weathering occurs. In general, a somewhat greater chemical stability of rocks and minerals seems to be achieved below the water table, in the saturated zone (Fig. 15-11).

The water table tends to follow the topography, but the relief of the water table is almost invariably much less than that of the topography. A typical relationship between water table and topography is shown in Fig. 15-12. Obviously, the water table must be at the level of rivers and lakes at their margins. The water table may, however, proceed downward from these bodies of running water, in which case rivers and lakes tend to add water to the ground, or it may proceed upward from these water bodies, and the resulting flow is from the ground into the rivers. The water table rises under hills but not as sharply as the surface topography.

The depth to the water table is obviously highly dependent on climate and type of rock. In humid regions saturated ground may be intersected only a few feet below the surface. In swamps the water table is at, or above, the land surface. In deserts, on the contrary, the water table may be many hundreds of feet below ground level. In general, all rocks below the water table are saturated with water until one reaches a level downward at which the high pressure of the overburden essentially reduces the pore space to zero. In some cases, however, impermeable strata may hold a body of water at a depth above the normal ground water table of the area. Such a situation is shown in Fig. 15-12, and it is apparent that the upper body of water can be penetrated in drilling a well, and the underlying material may be virtually dry.

Springs are formed where the water table intersects the surface or where special features permit movement of water from higher pressure areas out onto the ground surface. Deep notches or canyons in mountain sides, for example, may intersect the normal water table under the

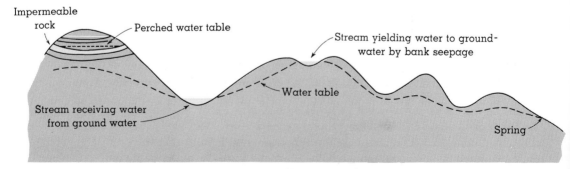

Fig. 15-12. Relationship of water table to topography.

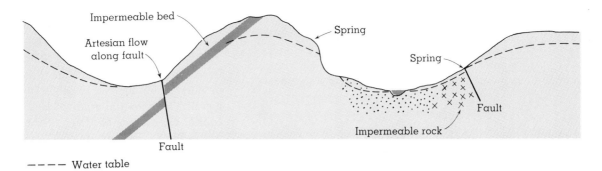

Artesian flow along fault

Impermeable bed

Spring

Spring

Fault

Impermeable rock

Fault

– – – – Water table

Fig. 15-13. Some major locations of springs.

mountain and may permit some outward flowage of the water at the intersection. Springs are commonly developed along fault or joint surfaces which permit great ease of movement of the water; for example, as in Fig. 15-13, water will move out into the ground under the driving force of the high pressure caused by the higher water table back in the mountain even though the water table might not normally intersect the ground surface at this point. In a similar fashion, springs might be formed along bedding surfaces, joints, or many other types of geologic features.

Movement

Water in the saturated zone below the water table moves in response to the force of gravity. The rate of movement is variable depending upon the permeability of the rock and the inclination of the water table (the potential gradient). Average rates of movement are in the range of 50 feet per year. The rates of movement can be measured experimentally by such devices as inserting dyes into water at one well and determining the time which it takes them to travel to another well. The movement of water is always in a direction from high potential, i.e., high pressure, to one of low potential. Naturally, the potential differences are related to the elevation of the water surface, and thus water invariably flows in the direction toward which the water table is sloping. A simple relationship can be established between the potential gradient, the permeability of the rocks through which the water is moving, and the velocity of movement. This relationship is known as Darcy's Law and can be expressed by the following equation

$$V = - k \frac{dh}{dZ}$$

where

V = velocity of flow

k = a constant

dh = difference in head at two points (Z_1 and Z_2)

dZ = difference in elevation at two points (Z_1 and Z_2)

This equation is applicable over any distance in which the potential gradient is uniform, that is, in which the surface of the water is a sloping

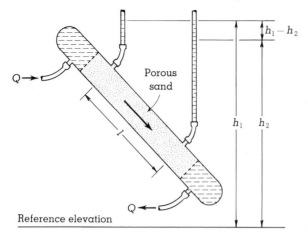

plane. Naturally, where the surface is curved it is possible to develop integrated forms of Darcy's Law from which an average velocity can be derived for a given distance interval. The potential gradient is, of course, expressable in terms of the difference in height between two points on the water's surface (the water table) (Fig. 15-14).

Reference elevation

Fig. 15-14. Tube for verification of Darcy's Law of fluid flow. For a given rate of flow (Q) and length of tube (*l*) the pressure difference ($h_1 - h_2$) is constant regardless of the orientation of the tube. (Courtesy of M. King Hubbert.)

Sculpturing by ground water

The effects of ground water are seen in the geologic record in two ways. Water in contact with soluble rocks, particularly carbonated water traversing limestone, may cause solution. Conversely, water may also cause precipitation of new minerals or growth of old minerals where saturation can be accomplished by evaporation or some other means. The typical result of solution is the development of caves in limestone country. The exact location of caves is always somewhat difficult to understand, but their general mode of formation is quite clear. The geologic requirements are a supply of carbonated water and an underground drainage system into which the saturated water, after dissolving the limestone, may be discharged. Obviously, if fluid flow is not reasonably fast, the water simply becomes saturated, and no additional solution takes place. Most caves appear to develop below the water table, although considerable solution may take place within the upper, unsaturated zone.

After a cave is formed, then precipitation may take place within it

Fig. 15-15. Cave deposits (stalactites and stalagmites) in Carlsbad Caverns, New Mexico. (Photo by D. K. Smith.)

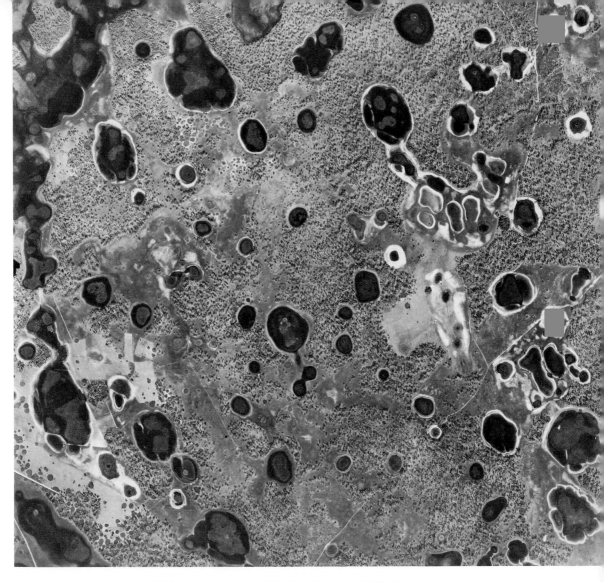

Fig. 15-16. Aerial view of sink holes in limestone in Florida. (Courtesy of U.S. Department of Agriculture.)

(Fig. 15-15). In part the precipitation occurs in small pools, perhaps left behind by the stream which occupied the cave floor. A far greater amount of precipitation, however, is occasioned by saturated water dripping from the almost invariably wet cave roofs. On exposure to the air in the cave, these waters lose carbon dioxide by evaporation and thus precipitate calcium carbonates. In this fashion, long growths may extend downward from the cave roof, and the projections thus formed are commonly called *stalactites*. It is also possible for the water to drip sufficiently fast to fall on the floor of the cave, where it then evaporates and deposits a *stalagmite* growing as a cylinder upward from the floor. In some cases the stalactites and stalagmites will join together to form a column extending from the floor all the way to the roof. Other types of cave de-

Fig. 15-17. Solution topography on limestone in Puerto Rico. (Photo by C. C. Almy)

posits are also found, and in some caves the streams which have existed previously or currently in the cave have deposited large amounts of clay, sand, or other normal stream sediments. This insoluble material is, in part, debris left behind by solution of the more soluble limestone.

Another feature of limestone solution occurs largely in the unsaturated zone above the water table. This is the development of large sinkholes, or solution pits, extending downward from the surface. In some limestone terrains, where surface erosion is limited, this method of erosion by solution becomes predominant, and the surface becomes honeycombed by a number of these pits (Fig. 15-16). The pits may be interconnected by small tunnels at depth. Naturally such features cannot be developed where surface erosion is so rapid that it out-paces solution. Thus, features of this type are generally found in flat regions where stream gradients are sufficiently small that physical movement of materials does not occur. Residues of insoluble material (clay and sand) may accumulate to great thicknesses in areas which have undergone simple limestone solution, and the soils of these areas may be extremely rich (Fig. 15-17).

Economic problems

One of the principal economic problems in connection with ground water is the method of its extraction. In most cases it is necessary to pump or, in more primitive areas, to ladle water out of the well by hand. Pumping always causes difficulties because the permeability of the surrounding rock is generally not sufficiently high that the water will flow rapidly into the well and maintain a constant level. Thus there is a zone around an actively pumping well in which the water table is tilted downward, much as is shown in Fig. 15-18. The amount of this "draw-down" is related to both the permeability and the rate of pumping. In fact, one method by which rock permeability can be measured around a well is to determine the elevation of the water table in the well for different rates of pumping.

In some areas it is not necessary to pump wells, and the water rises above the surface level by its own internal pressure. Such wells are called *artesian* and may originate in quite a number of ways. A common geologic situation which causes the developments of artesian wells in shown in Fig. 15-19. Here, water entering a permeable aquifer is confined underneath an impermeable unit as the beds dip downward. Naturally, the water at any particular point is under a pressure equal to that of the column of water above it. Thus, in theory, wherever an artesian aquifer is penetrated, the water should shoot forth to a height equal to that of the head. In actuality a certain amount of potential is lost during flowage through the rock, and the pressure at the well drops off slowly with distance from the source. Artesian wells are common in some aquifers throughout the western part of the Middle West; one famous example is the Dakota sandstone, a porous sand which accumulates water at its

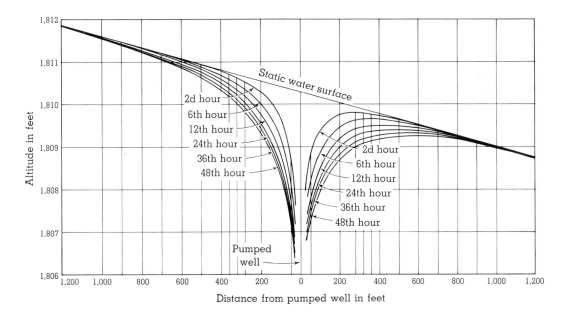

Fig. 15-18. Draw-down of water table by pumping of well. Times refer to total time after start of pumping. Static surface is normal water table gradient in area. (From L. K. Wenzel, *U.S. Geological Survey Water Supply Paper 679A*, 1936.)

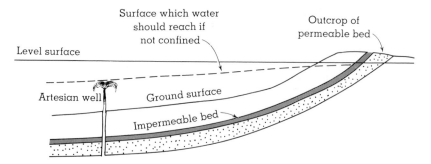

Fig. 15-19. Conditions for development of artesian well. The impermeable bed forces the water to flow below the level it would reach if flowing unconfined through a porous medium. If the ground surface is below this pressure surface, the well will flow above ground.

outcrop on the eastern side of the Rocky Mountains and extends under the plains states toward the east.

Another problem in connection with the production of water by pumping is found in areas near coastlines. This problem is caused by the fact that withdrawal of fresh water may permit the encroachment of salt water into the coastal sediments. Salt and fresh water generally remain quite separate, and contact between them is fairly sharp in the subsurface, with the denser salt water occupying a position below the fresh water. Naturally, withdrawal of the fresh water causes the salt-fresh contact to rise, though additional flow of fresh water from the higher land areas to landward would cause the contact to descend. The problem in coastal areas, therefore, is to withdraw the fresh water at a sufficiently slow rate that the normal water flow will prevent the salt water from rising into the wells.

The problems of ground water supply are numerous, and we have only briefly touched upon a few of them in this section. Enormous efforts are currently being made to develop and assess the ground water resources of the United States. This assessment, though particularly urgent in the western United States, is also becoming of vital importance throughout the entire country.

CHAPTER 16

MAN IN
GEOLOGIC PERSPECTIVE

◄ Drilling for oil off Alaska coast. (Shell photograph.)

PHYSICAL FACTORS IN THE ENVIRONMENT

Life has evolved on the earth with changing pace but without interruption over the past two or more billion years. During this immense span of time, life could have survived only if the physical, chemical, and biological conditions had remained rather constant. Sudden, world-wide, and catastrophic changes in temperature or any other physical condition are not evident in the geologic record. The lack of such sudden and sharp changes is an essential part of the concept of uniformitarianism. Temperature, for example, is but one of the myriad of interacting physical, chemical, and biological factors that have affected life throughout geologic time.

At first subjective glance, it would appear that the surface of the earth has a wide range of temperature from about $-100°$ F. to more than $150°$ F. These extremes, however, occur rarely and over very small areas. Much of mankind seldom sees snow, and only a small fraction of the ocean ever contains ice. Compared to other near-by bodies that orbit the sun, the range of temperature change on the terrestrial surface is small indeed. The essential physical mechanisms that result in this small temperature range are well understood in outline. The unequal heating of the earth's atmosphere causes convection, and the resultant winds blow so as to equalize temperatures. The hydrosphere acts as a global thermostat, with water evaporating during the day to lower the maximum temperature, and with the dew condensing at night to raise the minimum temperature. On a longer time scale, a decrease of a few tenths of a degree in the annual mean temperature of the earth will result in a year-by-year accumulation of snow to form glaciers. Conversely, as appears to be happening for the past century, an increase of a few tenths results in the melting back of the small high-altitude alpine glaciers and the larger high-latitude continental glaciers.

Some of the mechanisms that affect the range of terrestrial surface temperatures are not completely understood. The distribution of precipitation, for example, can be explained for the most part in terms of the prevailing circulation of air masses and the configuration of land surfaces. Yet, there still remain poorly defined and subtle mechanisms that affect precipitation. Droughts and the recent net lowering of the Great Lakes of North America are not fully understood. It is clear, however, that many of the physical mechanisms that affect and control the range of temperatures are delicately balanced and react quickly to offset any changes in temperature. These mechanisms appear adequate to have maintained rather constant surface temperatures throughout the geologic past. These natural mechanisms may well continue to so operate indefinitely, but it behooves mankind to study and to understand these mechanisms in much more detail so that man's advent as a special type of geologic agent is not marked by more self-inflicted, although unintended, harm.

Man may be considered a special type of geologic agent because of his great numbers and his intelligence. This intelligence has enabled him to invade an unusually wide variety of environments and to control increasingly great quantities of material and energy. Serious and planned attempts are being made to manipulate the physical mechanisms controlling the environment by such means as seeding of clouds and the diversion or dispersal of incipient hurricanes. To some, these attempts appear akin to an ordinary seven-year-old using a screw driver to adjust or improve a wrist watch. To others, it is proper that man should continue to modify his environment on an increasing scale, even if it requires the solution of the many difficult and unique legal problems that would arise from any effective cloud seeding or hurricane diverting. There is also the haunting possibility that man's activities may unintentionally trigger an upset in the delicate, interlocked balances and cycles of the natural physical mechanisms. Such upsets certainly occur on a short time scale, as when an inexperienced geologist accidentally kicks off an avalanche while crossing an unstable slope composed of rock rubble. It is more difficult to recognize longer-term events of this accidental type. Thus, the decline of the agricultural fertility of the classical lands around the Mediterranean has been ascribed to natural climatic changes by some and to deforestation by man and overgrazing by domestic goats by others.

Industrial activity in the twentieth century has been on such a scale that it provides a number of possibilities for triggering off some long-term change in the physical environment. Returning to the example of temperatures at the surface of the earth, it is possible that these temperatures have been raised by the carbon dioxide produced from man's combustion of coal, oil, and natural gas. Since 1900 such combustion has produced enough carbon dioxide to double the concentration in the atmosphere; however, geologic processes outlined below fixed enough carbon dioxide that its concentration in the atmosphere has increased at most by one-tenth, to approximately 0.033 percent. Any sustained increase in the carbon dioxide in the atmosphere will greatly affect the light transmission and absorption properties of the atmosphere. In particular, gaseous carbon dioxide absorbs strongly in the infrared, and this retains heat on the earth (Chapter 12); despite its low concentration, carbon dioxide is responsible for an important part of such absorption in the atmosphere. Any temperature increase caused by the addition of carbon dioxide to the atmosphere in this way could trigger further increases through at least two mechanisms.

The gaseous carbon dioxide in the atmosphere is in a finely balanced chemical equilibrium with the carbon dioxide dissolved in the oceans. The partition coefficient for this equilibrium is very temperature dependent, and if the oceans were slightly warmed, they would begin releasing carbon dioxide to the atmosphere. The oceans contain 25 to 30 times more carbon dioxide than the atmosphere, and so the amount releasable by warming of the ocean could be significant—even approaching "avalanche" proportions. To some extent, however, this mechanism is self-limiting because the depth of the ocean permits the colder, more carbon dioxide-rich water to sink out of immediate contact with the atmosphere. Another mechanism by which any warming of the atmosphere might be self-reinforcing lies in the decrease of the extent of snow cover in winter and the decrease in the area of perennial glacial ice. White ice and snow reflect more of the sun's rays back into space than does the underlying, darker ground. Hence, if, on the average, more and more darker ground were uncovered, the higher light absorption of this ground would raise the surface temperature.

It is also possible to argue that industrially produced carbon dioxide has played no important role in any slight warming trend during this century. The carbon dioxide content of the atmosphere is highly variable, being highest in industrial areas and falling to half the average value over the polar seas, where carbon dioxide is being absorbed into the cold water. Furthermore, the older analyses are few and may be inaccurate to such an extent that it is difficult to be sure of a one-tenth increase. It takes some hundreds to a thousand years for the oceans and atmosphere to equilibrate. Hence, much and perhaps all of the industrially produced carbon dioxide has been absorbed by the leaves of plants and incorporated by photosynthesis into hydrocarbons. Plants thrive when subjected to artificially high carbon dioxide concentrations, and the large surface areas of leaves only two cells thick represent an evolutionary response to the need of absorbing carbon dioxide at low concentrations. Certainly plants play a key role in regulating the carbon dioxide content of the atmosphere, and they may well have essentially removed the excess produced by the industrial combustion of fossil fuels.

Industrial activities may affect the earth's surface temperature by altering the distribution of precipitation. As mentioned earlier in this section, the global distribution of precipitation can be explained in large part by prevailing circulation of air masses and the configuration of the land surface. Other undefined and asymmetric factors may be locally important. Cloud-seeding is intended to meet any lack of suitable nuclei on which water vapor can condense. The particulate matter in the exhaust products of high-flying aircraft and the fine condensed material formed from the vaporization upon reentering of manmade satellites and rockets may provide new and differently distributed nuclei. To the extent that these artificial nuclei alter the distribution of all types of nuclei, they will affect the pattern of precipitation and hence the surface temperature.

Man's role as a geologic agent, manipulating or disturbing the physical mechanisms regulating conditions on the earth, is very new and poorly understood. The great size of the earth and the short period of time over which such possibilities have been studied and samples taken give rise to many uncertainties. The balances among—and the cycling through—the atmosphere, hydrosphere, and biosphere are fascinating in their complexity. An understanding of these complexities is overdue, as is the recognition of those critical points where action may or may not be taken. The building of dams, the actual or threatened extinction of whales and other species, and the deforestation and reforestation of vast areas are but a few of the actions to be studied.

CHEMICAL FACTORS IN THE ENVIRONMENT

In addition to favorable physical conditions such as temperature, the evolution and flourishing of terrestrial life requires chemical conditions in which all essential nutrients are adequately available and in which poisons are removed or reduced to healthy or tolerable levels. Industrial, including related agricultural and military, activities are modifying the chemical factors in the environment and even adding completely new ones. The sizable industrial addition to the carbon dioxide inventory of the atmosphere has already been discussed in connection with possible effects on surface temperatures and the growth of plants. The chemical factors that increase the productivity of plants and animals have been intensively investigated on account of the substantial economic benefits that chemical fertilization has yielded. The geologic processes that have operated throughout geologic time have not produced chemical conditions in every area that are optimum for modern forms of life. Certain elements or groups of elements may be overabundant to a toxic degree able in nutrient concentrations in some areas. By contrast, these same elements or groups of elements may be overabundant to a toxic degree in other areas. Less well known are the unintended modifications to the chemical environment brought about by man's activities, particularly large-scale industrial operations.

Modern industry uses substantial tonnages of heavy metals such as lead, thallium, and mercury. The history of the mining, smelting, and fabrication of these and other toxic elements provides ample and tragic examples of how locally man can poison himself and his surroundings. In these local industrial situations, it is generally easy to recognize and provide for any quick-acting and detrimental chemical factor. It is another matter, however, to recognize any slow-acting factor, particularly where these elements are spewed into the hydrosphere and atmosphere in previously unexperienced chemical forms and concentrations. For example, lead in gaseous or finely particulate form is released to the atmosphere through the exhaust of automobiles, as well as from the incineration of many of man's manufactured products. An anomalous increase in the lead concentration of the upper portions of the oceans is probably due to these new sources of airborne lead. As a result of this global circulation of lead, it may be very difficult to determine, for example, lead content in the blood of preindustrial man. It is a still more difficult problem to determine if this increase in available lead in the environment has or will have any significant good or bad effects. Lead in some forms and at lower-than-present concentrations has been in the environment throughout geologic time.

In contrast to lead is the use of chemical compounds, particularly organic, that have never been on the face of the earth before. Thousands of new compounds are created every year, and some of these are widely used in many aspects of the economy. A number of these compounds or their break-down products have sufficient chemical stability and concentration to be detected as they are circulated in the atmosphere, hydrosphere, and biosphere. Insecticides such as DDT, and the so-called "hard" or nonbiologically degradable detergents, are some of the better-under-stood examples. Some would consider cigarette smoke as another example, and as with cigarette smoke, it is not easy with these synthetic compounds to pinpoint detrimental effects to everyone's satisfaction. One economically attractive approach to the management of synthetics in the environment is to alter the compounds so that they retain their desirable properties but do not persist in nature. Thus, "soft" detergents have been made that are readily broken down or degraded by microorganisms that are present in every stream.

Man-induced nuclear reactions produce radioactive elements that for the most part were not present in the preindustrial environment. Some of these radioactive elements persist long enough to modify the physical environment in terms of the amount of ionizing radiation. As these man-made radioactive elements are circulated through the atmosphere, hydrosphere, and biosphere, they, as well as the naturally radioactive elements, may be dispersed or concentrated by a host of geologic and biologic processes. For the most part, the man-made elements appear to be dispersed so that their effects are not as great as those produced by the naturally radioactive elements. In some cases, however, a combination of factors can produce unusually high concentrations of fission products in man's food and in man himself. One of the better known examples concerns certain Alaskan Eskimos. Their proximity to atmospheric nuclear testing combined with the accidents of heavy precipitation brought down an unusually high amount of fallout in their area. Their area of flat-lying tundra underlain by permanently frozen ground did not allow much of the precipitation and fallout to be washed off to the sea or soaked into the ground. During the short summer, the lichens that dominate the flora blanket the ground densely, and much of the fallout concentrated on them as it fell or as the snow melted. The caribou graze heavily on this vegetation, and as each one ate the vegetation off of a large area it thus concentrated fallout products, particularly cesium-137, in its flesh. Those Eskimos whose diet contained a large proportion of caribou in turn retained some of the highest known concentrations of cesium-137. An exactly parallel combination of factors operated among some of the reindeer-eating Lapps of northern Scandinavia.

The effects, if any, of radioactive fallout on the Eskimos, of lead in the environment, and of various persistent hydrocarbons are largely unknown. Too much of any of these chemical factors, or indeed of almost any chemical factor, can be toxic. Lower concentrations are essential for nutrition in some cases and can be readily tolerated in many others. Certain of man's activities, such as automobile driving, are so obvious in their detrimental side-effects that the loss of life and limb can be ascertained. Of the possible long-term effects under study, probably only cigarette smoke is potentially on the same scale of life loss as the operation of automobiles. With each passing year it becomes, in many respects, more and more difficult to sample and reconstruct the preindustrial environment to which life, including man, has adjusted throughout geologic time. In terms of geologic perspective, man has the choice of either trying to understand and consciously to manage the physical and chemical factors in his environment or of continuing to rely upon the slow evolutionary responses to environmental change that have operated throughout geologic time. These slow evolutionary responses become more unsuccessful as man's life span increases and as man's ability to change his environment in shorter and shorter time increases.

BIOLOGICAL RESPONSE AND FACTORS IN THE ENVIRONMENT

Man can view in the living forms of life the products of an organic evolution that took place over two billion years. The countless millions of delicate adjustments of these organisms to the physical and chemical factors in their environment and to each other are truly marvelous. To sudden natural changes in the environment such as earthquakes, floods, epidemics, volcanic eruptions, or forest fires, many organisms have inadequate responses and die. Rarely are such disasters over a large enough area to eliminate a species. To slower changes such as climatic shifts, epidemic loss of part of the food supply, or the appearance of a new predator, many organisms can respond by migration. A species, in time, can develop an evolutionary response by evolving descendents more adapted to the new stress in the environment. For example, with DDT man has produced a new chemical stress in the environments of many insects. Some insect species have apparently responded to this stress by evolving DDT-resistant strains. To make this response, a species has to have a large enough genetic variance or pool so that some individuals have at least slightly higher-than-average DDT resistance. These individual insects must then live long enough to mate and reproduce; finally they must transmit to their progeny the DDT-resistant characteristic. This transmission via the genetic code must, in addition to the DDT-resistant characteristic, transmit a tremendous amount of information regarding each of the vital life processes of the species. On one hand, the transmission must be near perfect to avoid producing nonviable mutants; on the other hand, occasional errors in transmission might lead to viable mutants that were peculiar in having still higher resistance to DDT. With many insects such as the house fly producing a generation every ten days or so, a DDT-resistant strain might develop in a relatively short time. It is even possible that if DDT manufacture were to cease and the DDT characteristic proved genetically dominant, this characteristic would be propagated indefinitely. Many organisms have structures and instincts whose present usefulness is not apparent.

By selectively breeding domestic plants and animals, man has taken successful advantage of genetic variation. By introducing new species into environments to which they are not ecologically adjusted through the slow evolutionary mechanisms, man has hurt his economic interests in some cases. The introduction of the rabbit into Australia is but one of the better-known of many examples, for it has rapidly expanded into a serious menace to crops and grazing lands. A major means of trying to restore such disturbed ecological balances is the importation of the natural predators, parasites, or diseases of the species causing the upset. This method may prove to be a poor one if the new arrival in turn becomes a cause of ecological imbalance. No factors in the environment are tipped out of balance more quickly than the ecological ones. In several real senses, man himself can be considered out of ecological balance.

In more and more areas of the world, man is out of ecological balance in that he and other organisms are exposed to greater and greater concentrations of his chemical, organic, and radioactive wastes. Because the levels of these wastes are rising and show no signs of leveling off, they may be considered out of balance. Against many of these wastes or pollutants, many organisms have no genetically inherited response, except migration where possible. Fish, for example, are killed off by the millions in polluted lakes and streams. An evolutionary response will take much time, providing that the level of waste products finally stabilizes. If given enough time, man himself might evolve to a point where he could tolerate the worst smog and the densest cigarette smoke.

Another sense in which man is out of ecological balance is in the pressure his growing numbers exerts on food supplies in more and more regions of the world. The steady decline in the per capita food intake and the per capita income in many areas results from the fact that population growth is outstripping gains in productivity. A main cause of the rapidly expanding population results from the great success in controlling disease, particularly as it affects infant mortality. In other words, it is not so much a matter of more babies being born in each family as it is a matter of more infants surviving to maturity. Figure 16-1 illustrates a modern estimate of the rate of population growth, and it can be considered another, but highly important, example of how easily an ecological balance can be overturned. In nature as in past history, population pressures on food supplies have resulted in famines devastating local populations. Any future famine may, at first, take a special form, because the areas most seriously threatened generally have strong central governments with sufficient military force and transportation to insure a careful division of available food supplies.

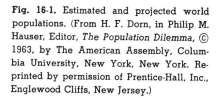

Fig. 16-1. Estimated and projected world populations. (From H. F. Dorn, in Philip M. Hauser, Editor, *The Population Dilemma*, © 1963, by The American Assembly, Columbia University, New York, New York. Reprinted by permission of Prentice-Hall, Inc., Englewood Cliffs, New Jersey.)

With equal but slowly diminishing shares, the death rate would increase slowly due to old age and various diseases, malnutrition being a contributing factor. Somehow a balance must be struck between population on one hand and available resources on the other. The smaller the population in this balance, the higher the standard of living. At balance the death rate and the birth rate would be equal, a condition that few regions have experienced in this century. In some ways the application of modern technology has worsened the problem in that, through health measures, it has had the effect of increasing the population growth faster than food production. In many areas it appears that population control will be necessary to give technological advance enough time to increase food productivity.

When viewing the population dilemma in geologic perspective, one is awed by the prospect that man must consciously develop global ecological balances and consciously manipulate the physical, chemical, and biological factors in the environment in order to avoid widespread want sooner or later. He must do this quickly, and his major guide and model is the imperfectly understood evolutionary one that operates over geologic time. Furthermore, to determine what balance between population and resources can be made, he must take stock of the earth and estimate the available mineral and energy resources.

THE FUTURE AVAILABILITY OF MINERALS AND ENERGY

Since the end of World War II, nearly every mineral material and fuel has been in quite adequate supply relative to world markets. The sulfur shortages of the early 1950s and the petroleum shortage during the Suez crisis of 1956 were caused by lack of milling and transport facilities rather than lack of proven reserves in the ground. There is no mineral material used in the past that is not used today because it has become exhausted or considerably more costly. Even with the great raw material demands of the postwar recovery, the large-tonnage metals such as iron, aluminum, copper, and zinc have been characterized by plentiful supplies and, indeed, by a few percent oversupply that has operated to keep prices low and steady. It is debatable whether the real prices of mineral commodities have substantially risen in this century. The fossil fuels, coal and oil, are being extracted at far below actual capacity. In short, as of today the immediate problem on the world markets is one of plentiful supply to oversupply. Furthermore, despite increased and increasing demands, immediate future reserves of minerals and energy sources are known for a longer projection into the future than at any time in the past. The many wants of the world are not presently caused by lack of minerals and fuels but by the lack of economic resources to buy what is available as well as the lack of organization and training to use it. If, however, the present world population or the future populations indicated in Figure 16-1 were to attain a high standard of living, the raw material and fuel demands would be greatly accelerated. The initial rate of this acceleration would, as at present, be dependent upon the rate of education, organization, and capital availability in the less industrialized regions.

Exact data for any balance between population and resources are lacking. The best population data are from the highly industrialized regions that have the smaller populations and the lower population growth rates. Data for the rapidly growing populations are either lacking, as in the case of mainland China, or generally unreliable. On the other side of the balance, little effort is made to study mineral and fuel resources by direct geological exploration. Estimates of mineral and fuel resources are based almost entirely on miscellaneous figures gathered from various sources. The major sources are profit-seeking groups that pay for most of the direct geologic exploration and development. Such groups have little economic or other interest in locating and proving out reserves that will take more than fifteen to twenty years to mine out. For the most part, investments are expected to pay out in fifteen or twenty years or sooner. Thus, our knowledge of proven reserves in the ground is almost totally determined by short-term economic, not long-term resource, considerations. Only the most naïve can make any connection between proven reserves and ultimate resources. Certain important resources, particularly coal, are known to be quite adequate for at least several centuries; knowledge of these larger-than-usual proven reserves arises from the geologic fact that coal beds are stratigraphic units with simple geometries; their volume can be accurately estimated with a very few inexpensive measurements of thickness and extent.

Striking a balance between population and resources is not a simple matter of putting one kind of counters in one pan and another kind in the other. Demographers, in their studies of populations, must attempt to assess future population increases in terms of changes in birth and death rates. Geologic estimates of resources must rest upon equally or more uncertain estimates of discovery rates and costs. In the early 1950s the known uranium reserves of the continental United States were inconsequential. Within a few years a concerted exploration effort made the United States a major uranium producer. So successful was this effort that many North American mines now operate at only 10 percent of capacity because currently uranium supply so greatly exceeds demand. After considering that many of the major uranium discoveries were made toward the end of the sustained exploration effort, no one can accurately estimate the ultimate resources of uranium except to say that present reserves are quite ample and that exploration methods are so highly developed that exploration costs are low. Backing up the unknown resources of higher-grade uranium ore are vast volumes of rock that contain extractable uranium in concentrations that may well become economic at some future date. The example of uranium in the resource situation is particularly important as it relates to the potential of nuclear energy discussed below.

Recent years are characterized by technological advances that have also increased the availability of other mineral resources. The synthesis of diamonds on an industrial scale has substantially freed the United States of dependence on overseas sources; this has been done with no increase in costs, but with some hope of lower costs in the future. New methods of exploration and of extraction from low-grade ore are operating to make the United States a net exporter of beryllium, whereas previously all supplies were imported. Improved techniques for extracting smaller and smaller amounts of helium from natural gas have substantially increased the known reserves of this important gas. Many supposedly played-out mining districts continue to be periodically revived by new ore discoveries or by better methods of extracting lower-grade ore.

Many of the successes in developing new reserves have depended upon the efficient extraction of ore of lower and lower grade; others have been caused by improved methods of geologic exploration. The question arises as to whether or not such successes, no matter how brilliant and profitable, are but temporary expedients in the long-term prospects of mankind. In particular, it is noteworthy that the average grade of ore mined has been declining throughout this century. So far, better extractive technology, including mechanization of the mines, and low energy costs have combined to keep real costs of metals at about the same level in this century. A vital consideration of resource availability is whether or not improvements in technology, combined with low energy costs, can continue to keep the costs of mineral materials from rising. Any significant rise in such costs would need careful attention. A favorable geologic fact is that as ore grades become lower, a larger absolute amount of material will be found in that grade; in other words, cutting the acceptable ore grade to one-tenth or less will result in tens or even hundreds of times more material being available.

Technology has been termed the "inexhaustible resource." Broad segments of a modern industrial economy experience a steady productivity increase of several percent year after year. The exploration and extractive segments are no exceptions. In recent years the use of helicopters and solid-state electronics for field instrumentation have greatly increased mineral productivity in terms of the area explored per man-day. The military have developed many completely novel infrared and other techniques for the remote and rapid sensing of terrane; these techniques hold great but untapped promise in mineral exploration. Electronic computers are widely used in the gathering and reduction of geologic and geophysical data with great increases in quality, rapidity, and productivity. In exploration and extraction, as in so many other applications, the actual and potential increases of productivity brought about with computers are so great that some persons are predicting a second industrial revolution. Certainly the advancing technology of mineral exploration and extraction shows no striking signs of faltering. There are, however, a few possible signs of slowing, and they are of special interest because they concern major current sources of energy.

Petroleum exploration represents an unusually high level of technological development in terms of manpower, research expenditure, and scale. Although not complete or ideal, the production and reserve statistics for petroleum are much better than those for most mineral resources. These statistics have provided the fuel for lively debate regarding ultimate petroleum production. Certainly petroleum and all the other fossil fuels are exhaustible in the sense that they are presently being consumed at much greater rates than they are being produced in nature. It is also likely that petroleum production in the future will taper off rather than dropping from some peak rate to zero. The hotly debated question concerns the time of peak production, which in turn is related to the total resources ultimately available. Figure 16-2 represents a recent estimate of ultimate world production. If we consider the important role of petroleum in supplying low-cost energy to the United States (see Fig. 16-3), the serious depletion of this energy source in one hundred years or so is an important factor in any attempt to balance population and resources.

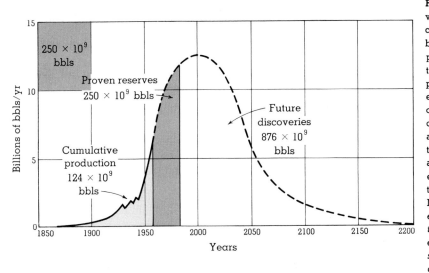

Fig. 16-2. Ultimate world production of crude oil, given in billion barrels (bbls) per year. Note that the total area under the production curve must equal the total amount of oil ultimately produced. The curve of actual production up to the present is shown as a solid line, and the extrapolated production is dashed. (After M. King Hubbert, *Energy Resources, National Academy of Sciences—National Research Council Publication 1000-D, 1962.*)

If the entire world and all fossil fuel sources (see Fig. 16-4) are included, the depletion of these sources of energy could be expected within a thousand years or so. The depletion is not inevitable, however; in Fig. 16-3 the relative decline of coal is not caused by any lack of cheap coal, but by the convenience of other fuels. As this book is written, nuclear fuels are becoming competitive in more and more applications, and they may reduce petroleum usage as petroleum has diminished coal usage. The large potential reserves of uranium for nuclear fuel have been discussed earlier in this chapter. Together with those of thorium, such reserves represent a potential souce of low-cost energy for a very long time into the future. With this low-cost energy and ever-increasing technology, it

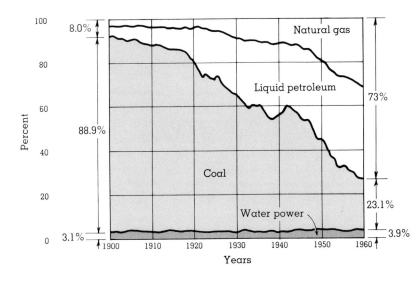

Fig. 16-3. Consumption of energy in the United States since 1900. (After M. King Hubbert, *Energy Resources, National Academy of Sciences—National Research Council Publication 1000-D, 1962.*)

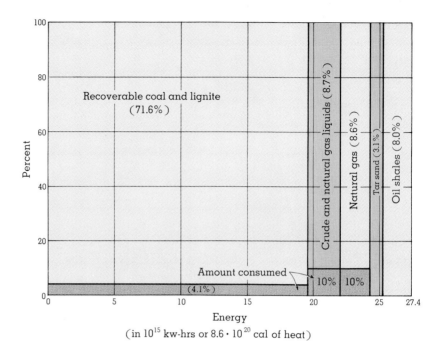

Fig. 16-4. Total world energy of fossil fuels. (After M. King Hubbert, *Energy Resources, National Academy of Sciences—National Research Council Publication 1000-D, 1962.*)

might be possible to continue for some time to supply many minerals and materials at near-present prices.

Despite the promise of nuclear energy, and even should it prove to be considerably cheaper than present sources, some mineral resources may well have the production history projected for petroleum in Fig. 16-2. Helium, once released to the atmosphere, escapes into outer space and is lost forever. The dispersal of lead through automobile exhausts proceeds at a rate greatly exceeding natural processes of concentration. Silver dissolved in used photographic developing solutions is often washed down the drain. Every case of such element dispersal can be considered one of ecological imbalance that must sooner or later be rectified either by substitution of a more plentiful material or by recycling. Recycling can take the form of recovery of waste and scrap in a single plant where, for example, silver is recovered from spent photographic developing solutions. Recycling can be on a global scale, as with the fixation from the atmosphere of nitrogen that will return to the atmosphere, or as in the extraction from the ocean of magnesium that will return to the ocean long before the oceans show any sign of magnesium depletion. Within the memory of living man, the United States has moved from nearly complete depletion of virgin forests at the beginning of the century to a steady state where reforestation matches forest production plus losses.

Currently man is reproducing his species in many regions at close to the maximum biologically possible. Any species that reproduces at its maximum limit requires but a few generations to produce a mass of individuals equal to the weight of the earth. Long before this can happen, however, the high fertility of any species, except man, would be offset by high death rates owing to disease and starvation. Man has the option to consciously bring his fertility rate into balance with the low death rates brought about by modern medicine and hygiene. His mineral and fuel resources appear adequate to support such an effort if the two rates are brought into balance within the next few generations. The naturally evolved recycling of materials through the atmosphere, hydrosphere, and biosphere, provide examples of the recycling and balances that man can impose upon himself and the earth.

IDENTIFICATION
OF MINERALS

The general procedures for recognizing different minerals are discussed in Chapter 6. The charts given in this Appendix subdivide twenty-one common minerals into groups with distinct physical properties. This subdivision is one of convenience for the identification of minerals and is not related to any basic chemical or crystallographic classifications which we might make. The three major subdivisions are:

1. Minerals with metallic luster
2. Minerals with nonmetallic luster and good cleavage
3. Minerals with nonmetallic luster and poor or no cleavage

METALLIC LUSTER

mineral	formula	color	cleavage	hardness	comments
Galena	PbS	Shiny, dark gray	Cubic (3 directions at 90° to each other)	2–3	Commonly forms perfect cubes; main ore of lead
Pyrite	FeS_2	Light yellow	None	6	May form modified cubes; common in most ore deposits but generally not valuable
Chalcopyrite	$CuFeS_2$	Dark yellow	None	4	Common ore of copper
Magnetite	Fe_3O_4	Black	None	6	The only common mineral which is attracted to a magnet

NONMETALLIC LUSTER; GOOD CLEAVAGE

mineral	formula	color	cleavage	hardness	comments
Sphalerite	ZnS	Dark reddish brown; lighter in thin pieces	Excellent in 6 directions	4	Main ore of zinc
Gypsum	$CaSO_4 \cdot 2H_2O$	White	Excellent in 1 direction; less well-developed perpendicular to main direction; forms plates	2	Good crystals are easy to identify; fine-grained varieties are recognized mainly by exceptional softness
Biotite	$K(Mg,Fe)_3AlSi_3O_{10}(OH)_2$	Black	Forms flexible elastic sheets	3	In igneous and metamorphic rocks
Muscovite	$KAl_2AlSi_3O_{10}(OH)_2$	White	Forms flexible elastic sheets	3	In igneous and metamorphic rocks; best crystals are from pegmatites
Amphibole group	$(Ca, Al, Mg, Fe, Na, etc.)_7Si_8O_{22}(OH)_2$	Common varieties are black	2 good cleavages intersecting at an angle of 120°	5	In igneous and metamorphic rocks; common variety is hornblende
Pyroxene Group	$(Ca, Mg, Fe)SiO_3$	Common varieties are black; may have slight greenish appearance	2 fairly good cleavages intersecting at 90°; cleavage not as well developed as in amphiboles	5	In igneous and metamorphic rocks; common variety is augite
Chlorite	Similar to biotite but with additional Mg-$(OH)_2$ and no K	Dark green	Good in 1 direction; forms flexible, non-elastic sheets	2	Best developed in metamorphic rocks
Plagioclase	Complete range from $NaAlSi_3O_8$ (albite) to $CaAl_2Si_2O_8$ (anorthite)	Generally white to light gray; appears white in most igneous rocks	2 fairly good cleavages at about 90° to each other; generally not as well developed as in potassium feldspar	6	Commonly has fine striation caused by twinning

mineral	formula	color	cleavage	hardness	comments
Potassium feldspar	$KAlSi_3O_8$ (high-temperature forms contain some Na in place of K)	Pink or white; all pink feldspar is potassium feldspar	Good in 2 directions at about 90° to each other; poorer in a third direction	6	Microline is common form in granitic and metamorphic rocks; a high-temperature form (sanidine) is crystallographically different from microline and occurs in volcanic rocks; the term "orthoclase" is commonly used to refer to any potassium feldspar
Calcite	$CaCO_3$	Generally white or colorless	Excellent in 3 directions; forms rhombs with approximately 60° angles between faces	3	Fizzes with HCl; common in sediments; well-formed, transparent crystals are from ore deposits; major constituent of marble
Dolomite	$CaMg(CO_3)_2$	White or pink	Good in 3 directions, similar to calcite; less perfect than calcite, and cleavage faces may be curved	4	In sedimentary rocks and ore deposits; powder fizzes in HCl
Halite	$NaCl$	White	Cubic (3 directions at 90° to each other)	2	A common evaporite; salty taste is diagnostic

NONMETALLIC LUSTER; POOR OR NO CLEAVAGE

mineral	formula	color	cleavage	hardness	comments
Quartz	SiO_2	Generally colorless or white	None	7	Common in all kinds of rocks
Olivine	$(Mg,Fe)_2SiO_4$	Green	None	7	In peridotites and other basic igneous rocks; common as phenocrysts in basalts
Garnet	$(Ca, Mg, Fe)_3$ $(Al, Fe, Cr)_2$ $(SiO_4)_3$	Generally red; green and brown also common	None	7	Mainly as large crystals in metamorphic rocks
Hematite	Fe_2O_3	Red	None in red, fine-grained varieties	Fine-grained varieties appear to be very soft	In sediments; major ore of iron
Limonite	Hydroxide of ferric iron	Yellow-brown	None	Fine-grained varieties are soft	Common brownish weathering product in all types of rocks

INDEX

Set in Linotype Baskerville

Format by Frances Torbert Tilley

Composition by American Book–Stratford Press, Inc.

Printed by The Murray Printing Company

Manufactured by American Book–Stratford Press, Inc.

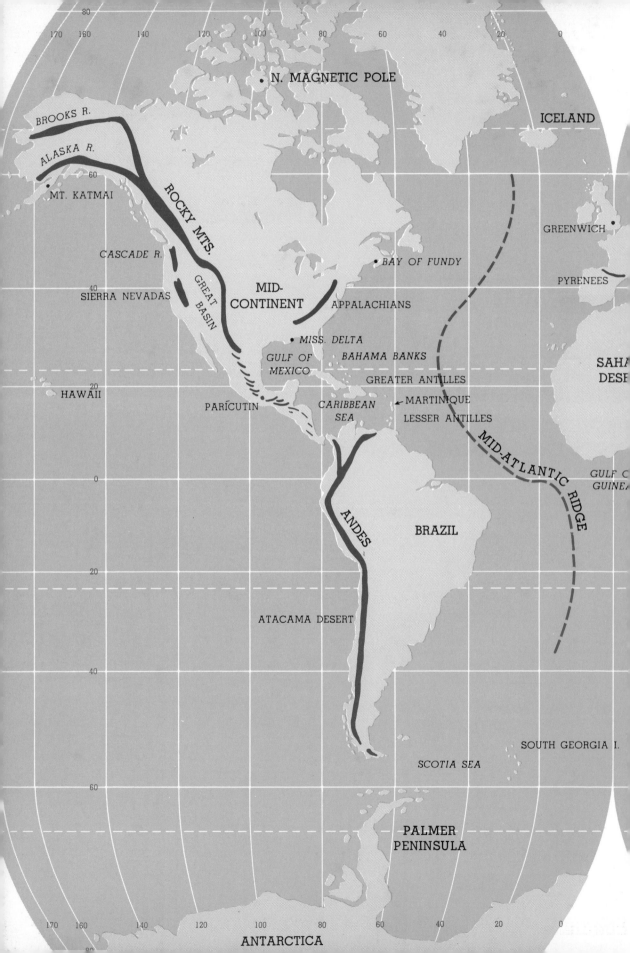